Elec
for
volume 1

G. Waterworth
Lecturer in electrical engineering,
Leeds Polytechnic

illustrated by
R. P. Phillips
Lecturer in mechanical engineering,
Carlett Park College of Technology

Edward Arnold
A division of Hodder & Stoughton
LONDON   MELBOURNE   AUCKLAND

© 1980 G. Waterworth and R. P. Phillips

First published in Great Britain 1980
Reprinted 1983 (with corrections), 1986, 1989, 1990, 1991,
1992 (twice)

British Library Cataloguing in Publication Data

Waterworth, G
   Electrical principles for technicians.
   Vol. 1
   1. Electric engineering
   I. Title.   II. Phillips, R P
   621.3   TK145

   ISBN 0-7131-3421-6

Typeset by Reproduction Drawings Ltd, Sutton, Surrey.
Printed and bound in Great Britain for Edward Arnold, a division of
Hodder and Stoughton Limited, Mill Road, Dunton Green,
Sevenoaks, Kent TN13 2YA by J. W. Arrowsmith Ltd, Bristol.

Contents

Preface

This book aims to develop the understanding of electrical principles required by technician students as a basis for a range of specialisms in electrical, electronic, and communications engineering. The objectives of the Technician Education Council standard units Electrical Principles II (U75/019) and Electrical and Electronic Principles II (U76/359) are covered, including an introduction to semiconductor diodes and transistors for the benefit of students not taking separate units in electronics.

To help the student obtain a real working grasp of the subject matter, I have made considerable use of analogies in discussing electrical phenomena and have tried to integrate worked examples with the text to relate the principles under discussion to their practical applications. A selection of problems, with answers, is provided at the end of each chapter, to give practice in using the concepts discussed, and examples of actual industrial equipment and components are given wherever appropriate.

I would like to thank the following organisations for permission to reproduce photographs: Jackson Brothers (London) Ltd (fig. 3.14), RS Components Ltd (fig. 3.15), GEC Machines Ltd (pages 91 and 133), GEC Power Transformers Ltd (page 122), IMO Precision Controls Ltd (fig. 5.19), Avo Ltd, Dover, England (fig. 8.7), the Solarton Electronic Group Ltd (fig. 8.14), Tektronix UK Ltd (fig. 8.22), and Ferranti Electronics Ltd (page 239).

The following questions are taken from or based on examination questions set by the Union of Lancashire and Cheshire Institutes (now incorporated in the North Western Regional Advisory Council for Further Education) and are reproduced here by permission of the NWRAC as they are of an appropriate standard for these TEC units: chapter 2, questions 44 to 58, chapter 3, questions 19 to 21 and 24 to 32; chapter 4, questions 17 to 30; chapter 5, questions 25 to 27, 36 to 38, and 59; chapter 6, questions 28 to 33, chapter 7, questions 8 to 12, 15 to 19, 21, 23 to 25, 29 to 33, and 37 to 44; chapter 8, questions 32, 36 to 45, and 69 to 79. The NWRAC accepts no responsibility for the answers quoted for these questions.

G. Waterworth

1   Units

1.1 Introduction

In all branches of science and engineering where measurements are performed, there is a need for a practical system of units, and it is obviously desirable that the same system of units should be used by everybody. The International System of units (SI units) is just such a practical system and has evolved into its present form in response to a wide range of requirements. The system is based on seven 'base' units which have been chosen as a small number of convenient and acceptable units from which the other units of the system may be derived.

The seven base units include, of course, the units of mass, length, and time, while the remaining four are the units of electric current, temperature, luminous intensity, and amount of substance – Table 1.1.

Table 1.1 The SI base units

Quantity	Unit	Abbreviation
Mass	kilogram	kg
Length	metre	m
Time	second	s
Electric current	ampere	A
Temperature	kelvin	K
Luminous intensity	candela	cd
Amount of substance	mole	mol

All other units are called 'derived' units, since they can be derived from these seven base units by making use of equations relating the quantities concerned. Since the SI is a 'coherent' system of units, no numerical factor other than 1 is used in forming derived units.

Many of the derived units have their own names and symbols.

Example   If electric charge Q is related to electric current I and time t by the equation $Q = It$, derive the SI unit of charge, the coulomb (abbreviation C), in terms of SI base units.

$$Q = It$$

Since the SI is a coherent system, when $I = 1$ ampere and $t = 1$ second then Q will be 1 coulomb;

i.e. $\qquad\qquad Q = 1$ ampere × 1 second

$\qquad\qquad\qquad = 1$ coulomb

∴ $\qquad$ 1 coulomb = 1 ampere second

or $\qquad\qquad$ 1 C = 1 A s

In a similar way, other derived units may be obtained as shown below.

1.2 Mechanical units

Force (symbol F)

If a body at rest or moving in a straight line with constant speed has a force applied to it, then (neglecting any friction effects) the body will accelerate. The acceleration a is related to the force F and the mass of the body m by Newton's second law of motion, which may be stated as

$$F = ma$$

If $m = 1$ kg and $a = 1$ m/s² then F is defined as 1 newton (abbreviation N);

i.e. $\quad$ 1 newton = 1 kilogram × 1 metre/second²

$\qquad\qquad\qquad = 1$ kilogram metre/second²

or $\qquad\qquad$ 1 N = 1 kg m/s²

i.e. one newton is that constant force which if applied to a mass of 1 kg will cause it to accelerate at 1 metre per second per second.

Torque (symbol T)

Torque is the effect that causes rotation about a point when a force acts at a distance from that point. Most electric motors produce mechanical torque as their output, and this is used to drive mechnical loads such as lathes, pumps, fans, etc. Torque T is defined as the product of force F and the perpendicular distance l from the line of action of the force to the centre of rotation;

i.e. $\quad T = Fl$

When $F = 1$ N and $l = 1$ m, we have

$\qquad T = 1$ newton × 1 metre

$\qquad\quad = 1$ newton metre

Hence the unit of force is the newton metre (N m), where 1 newton metre is the torque produced by a force of 1 newton acting at 1 metre from the centre of rotation.

Example 1   Calculate the torque produced by a force of 2.5 N applied 10 cm from the centre of rotation.

$$T = Fl$$

where $F = 2.5 \, \text{N}$ and $l = 10 \, \text{cm} = 0.1 \, \text{m}$

$\therefore$ $T = 2.5 \, \text{N} \times 0.1 \, \text{m}$

$= 0.25 \, \text{N m}$

i.e. the torque produced is 0.25 N m.

Energy (symbol W)

Energy may be described as a capacity to do work. However, it should be noted that when work is done energy is not lost but rather converted from one form into another.

In mechanical terms, energy converted to work is defined as the product of force F and the distance s through which the force is exerted in the direction of the force;

i.e. $W = Fs$

When $F = 1 \, \text{N}$ and $s = 1 \, \text{m}$ we have

$W = 1 \, \text{newton} \times 1 \, \text{metre}$

$= 1 \, \text{newton metre}$

Hence the unit of energy or work done is the newton metre. In the context of energy, this unit is given the special name 'joule' (abbreviation J);

i.e.   1 joule $= 1$ newton metre

or $1 \, \text{J} = 1 \, \text{N m}$

i.e. one joule is the energy converted when a force of 1 newton is exerted through a distance of 1 metre in the direction of the force.

Example 2   Calculate the energy converted when a trolley is brought uniformly to rest through a distance of 8 m by a braking force of 45 N.

$$W = Fs$$

where $F = 45 \, \text{N}$ and $s = 8 \, \text{m}$

$\therefore$ $W = 45 \, \text{N} \times 8 \, \text{m}$

$= 360 \, \text{J}$

i.e. the energy converted is 360 J.

An alternative equation for the energy converted in a *rotary* system may be considered. If a torque of T N m is exerted through an angular distance θ radians then the energy converted is

$$W = T\theta$$

Example 3   Calculate the energy converted in 1 minute if a motor running at 3000 rev/min produces a constant torque of 20 N m.

The motor speed is 3000 rev/min; therefore in 1 minute the motor rotates through 3000 revolutions.

But   3000 revolutions $= 3000 \times 2\pi$ radians

$\therefore$ $\qquad\qquad\qquad \theta = 3000 \times 2\pi$ rad

Now $W = T\theta$

where $T = 20$ N m   and $\theta = 3000 \times 2\pi$ rad

$\therefore$ $W = 20$ N m $\times 3000 \times 2\pi$ rad

$\qquad = 377 \times 10^3$ J

i.e. the energy converted in 1 minute is 377×10^3 J.

Power (symbol P)

Power is a measure of the rate at which energy is converted from one form to another, and is defined as the energy converted W divided by the time t taken for the conversion;

i.e. $P = \dfrac{W}{t}$

When $W = 1$ J and $t = 1$ s then the power P is defined as 1 watt (abbreviation W);

i.e.   1 watt $= 1$ joule/1 second

$\qquad\qquad = 1$ joule/second

or   1 W $= 1$ J/s

i.e. one watt is the power when one joule of energy is converted in one second.

   The energy conversion may take any form; for example, electrical energy may be converted into mechanical energy or heat energy, nuclear energy may be converted into electrical energy, and so on.

Example 4   Calculate the energy converted into heat by a 1 kW (1000 W) heater in 1 h.

$$W = Pt$$

where $P = 1000$ W   and $t = 1$ h $= 3600$ s

$$\therefore \quad W = 1000\ \text{W} \times 3600\ \text{s}$$
$$= 3.6 \times 10^{6}\ \text{J}$$

i.e. the energy converted is 3.6×10^{6} J.

In performing calculations on rotating electrical machines, it is often convenient to express the power of the rotary system in terms of the torque T and the angular velocity ω.

Now the energy W converted in a rotary system is given by

$$W = T\theta$$

and
$$P = \frac{W}{t}$$

$$\therefore \quad P = \frac{T\theta}{t}$$

but
$$\frac{\theta}{t} = \omega$$

$$\therefore \quad P = T\omega \quad \text{or} \quad T = P/\omega$$

where T is the torque in N m, and ω is the angular velocity in rad/s.

Example 5   Calculate the mean torque available at the flywheel of a 2 kW motor running at 1000 rev/min.

$$T = P/\omega$$

where
$$P = 2\ \text{kW} = 2000\ \text{W}$$

and
$$\omega = 1000\ \text{rev/min} = 1000 \times \frac{2\pi}{60}\ \text{rad/s} = 104.7\ \text{rad/s}$$

$$\therefore \quad T = \frac{2000\ \text{W}}{104.7\ \text{rad/s}}$$
$$= 19.1\ \text{N m}$$

i.e. the mean torque is 19.1 N m.

1.3 Electrical units

Electric current (symbol I)
Electric current is a measure of the rate of flow of electrons through a conductor. The unit is the ampere (abbreviation A) and it is the only electrical base unit. The formal definition of the ampere is 'that constant current which, if maintained in two straight parallel conductors of infinite length, of negligible circular cross-section, and placed 1 metre apart in a vacuum, would produce

between these conductors a force equal to 2×10^{-7} newton per metre length.'

Since it is a base unit, it is not necessary to define the ampere in terms of other units.

Electric charge (symbol Q)

Electrons have a negative electric charge. If a body has an excess of electrons then it possesses a negative charge. If it has a shortage of electrons then it possesses a positive charge. The charge on an electron is so small that a much larger practical unit of charge is chosen.

The charge Q that has been transported through a conductor in a time t is related to the current I by the equation

$$Q = It$$

If a current of 1 A flows for 1 s then the charge transported is 1 coulomb (abbreviation C):

$$1 \text{ coulomb} = 1 \text{ ampere} \times 1 \text{ second}$$
$$= 1 \text{ ampere second}$$

or $\qquad 1 \text{ C} = 1 \text{ A s}$

i.e. one coulomb is defined as the quantity of electricity transported in one second by a current of one ampere.

Example 1   Calculate the total charge that flows through a conductor in 20 s if the current is maintained constant at 10 A.

$$Q = It$$

where $\qquad I = 10 \text{ A} \quad$ and $\quad t = 20 \text{ s}$

$\therefore \qquad Q = 10 \text{ A} \times 20 \text{ s}$

$\qquad\qquad = 200 \text{C}$

i.e. the total charge is 200 C.

Potential difference (symbol V)

Potential difference in an electric circuit may be likened to pressure difference in a fluid circuit. When fluid flows through a pipe there is a drop in pressure along the length of the pipe due to the resistance to flow. Similarly, when current flows through a conductor, there is a potential difference between two points in the conductor due to the resistance of the conductor.

The potential difference V between two points is defined in terms of the energy W used in transporting a charge Q across that potential difference and is given by the equation

$$V = \frac{W}{Q}$$

This definition is often found difficult to understand, but it is worth noting that some work must be done in moving an electric charge (electrons) around a circuit, and we may therefore define potential difference in terms of this work done and the quantity of charge moved.

When the work done is one joule and the charge transported is one coulomb then the potential difference is defined as one volt (abbreviation V);

i.e.   1 volt $= \dfrac{1\ \text{joule}}{1\ \text{coulomb}}$

$= 1$ joule/coulomb

or $1\ V = 1\ J/C$

i.e. one volt is defined as the potential difference between two points in a circuit if one joule of work is done in moving one coulomb of charge between these two points.

The term 'potential difference' is usually abbreviated to p.d.

Example 2   Calculate the work done in moving 5 C of charge across a p.d. of 200 V.

$V = W/Q$ $\therefore$ $W = QV$

where $Q = 5\ C$ and $V = 200\ V$

$\therefore$ $W = 5\ C \times 200\ V$

$= 1000\ J$

i.e. the work done is 1000 J.

Electromotive force (symbol E)

When connected across a conductor, a generator or electric cell will cause a current to flow. The generator or cell is therefore said to possess an electromotive force. A comparison may be made with a fluid system: the electromotive force is analogous to the head of pressure which causes the fluid to flow, while the p.d. is analogous to the pressure drop along the length of the pipe.

Electromotive force is usually abbreviated to e.m.f. and has the same units as p.d. (i.e. volts).

The energy transferred or work done (W) by a generator or cell in transporting a charge of Q coulombs across an e.m.f. of E volts is

$W = QE$

Example 3   A 12 V car battery supplies a current of 25 A for 6 s when used to start a motor car. Calculate the energy used.

$W = QE$

where $Q = It = 25\ A \times 6\ s = 150\ C$ and $E = 12\ V$

7

$$\therefore \quad W = 150 \text{ C} \times 12 \text{ V}$$

$$= 1800 \text{ J}$$

i.e. the energy used is 1800 J.

Electrical resistance (symbol R)

In electric circuits, the term 'resistance' means resistance to flow of electric current. A high resistance will allow only a small current to flow, while a low resistance will allow a large current to flow. This may be likened to the flow of fluid through a pipe, where the bore of the pipe affects the flow rate.

The resistance R of a circuit in which a potential difference V causes a current I to flow is given by

$$R = \frac{V}{I}$$

When $V = 1$ V and $I = 1$ A then R is defined as 1 ohm (symbol Ω);

i.e.   1 ohm $= 1$ volt/1 ampere

$$= 1 \text{ volt/ampere}$$

or $1 \Omega = 1$ V/A

i.e. one ohm is defined as the resistance between two points such that a potential difference of one volt between the two points causes a current of one ampere to flow.

The equation for resistance is often referred to as Ohm's law and written in the form

$$V = IR$$

Example 4   Calculate the resistance of a circuit which takes a current of 5 A from an e.m.f. of 20 V.

$$R = V/I$$

where $V = 20$ V   and $I = 5$ A

$$\therefore \quad R = 20 \text{ V}/5 \text{ A}$$

$$= 4 \ \Omega$$

i.e. the resistance of the circuit is 4 Ω.

Energy in electric circuits

When an electric current flows through a resistance, heat is generated and electrical energy is thus converted into heat energy. The heat W generated by a current I flowing in a resistance R for a time t is given by

$$W = I^2 R t$$

Example 5 Calculate the heat generated in 1 minute by a 240 V electric heater which has a resistance of 8.3 Ω.

$$W = I^2Rt$$

where $\quad I = V/R = 240 \text{ V}/8.3 \ \Omega = 28.9 \text{ A} \qquad R = 8.3 \ \Omega$

and $\quad t = 1 \text{ min} = 60 \text{ s}$

$\therefore \quad W = (28.9 \text{ A})^2 \times 8.3 \ \Omega \times 60 \text{ s}$

$\qquad = 0.416 \times 10^6 \text{ J}$

i.e. the heat generated is 0.416×10^6 J.

The kilowatt hour

An alternative unit for energy which is often used by electrical engineers is the kilowatt hour (kW h). This is the quantity of energy converted into some other form if 1 kW is supplied for 1 hour:

$$1 \text{ kW h} = 1 \text{ kW} \times 1 \text{ h}$$

This unit is commonly used when calculating the quantity of electrical energy supplied to a domestic or industrial consumer by the electricity board.

Example 6 Calculate the energy in kW h consumed by a 150 W electric light bulb in 24 h.

$$\text{Energy (kW h)} = \text{power (kW)} \times \text{time (h)}$$

where $\quad \text{power} = 150 \text{ W} = 0.15 \text{ kW} \quad \text{and} \quad \text{time} = 24 \text{ h}$

$\therefore \quad \text{energy} = 0.15 \text{ kW} \times 24 \text{ h} = 3.6 \text{ kW h}$

i.e. the energy consumed is 3.6 kW h.

Power in electric circuits

The power or rate of energy transfer in an electric circuit may be found from

$$P = \frac{W}{t} = \frac{I^2Rt}{t} = I^2R \text{ watts}$$

Two alternative equations may be derived:

$$P = I^2R = (IR)I$$

$\therefore \qquad P = VI$

and $\quad P = I^2R = (V/R)^2R$

$\therefore \qquad P = V^2/R$

These three equations are used to calculate the power in d.c. electric circuits. The equation for the power in a.c. circuits is considered in chapter 7.

Example 7 Calculate the power supplied by a 200 V d.c. generator when feeding a current of 15 A.

$$P = VI$$

where $V = 200$ V and $I = 15$ A

$\therefore$ $P = 200$ V $\times$ 15 A

$= 3000$ W $= 3$ kW

i.e. the power supplied is 3 kW.

Example 8 A 2 kW (2000 W) electric heater takes a current of 12.5 A. Calculate its resistance.

$$P = I^2R \qquad \therefore \quad R = P/I^2$$

where $P = 2000$ W and $I = 12.5$ A

$\therefore$ $R = 2000$ W$/(12.5$ A$)^2 = 12.8\ \Omega$

i.e. the resistance is 12.8 Ω.

Example 9 Calculate the power dissipated by a 100 Ω resistor connected across an e.m.f. of 50 V.

$$P = V^2/R$$

where $V = 50$ V and $R = 100\ \Omega$

$\therefore$ $P = (50$ V$)^2/100\ \Omega = 25$ W

i.e. the power dissipated is 25 W.

Example 10 A 200 V d.c. electric generator has a mechanical power input of 2.5 kW (2500 W). Assuming 80% efficiency, calculate the electrical power output and the current supplied by the generator.

Output power = efficiency $\times$ input power

$$= \tfrac{80}{100} \times 2500 \text{ W}$$

$$= 2000 \text{ W} = 2 \text{ kW}$$

Now $I = P/V$

where $P = 2000$ W and $V = 200$ V

$\therefore$ $I = 2000$ W$/200$ V

$= 10$ A

i.e. the output power is 2 kW and the current supplied is 10 A.

1.4 Multiples and submultiples of units

A set of multiples and submultiples of SI units is recommended to make it possible to write any quantity in a concise form. For example, a length of 0.001 m is better written as 1 mm. The recommended multiplying factors are arranged in multiples of 10^3, and each is given a prefix as shown in Table 1.2.

Table 1.2 Multiplying factors for use with SI units

Unit multiplying factor	Prefix	Symbol
10^9	giga	G
10^6	mega	M
10^3	kilo	k
10^{-3}	milli	m
10^{-6}	micro	μ
10^{-9}	nano	n
10^{-12}	pico	p

It is usual to use a prefix such that the number preceding the unit is between 0.1 and 1000.

Example 1　Write the following in a more concise form: (a) 0.000 015 A, (b) 0.01 m, (c) 11 000 V, (d) 100 000 kW.

Answers　(a) 15 μA, (b) 10 mm, (c) 11 kV, (d) 100 MW

Example 2　Calculate the current and the power dissipation in a 4.7 kΩ resistor which is connected across a 12 V e.m.f.

$$I = V/R$$

where　$V = 10$ V　and　$R = 4.7$ k$\Omega = 4700$ Ω

$\therefore$　　$I = 12$ V/4700 Ω

　　　$= 0.0026$ A $= 2.6$ mA

and　$P = VI$

　　　$= 12$ V $\times 0.0026$ A

　　　$= 0.031$ W $= 31$ mW

i.e. the current is 2.6 mA and the power dissipation is 31 mW.

Example 3　Calculate the power consumed by a resistive load which takes a current of 200 A from a 33 kV supply.

$$P = VI$$

where　$V = 33$ kV $= 33 000$ V　and　$I = 200$ A

11

$$\therefore \quad P = 33\,000 \text{ V} \times 200 \text{ A}$$
$$= 6.6 \times 10^6 \text{ W} = 6.6 \text{ MW}$$

i.e. the power consumed is 6.6 MW.

1.5 Preferred units

In performing calculations it is advisable to use preferred units, since this ensures that the units of the final answer are correct; for example, the metre is the preferred unit for the measurement of length, as opposed to, say, the millimetre or kilometre. After the calculation has been performed, the answer is converted to the most concise form for final presentation. Using this procedure reduces the likelihood of unit errors.

Particular care should be taken when working with area or volume. It should be noted that

$$1 \text{ mm} = 10^{-3} \text{ m} \qquad 1 \text{ mm}^2 = 10^{-6} \text{ m}^2 \qquad 1 \text{ mm}^3 = 10^{-9} \text{ m}^3$$

Example   A conductor of square cross-section has a side length of 2 mm. Calculate the cross-sectional area.

$$A = l^2$$

where $l = 2 \text{ mm} = 2 \times 10^{-3} \text{ m}$

$$\therefore \quad A = (2 \times 10^{-3} \text{ m})^2$$
$$= 4 \times 10^{-6} \text{ m}^2$$

This may also be written as 4 mm^2.

1.6 Instantaneous values

If a quantity is constantly changing, such as for example a sinusoidal alternating voltage (see chapter 6), then the value at any particular instant is referred to as the *instantaneous value*. It is usual to use a small letter to represent instantaneous values and a capital letter to represent fixed (or d.c.) values.

Exercises on chapter 1

1   Calculate the current taken by a 19 Ω electric heater when supplied from a voltage of 240 V.   [12.63 A]

2   Calculate the resistance of an electric light bulb which takes 0.25 A from 240 V.   [960 Ω]

3   Calculate the quantity of electricity transported if a current of 15 A flows for 1 hour.   [54 kC]

4   Calculate the torque produced by a motor which drives a flywheel of diameter 1 m with a tangential force of 25 N.   [12.5 Nm]

5   The insulation resistance between a conductor and earth is 25 MΩ. Calculate the leakage current and the power absorbed if the supply voltage is 240 V.   [9.6 μA; 2.3 mW]

6   A motor drives a belt via a flywheel of diameter 0.8 m. The force on the belt is 200 N. Calculate the output torque.   [80 N m]

7   Derive the SI units of force, energy, and power in terms of base units.
  If a mass of 20 kg is made to accelerate uniformly at 4 m/s^2 for 10 s, calculate (a) the force required, (b) the energy consumed in 10 s.   [80 N; 3.2 kJ]

8   An electric motor is rated at 50 kW and runs at 1500 rev/min. Calculate the mean torque available at the flywheel if the motor runs at its full rated power.   [318.5 N m]

9   State the SI units of power and energy.
  An electric fire operating from a 240 V supply has two elements connected in parallel, each element having a resistance of 60 Ω. Calculate (a) the power input to the fire, (b) the energy supplied in kW h if the fire is used for 10 hours.   [1.92 kW; 19.2 kW h]

10   A current of 5 A flows for 10 minutes between two points at a potential difference of 240 V. Calculate (a) the quantity of electricity delivered, (b) the energy converted in kW h, (c) the cost of the energy at 5 p per kW h.   [3 kC; 0.2 kW h; 1 p]

11   An electric motor produces a torque of 25 N m and rotates at 1000 rev/min. Calculate the power of the motor and the work in joules done in 1 minute.   [2.617 kW; 157 kJ]

12   A linear motor has a mass of 200 kg and can accelerate uniformly from rest at 5 m/s^2 through a distance of 30 m. Calculate (a) the force produced by the motor, (b) the work done by the motor in this distance.   [1 kN; 30 kJ]

13   Calculate the energy in kW h converted by an electric motor running at 2000 rev/min and producing an average torque of 35 N m for 1 hour.   [7.33 kW h]

14   A solar panel on a satellite delivers 1.2 A from 30 V for a period of 60 days. Calculate (a) the power, (b) the energy converted in kW h.   [36 W; 51.84 kW h]

15   A 3 kW heater is switched on for 1.5 hours. Calculate the energy converted, in kW h and in joules. Hence state the relationship between joules and kW h.   [4.5 kW h; 12.96 MJ]

16   A motor has a brake test performed on it using a rope wound around a flywheel with a constant force of 250 N applied to the rope. If the motor runs at 1800 rev/min and the diameter of the flywheel is 0.6 m calculate the power developed.   [14.13 kW]

17   Name the SI unit of electrical energy.
  The cost of operating two 3 kW electric heaters for 8 hours is 48 p. Calculate the cost of energy per kW h.   [2 p]

18   A 3 kW immersion heater is designed to operate from a 250 V supply. Calculate its resistance and the current taken by the heater when operating at its rated voltage.
  If the heater is now used on a 200 V supply, what will be the power dissipated, assuming that the resistance remains the same?   [20.83 Ω; 12 A; 1.92 kW]

19   Calculate the cost of operating a 5 kW electric motor for 12 hours if energy is charged at 2 p per kilowatt hour. If the supply voltage is 400 V, calculate the supply current.   [120 p; 12.5 A]

20   An electric motor takes a current of 10 A when connected to a 240 V a.c. supply. Calculate its efficiency if its mechanical output is 2 kW. [Efficiency = (output power/input power) × 100%]   [83.3%]

21   Explain the meaning of the terms 'electrical energy' and 'electrical power', stating the units in which each is measured.

The cost of operating a 3 kW heater for 2 hours a day for $4\frac{1}{2}$ days is 54 p. Calculate the cost of energy per kilowatt hour.   [2 p]

22   A machine has an electrical energy input of 200 kW h and a mechanical energy output of 5.4×10^8 J. Calculate (a) the output energy in kW h, (b) the efficiency of the conversion process.   [150 kW h; 75%]

23   A colliery pump with an operating efficiency of 0.8 per unit is driven by a d.c. motor and has an output of 60 kW. Given that when operating with the above loading the motor has an efficiency of 0.75 per unit, calculate (a) the input power, in kW, to the pump; (b) the input power, in kW, to the motor; (c) the annual cost of the energy consumed, with electricity at 1 p per unit, if the pump is in continuous use for 40 hours each week, 50 weeks each year.   [75 kW; 100 kW; £2000]

24   A 200 V generator supplies a lighting load of sixty 100 W lamps, a heating load of 24 kW, and other loads totalling 25 A. Calculate the power output of the generator.   [35 kW]

25   Convert to preferred units (a) 25 cm, (b) 2.7 mA, (c) 6.6 GW, (d) 2500 nA, (e) 33 kV.

26   Convert to a more concise form (a) 200 000 kW, (b) 0.0024 m, (c) 0.0027 A, (d) 11 000 V, (e) 0.000 050 C.

2   Electric circuits

2.1 Introduction
A simple electric circuit consisting of a cell (E) and a resistor (R) is shown in fig. 2.1. Notice that, for current to flow, the circuit must be a complete closed path, otherwise there is said to be an 'open circuit' and no current will flow.

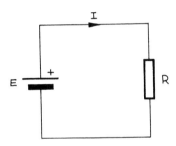

Fig. 2.1 A simple electric circuit

The cell is a source of energy, and the voltage it develops is defined as an electromotive force (e.m.f.). The resistor is a dissipator of energy and the voltage across it is defined as a potential difference (p.d.). Both e.m.f. and p.d. are measured in volts. Notice that in this case the e.m.f. is equal to the p.d.

The direction of current flow in a circuit is conventionally taken as being from the positive terminal to the negative terminal of the e.m.f. source; thus the current flow in the circuit of fig. 2.1 is in the direction shown. (In fact, the flow of electrons which constitutes the current is from the negative to the positive terminal, but it is always the conventional-current direction that is considered in calculations.)

2.2 Resistors in series
When resistors are connected in series, as shown in fig. 2.2, their resultant resistance is equal to the sum of their separate values. The total resistance is given by

$$R_T = R_1 + R_2 + R_3$$

The proof of this equation is as follows.

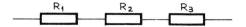

Fig. 2.2 Resistors in series

Referring to fig. 2.2, suppose that the voltage across R_1 is V_1, the voltage across R_2 is V_2, the voltage across R_3 is V_3, and the total voltage is V_T.

Since there is only one path for current to flow in, the same current I flows in each resistor; therefore

$$V_T = IR_T \qquad V_1 = IR_1 \qquad V_2 = IR_2 \qquad V_3 = IR_3$$

But the total voltage is given by

$$V_T = V_1 + V_2 + V_3$$
$$\therefore \quad IR_T = IR_1 + IR_2 + IR_3$$

Dividing throughout by I,

$$R_T = R_1 + R_2 + R_3$$

The current flowing through the resistors may be found from

$$I = \frac{V}{R_T} = \frac{V}{R_1 + R_2 + R_3}$$

Example   Three resistors, of values 100 Ω, 220 Ω, and 470 Ω, are connected in series. Calculate the total resistance, and find the current flow if 50 V is applied across the combination.

$$R_T = R_1 + R_2 + R_3$$
$$= 100\ \Omega + 220\ \Omega + 470\ \Omega$$
$$= 790\ \Omega$$

i.e. the total resistance is 790 Ω.

$$I = \frac{V}{R_T}$$
$$= \frac{50\ \text{V}}{790\ \Omega}$$
$$= 0.063\ \text{A} = 63\ \text{mA}$$

i.e. a current of 63 mA flows.

2.3 Resistors in parallel
When resistors are connected in parallel, as shown in fig. 2.3, their total resistance is given by the equation

16

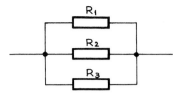

Fig. 2.3 Resistors in parallel

$$\frac{1}{R_T} = \frac{1}{R_1} + \frac{1}{R_2} + \frac{1}{R_3}$$

The proof of this equation is as follows.

Referring to fig. 2.3, suppose that the current in R_1 is I_1, the current in R_2 is I_2, the current in R_3 is I_3, and the total current is I_T.

Since the voltage (V) across each resistor is the same, then

$$I_T = \frac{V}{R_T} \qquad I_1 = \frac{V}{R_1} \qquad I_2 = \frac{V}{R_2} \qquad I_3 = \frac{V}{R_3}$$

But the total current is given by

$$I_T = I_1 + I_2 + I_3$$

$$\therefore \quad \frac{V}{R_T} = \frac{V}{R_1} + \frac{V}{R_2} + \frac{V}{R_3}$$

Dividing throughout by V,

$$\frac{1}{R_T} = \frac{1}{R_1} + \frac{1}{R_2} + \frac{1}{R_3}$$

It is worth noting that the resultant resistance (R_T) is always less than the value of the smallest resistor in the combination.

Example 1 Three resistors, of values 100 Ω, 200 Ω, and 400 Ω, are connected in parallel. Calculate the total resistance and find the current flow if 200 V is applied across the combination.

$$\frac{1}{R_T} = \frac{1}{R_1} + \frac{1}{R_2} + \frac{1}{R_3}$$

$$= \frac{1}{100 \, \Omega} + \frac{1}{200 \, \Omega} + \frac{1}{400 \, \Omega}$$

$$= \frac{4 + 2 + 1}{400 \, \Omega} = \frac{7}{400 \, \Omega}$$

17

$$\therefore \quad R_T = \frac{400\ \Omega}{7} = 57.14\ \Omega$$

$$I = \frac{V}{R_T} = \frac{200\ \text{V}}{57.14\ \Omega}$$

$$= 3.5\ \text{A}$$

i.e. the total resistance is 57.14 Ω and a current of 3.5 A flows.

The case of two resistors in parallel is worth considering in more detail.

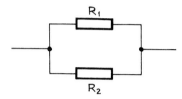

Fig. 2.4 Two resistors in parallel

For the arrangement shown in fig. 2.4,

$$\frac{1}{R_T} = \frac{1}{R_1} + \frac{1}{R_2}$$

$$\therefore \quad \frac{1}{R_T} = \frac{R_1 + R_2}{R_1 R_2}$$

$$\therefore \quad R_T = \frac{R_1 R_2}{R_1 + R_2}$$

$$= \frac{\text{product}}{\text{sum}}$$

This equation is often used and is therefore worth remembering.

Example 2 Find the resultant resistance of 5 Ω and 15 Ω connected in parallel.

$$R_T = \frac{\text{product}}{\text{sum}}$$

$$= \frac{5\ \Omega \times 15\ \Omega}{5\ \Omega + 15\ \Omega} = \frac{75\ \Omega}{20} = 3.75\ \Omega$$

i.e. the resultant resistance is 3.75 Ω.

18

In the particular case of the two parallel resistors being equal ($R_1 = R_2$), then

$$R_T = \frac{product}{sum}$$

$$= \frac{R_1{}^2}{2R_1}$$

$$= \frac{R_1}{2}$$

Example 3 Find the resultant resistance of two 680 Ω resistors connected in parallel.

$$R_T = \frac{R}{2} = \frac{680\ \Omega}{2}$$

$$= 340\ \Omega$$

i.e. the resultant resistance is 340 Ω.

2.4 Resistors in series–parallel combinations

Finding the resultant resistance of combinations of resistors with both series and parallel connections is best understood by considering the following examples.

Example 1 Calculate the total resistance of the arrangement shown in fig. 2.5.

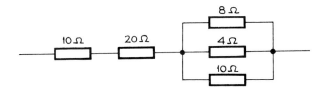

Fig. 2.5

First find the resultant of the three resistors in parallel:

$$\frac{1}{R} = \frac{1}{8\ \Omega} + \frac{1}{4\ \Omega} + \frac{1}{10\ \Omega}$$

$$= \frac{5 + 10 + 4}{40\ \Omega} = \frac{19}{40\ \Omega}$$

$$R = \frac{40\ \Omega}{19} = 2.1\ \Omega$$

19

The total resistance is then given by

$$R_T = 10 \, \Omega + 20 \, \Omega + 2.1 \, \Omega$$
$$= 32.1 \, \Omega$$

i.e. the total resistance is $32.1 \, \Omega$.

Example 2 Calculate the total resistance of the arrangement shown in fig. 2.6.

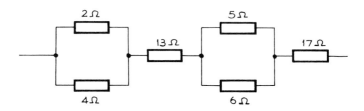

Fig. 2.6

First find the resultant of the $2 \, \Omega$ and $4 \, \Omega$ in parallel:

$$R_1 = \frac{\text{product}}{\text{sum}}$$
$$= \frac{4 \, \Omega \times 2 \, \Omega}{4 \, \Omega + 2 \, \Omega}$$
$$= \frac{8 \, \Omega}{6} = 1.33 \, \Omega$$

Now find the resultant of the $5 \, \Omega$ and $6 \, \Omega$ in parallel:

$$R_2 = \frac{5 \, \Omega \times 6 \, \Omega}{5 \, \Omega + 6 \, \Omega}$$
$$= \frac{30 \, \Omega}{11} = 2.73 \, \Omega$$

The total resistance is then given by

$$R_T = 1.33 \, \Omega + 13 \, \Omega + 2.73 \, \Omega + 17 \, \Omega$$
$$= 34.06 \, \Omega$$

i.e. the total resistance is $34.06 \, \Omega$.

Example 3 Calculate the total resistance of the arrangement shown in fig. 2.7.

20

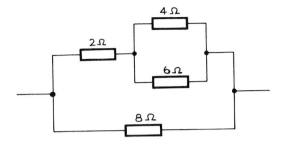

Fig. 2.7

First find the resultant of the 4 Ω and 6 Ω in parallel:

$$R_1 = \frac{4\,\Omega \times 6\,\Omega}{4\,\Omega + 6\,\Omega}$$

$$= \frac{24\,\Omega}{10} = 2.4\,\Omega$$

This resistance is now taken in series with the 2 Ω resistor:

$$R_2 = 2.4\,\Omega + 2\,\Omega$$

$$= 4.4\,\Omega$$

This resistance is now taken in parallel with the 8 Ω resistor:

$$R_T = \frac{4.4\,\Omega \times 8\,\Omega}{4.4\,\Omega + 8\,\Omega}$$

$$= \frac{35.2\,\Omega}{12.4} = 2.84\,\Omega$$

i.e. the total resistance is 2.84 Ω.

2.5 The potential-divider

An important rule which applies to resistors connected in series is that, when a voltage is applied across the combination, 'the ratio of the voltage across any one resistor to the total applied voltage is equal to the ratio of that resistor to the total resistance.' This is known as the potential-divider rule.

In the circuit of fig. 2.8, the voltage V_1 across R_1 is given by

$$\frac{V_1}{V} = \frac{R_1}{R_1 + R_2}$$

21

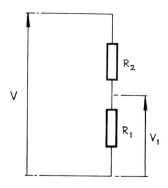

Fig. 2.8 Potential-divider

Example 1   Two resistors, of values 100 Ω and 400 Ω, are connected in series across a 50 V supply. Using the potential-divider rule, calculate the voltage across the 100 Ω resistor.

$$\frac{V_1}{V} = \frac{R_1}{R_1 + R_2}$$

$$\frac{V_1}{50 \text{ V}} = \frac{100 \ \Omega}{400 \ \Omega + 100 \ \Omega}$$

$$= 100/500 = 0.2$$

$$\therefore \quad V_1 = 50 \text{ V} \times 0.2 = 10 \text{ V}.$$

i.e. the voltage across the 100 Ω resistor is 10 V.

Example 2   Three 470 Ω resistors are connected in series across a 10 V supply. Calculate the voltage across each resistor.

$$\frac{V_1}{10 \text{ V}} = \frac{470 \ \Omega}{470 \ \Omega + 470 \ \Omega + 470 \ \Omega} = \frac{1}{3}$$

$$\therefore \quad V_1 = \frac{10 \text{ V}}{3} = 3.33 \text{ V}$$

i.e. the voltage across each resistor is 3.33 V.

2.6 The current-divider

An important rule which applies to *two* resistors connected in parallel is that, when a current flows through the combination, 'the ratio of the current in any one resistor to the total current is equal to the ratio of the opposite resistor to the sum of the resistors.' This is known as the current-divider rule.

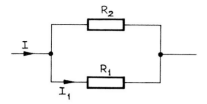

Fig. 2.9 Current-divider

In the arrangement shown in fig. 2.9, the current I_1 in R_1 is given by

$$\frac{I_1}{I} = \frac{R_2}{R_1 + R_2}$$

Example Two resistors, of values 2 Ω and 3 Ω, are connected in parallel and take a total current of 10 A. Calculate the current in the 2 Ω resistor.

$$\frac{I_1}{I} = \frac{3\ \Omega}{3\ \Omega + 2\ \Omega} = \frac{3}{5}$$

$$= 0.6$$

$$\therefore \quad I_1 = 10\ \text{A} \times 0.6 = 6\ \text{A}$$

i.e. the current in the 2 Ω resistor is 6 A.

2.7 Calculations involving series–parallel circuits
Finding the potential differences and currents in series–parallel combinations of resistors is best understood by considering the following examples.

Example 1 In the circuit of fig. 2.10, calculate the potential difference across (a) the 2 Ω resistor, (b) the 8 Ω and 4 Ω in parallel.

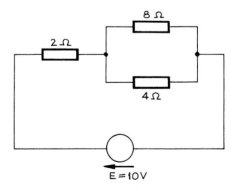

Fig. 2.10

23

The resultant of the 8 Ω and 4 Ω in parallel is found as follows:

$$R = \frac{\text{product}}{\text{sum}}$$

$$= \frac{4\,\Omega \times 8\,\Omega}{4\,\Omega + 8\,\Omega}$$

$$= \frac{32\,\Omega}{12} = 2.67\,\Omega$$

Now, using the potential-divider rule,

a) p.d. across 2 Ω $= \left(\dfrac{2\,\Omega}{2\,\Omega + 2.67\,\Omega}\right) 10\,V$

$$= 4.28\,V$$

b) p.d. across 8 Ω and 4 Ω $= \left(\dfrac{2.67\,\Omega}{2\,\Omega + 2.67\,\Omega}\right) 10\,V$

$$= 5.72\,V$$

Example 2   For the circuit of fig. 2.11, calculate the current in (a) the 20 Ω resistor, (b) the 100 Ω resistor, (c) the 40 Ω resistor.

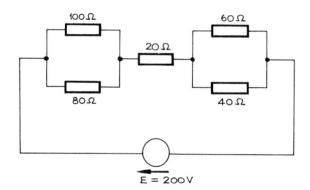

Fig. 2.11

The resultant of 80 Ω and 100 Ω in parallel is found from

$$R_1 = \frac{100\,\Omega \times 80\,\Omega}{100\,\Omega + 80\,\Omega}$$

$$= \frac{8000\,\Omega}{180} = 44.44\,\Omega$$

24

The resultant of 60 Ω and 40 Ω in parallel is found from

$$R_2 = \frac{60 \, \Omega \times 40 \, \Omega}{60 \, \Omega + 40 \, \Omega}$$

$$= \frac{2400 \, \Omega}{100} = 24 \, \Omega$$

a) The total current is given by

$$I_T = \frac{E}{R_T}$$

$$= \frac{200 \text{ V}}{R_1 + R_2 + 20 \, \Omega}$$

$$= \frac{200 \text{ V}}{44.44 \, \Omega + 24 \, \Omega + 20 \, \Omega}$$

$$= \frac{200 \text{ V}}{88.44 \, \Omega} = 2.26 \text{ A}$$

i.e. the current in the 20 Ω resistor is 2.26 A.

b) To find the current in the 100 Ω resistor, use the current-divider rule:

$$\frac{I_1}{I_T} = \frac{80 \, \Omega}{100 \, \Omega + 80 \, \Omega}$$

$$= 80/180 = 0.44$$

$$\therefore \quad I_1 = 0.44 \times 2.26 \text{ A}$$

$$= 1.00 \text{ A}$$

i.e. the current in the 100 Ω resistor is 1.00 A.

c) To find the current in the 40 Ω resistor:

$$\frac{I_2}{I_T} = \frac{60 \, \Omega}{60 \, \Omega + 40 \, \Omega}$$

$$= 60/100 = 0.6$$

$$\therefore \quad I_2 = 0.6 \times 2.26 \text{ A}$$

$$= 1.36 \text{ A}$$

i.e. the current in the 40 Ω resistor is 1.36 A.

2.8 Kirchhoff's laws

To simplify the procedures involved in performing calculations on electric circuits, two laws are available which are due to Kirchhoff.

Kirchhoff's first law

Kirchhoff's first law states that 'At a junction in an electric circuit, the sum of the currents flowing towards the junction is equal to the sum of the currents flowing away from the junction.'

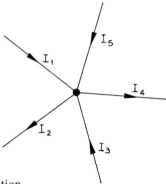

Fig. 2.12 Current junction

Applying this law to the circuit of fig. 2.12,

$$I_1 + I_3 + I_5 = I_2 + I_4$$

Although this law is fairly obvious, it is very useful.

Kirchhoff's second law

Kirchhoff's second law states that 'Around any closed loop in a network, the sum of the e.m.f.'s acting around the loop is equal to the sum of the potential drops around the same loop.'

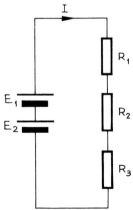

Fig. 2.13 A closed loop

Applying this law to the circuit of fig. 2.13,

$$E_1 + E_2 = IR_1 + IR_2 + IR_3$$

Notice that the e.m.f.'s on one side of the equation balance with the p.d.'s on the other side.

To find whether an e.m.f. or a p.d. should be positive or negative in the equation, a useful convention is as follows.

> When you are going around the loop in a particular direction, if the e.m.f. is such as to drive current in the same direction as you are going, then that e.m.f. is considered positive. If the e.m.f. acts in the opposite direction, then it is negative.
> When you are going around the loop, if the direction of the current in a resistance is the same as the direction in which you are going, then the p.d. across the resistance is considered positive. If the current is in the opposite direction to the way you are going, the p.d. is negative.

Notice that the direction of the current is only assumed, and in some examples the current will turn out negative, thus showing that the current flow is in the opposite direction.

Example 1   A 15 V d.c. generator, with an internal resistance of 2 Ω is used to charge a 12 V car battery which has an internal resistance of 1 Ω. Calculate the charging current.

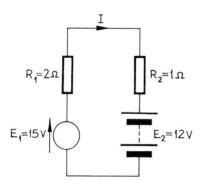

Fig. 2.14

The circuit diagram of the arrangement is shown in fig. 2.14. The senses of E_1 and E_2 are such that they oppose each other. Assuming the direction of the current as being from the generator to the battery, and equating e.m.f.'s with p.d.'s,

$$E_1 - E_2 = IR_1 + IR_2$$

$$\therefore \quad E_1 - E_2 = I(R_1 + R_2)$$

$$\therefore \qquad I = \frac{E_1 - E_2}{R_1 + R_2}$$

where $E_1 = 15$ V $E_2 = 12$ V $R_1 = 2\,\Omega$ and $R_2 = 1\,\Omega$

$$\therefore \quad I = \frac{15\text{ V} - 12\text{ V}}{2\,\Omega + 1\,\Omega} = \frac{3\text{ V}}{3\,\Omega}$$

$$= 1\text{ A}$$

i.e. the charging current is 1 A.

Notice that, if we had originally assumed the current flow to be in the opposite direction, then the final result would have turned out negative.

Circuits which have more than one closed loop require more than one equation. We require as many equations as there are unknowns, and these equations are then solved as a set of simultaneous equations.

Example 2   A 2 V accumulator with an internal resistance of 1 Ω and a 6 V generator with an internal resistance of 2 Ω both feed current into a 5 Ω resistor. Calculate the current in each loop of the network and the total current in the 5 Ω resistor.

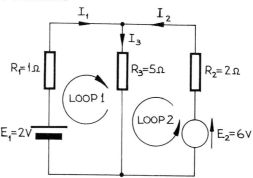

Fig. 2.15

The circuit is as shown in fig. 2.15. Notice that each internal resistance is represented as a resistance in series with its corresponding voltage source. We shall assume the direction of currents to be as shown.

There are three unknowns, so we need three equations.

Using Kirchhoff's first law,

$$I_1 + I_2 = I_3 \tag{i}$$

Using Kirchhoff's second law,

for loop 1:

$$E_1 = I_1 R_1 + I_3 R_3 \tag{ii}$$

for loop 2:

$$E_2 = I_2 R_2 + I_3 R_3 \tag{iii}$$

28

We now have three equations and may solve for I_1, I_2, and I_3.

Inserting the values and substituting for I_3 in equation (ii),

$$2 \text{ V} = I_1 \text{ A} \times 1 \text{ } \Omega + (I_1 + I_2) \text{ A} \times 5 \text{ } \Omega$$

$$\therefore \quad 2 \text{ V} = I_1 \text{ A} \times (1 + 5) \text{ } \Omega + I_2 \text{ A} \times 5 \text{ } \Omega$$

$$\therefore \quad 2 = 6 I_1 + 5 I_2 \tag{iv}$$

Similarly for equation (iii):

$$6 \text{ V} = I_2 \text{ A} \times 2 \text{ } \Omega + (I_1 + I_2) \text{ A} \times 5 \text{ } \Omega$$

$$\therefore \quad 6 \text{ V} = I_1 \text{ A} \times 5 \text{ } \Omega + I_2 \text{ A} \times (2 + 5) \text{ } \Omega$$

$$\therefore \quad 6 = 5 I_1 + 7 I_2 \tag{v}$$

Multiplying equation (iv) by 5 and equation (v) by 6,

$$10 = 30 I_1 + 25 I_2 \tag{vi}$$

$$36 = 30 I_1 + 42 I_2 \tag{vii}$$

Subtracting equation (vi) from equation (vii),

$$26 = 17 I_2$$

$$\therefore \quad I_2 = \frac{26}{17} = 1.53$$

Substituting for I_2 in equation (iv),

$$2 = 6 I_1 + 5 \times 1.53$$

$$\therefore \quad 6 I_1 = 2 - 7.65 = -5.65$$

$$\therefore \quad I_1 = -0.94$$

Substituting I_1 and I_2 into equation (i),

$$I_3 = -0.94 + 1.53$$

$$= 0.59$$

i.e. the currents are 1.53 A, 0.94 A, and 0.59 A.

Notice that I_1 has worked out negative and therefore the current is in the opposite direction to that originally assumed. The generator is thus charging the battery as well as supplying the load resistor.

Example 3   Calculate the currents I_1 A and I_2 A in the network shown in fig. 2.16.

Notice that Kirchhoff's first law has already been applied to the current junctions.

Applying Kirchhoff's second law to loop 1, in which the e.m.f. is zero,

$$0 \text{ V} = 2 \text{ } \Omega \times I_1 \text{ A} + 6 \text{ } \Omega \times (I_1 - I_2) \text{ A} - 9 \text{ } \Omega \times (2 - I_1) \text{ A}$$

29

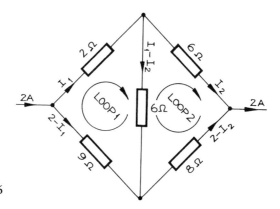

Fig. 2.16

$\therefore \qquad 0 = I_1 (2 + 6 + 9) - 6 I_2 - 18$

$\therefore \quad 17 I_1 - 6 I_2 = 18$ (i)

Applying Kirchhoff's second law to loop 2,

$\qquad 0 \text{ V} = 6\,\Omega \times I_2 \text{ A} - 8\,\Omega \times (2 - I_2)\text{ A} - 6\,\Omega \times (I_1 - I_2)\text{ A}$

$\therefore \qquad 0 = -6 I_1 + I_2 (6 + 8 + 6) - 16$

$\therefore \quad -6 I_1 + 20 I_2 = 16$ (ii)

Multiplying equation (i) by 6 and equation (ii) by 17,

$\qquad 102 I_1 - 36 I_2 = 108$ (iii)

$\qquad -102 I_1 + 340 I_2 = 272$ (iv)

Adding equations (iii) and (iv),

$\qquad 304 I_2 = 380$

$\therefore \qquad I_2 = 1.25$

Substituting for I_2 in equation (i),

$\qquad 17 I_1 - 6 \times 1.25 = 18$

$\therefore \quad 17 I_1 = 18 + 7.5 = 25.5$

$\therefore \qquad I_1 = 1.5$

i.e. the currents are 1.5 A and 1.25 A.

2.9 The superposition theorem

This theorem may be used as an alternative to Kirchhoff's laws.

The basic assumption is that the current in any branch of a network may be found by considering the current due to each generator separately and then adding all these individual currents together to find the resultant current. When considering the effect of each separate generator, the other voltage generators must be replaced by a short circuit (or by their internal resistances).

Example 1 Applying the superposition theorem to the network of fig. 2.17, calculate the current in the 6 Ω resistor.

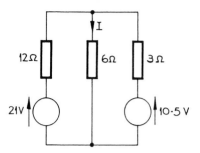

Fig. 2.17

Consider first the current due to the 21 V generator. Replacing the 10.5 V generator by its internal resistance gives the circuit of fig. 2.18(a).

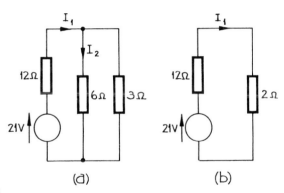

Fig. 2.18

The resultant of 6 Ω in parallel with 3 Ω is (6 Ω × 3Ω)/(6 Ω + 3Ω) = 18 Ω/9 = 2 Ω; therefore the circuit is equivalent to fig. 2.18(b).

$$\therefore \quad I_1 = \frac{21\ V}{12\ \Omega + 2\ \Omega} = \frac{21\ V}{14\ \Omega} = 1.5\ A$$

Now from fig. 2.18(a), using the current-divider rule,

$$I_2 = \left(\frac{3}{6+3}\right) I_1 = \frac{3}{9} \times 1.5\ A = 0.5\ A$$

Next consider the current due to the 10.5 V generator. Replacing the 21 V generator by its internal resistance gives the circuit of fig. 2.19(a).
  The resultant of 6 Ω in parallel with 12 Ω is (6 Ω × 12 Ω)/(6 Ω + 12 Ω) = 72 Ω/18 = 4 Ω; therefore the circuit is equivalent to fig. 2.19(b).

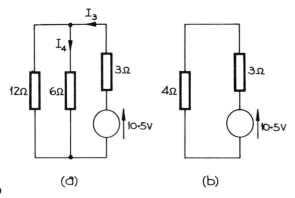

(d)   (b)

Fig. 2.19

$$\therefore \quad I_3 = \frac{10.5 \text{ V}}{4 \, \Omega + 3 \, \Omega} = \frac{10.5 \text{ V}}{7 \, \Omega} = 1.5 \text{ A}$$

Now from fig. 2.19(a), using the current-divider rule,

$$I_4 = \left(\frac{12}{12 + 6}\right) I_3 = \frac{12}{18} \times 1.5 \text{ A} = 1 \text{ A}$$

Now, adding the individual currents to find the total current due to both generators,

$$I = I_2 + I_4 = 0.5 \text{ A} + 1.0 \text{ A} = 1.5 \text{ A}$$

i.e. the current in the 6 Ω resistor is 1.5 A

Example 2 An 11 V generator with an internal resistance of 6 Ω and a 10 V generator with an internal resistance of 3 Ω are connected in opposition across a resistive network as shown in fig. 2.20. Using the superposition theorem, calculate the current in the 8 Ω resistor.

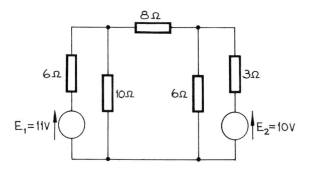

Fig. 2.20

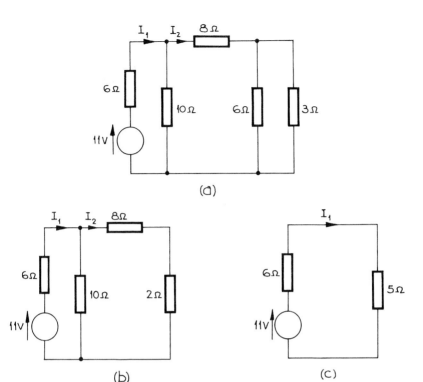

Fig. 2.21

Consider first the current due to E_1 by replacing the generator E_2 by its internal resistance. This gives the circuit of fig. 2.21(a).

The resultant of 6 Ω and 3 Ω in parallel is given by $(6\ \Omega \times 3\ \Omega)/(6\ \Omega + 3\Omega)$ = 18 Ω/9 = 2 Ω; therefore the circuit is equivalent to fig. 2.21(b).

The resultant of 10 Ω in parallel with 8 Ω + 2 Ω is $(10\ \Omega \times 10\ \Omega)/$ (10 Ω + 10 Ω) = 100 Ω/20 = 5 Ω; therefore the circuit is equivalent to fig. 2.21(c).

$$\therefore \quad I_1 = \frac{11\text{ V}}{6\ \Omega + 5\ \Omega} = 1\text{ A}$$

therefore, from fig. 2.21(b),

$$I_2 = \frac{10}{20} \times I_1 = 0.5\text{ A}$$

Now consider the current due to E_2 by replacing the generator E_1 by its internal resistance. We then have the circuit of fig. 2.22(a).

The resultant of 6 Ω and 10 Ω in parallel is given by $(6\ \Omega \times 10\ \Omega)/$ (6 Ω + 10 Ω) = 60 Ω/16 = 3.75 Ω; therefore the circuit is equivalent to fig. 2.22(b).

33

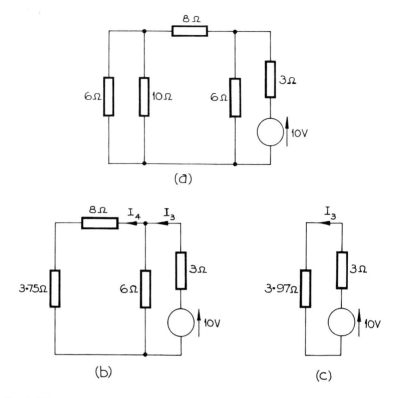

Fig. 2.22

The resultant of 6 Ω in parallel with 8 Ω + 3.75 Ω is (6 Ω × 11.75 Ω)/
(6 Ω + 11.75 Ω) = 3.97 Ω; therefore the circuit is equivalent to fig. 2.22(c).

$$\therefore \quad I_3 = \frac{10\ V}{3\ \Omega + 3.97\ \Omega} = 1.43\ A$$

From fig. 2.22 (b),

$$I_4 = \left(\frac{6}{6 + 11.75}\right) I_3 = \frac{6}{17.75} \times 1.43\ A = 0.48\ A$$

Now, by the superposition theorem, the resultant current in the 8 Ω resistor
is

$$I = I_2 - I_4$$

$$= 0.5\ A - 0.48\ A$$

$$= 0.02\ A$$

i.e. the current in the 8 Ω resistor is 0.02 A, flowing from left to right.

It is important, when performing calculations on networks, to look for the simplest method of solution and to use a procedure which involves the least amount of calculation.

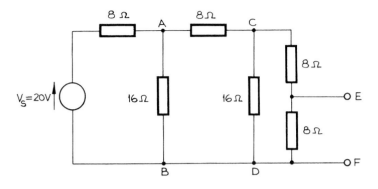

Fig. 2.23

Example 3   Find the voltage across EF in the circuit of fig. 2.23.

This problem is easily solved by noting that
i) the resistance between CD is 8 Ω,
ii) the resistance between AB is 8 Ω.

$$\therefore \quad V_{AB} = \tfrac{1}{2} V_s \quad = (20 \text{ V})/2 = 10 \text{ V}$$

$$\therefore \quad V_{CD} = \tfrac{1}{2} V_{AB} = (10 \text{ V})/2 = 5 \text{ V}$$

$$\therefore \quad V_{EF} = \tfrac{1}{2} V_{CD} = (5 \text{ V})/2 = 2.5 \text{ V}$$

i.e the voltage across EF is 2.5 V.

Exercises on chapter 2
1   Calculate the current which flows when 240 V is connected across a 1.5 kΩ resistor.   [0.16 A]
2   A resistor has 15 V across it and a current of 2.2 mA flows. Calculate the resistance.   [6.8 kΩ]
3   An electric-fire element has a resistance of 65 Ω. Calculate the current flow when 240 V is connected across it.   [3.69 A]
4   An electric-light bulb takes a current of 0.25 A when connected across a 240 V supply. Calculate the resistance of the bulb.   [960 Ω]
5   A cable of resistance 0.1 Ω carries a current of 20 A. Calculate the voltage drop along the cable.   [2 V]
6   A voltage of 0.1 V is connected across a resistance of 22 mΩ. Calculate (a) the current flow, (b) the total charge that has flowed in 30 minutes. [4.55 A; 8.2 kC]
7   Two 570 Ω resistors placed in series are connected across a 400 V supply. Calculate the current.   [0.39 A]

8   A $1.8\,k\Omega$ resistor is supplied from a $20\,V$ source. Calculate (a) the current, (b) the charge that would flow in $2\,s$.   [$11\,mA$; $22\,mC$]

9   Two $20\,\Omega$ resistors are connected in parallel and this group is then connected in series with a $4\,\Omega$ resistor. What is the total effective resistance of the circuit?   [$14\,\Omega$]

10   An experiment to find the resistance of a coil gave the following readings on an ammeter and voltmeter:

Voltage (V)	0	1.1	1.95	3.15	3.9
Current (A)	0	0.5	1	1.5	2

Plot a graph of voltage against current and hence find the resistance of the coil.

11   When the four identical hotplates on a cooker are all in use, the current taken from a $240\,V$ supply is $33.3\,A$. Calculate (a) the resistance of each hotplate, (b) the current taken when only three hotplates are switched on. The hotplaces are connected in parallel.   [$28.8\,\Omega$; $25\,A$]

12   Calculate the total current when six $120\,\Omega$ torch bulbs are connected in parallel across a $9\,V$ supply of negligible internal resistance.   [$0.45\,A$]

13   When two identical fans are connected in series across a $240\,V$ supply, the total current is $0.52\,A$. Calculate (a) the voltage across each fan, (b) the resistance of each fan, (c) the current taken if the two fans are connected in parallel across the supply.   [$120\,V$; $231\,\Omega$; $2.08\,A$]

14   An electric kettle takes $12.5\,A$ from a $240\,V$ supply. Calculate the current that would flow if the kettle were connected across a $110\,V$ supply.   [$5.7\,A$]

15   The heating element of an indirectly heated thermionic valve takes a current of $0.38\,A$ when connected across $6.3\,V$. Calculate the current taken when eight such elements are connected in parallel across the same voltage. If the elements were connected in series, what would be the voltage required across the combination to give a current of $0.38\,A$?   [$3.04\,A$; $50.4\,V$]

16   A $200\,V$ generator supplies the following loads connected in parallel: five $400\,\Omega$ bulbs, eight $667\,\Omega$ bulbs, a $20\,\Omega$ electric fire, and an additional load taking $12.6\,A$. Calculate the total current supplied by the generator.   [$27.5\,A$]

17   A $12\,\Omega$ resistor is connected in parallel with a $15\,\Omega$ resistor and the combination is connected in series with a $9\,\Omega$ resistor and fed from a $12\,V$ supply. Calculate (a) the total resistance, (b) the current in the $9\,\Omega$ resistor, (c) the current in the $12\,\Omega$ resistor.   [$15.67\,\Omega$; $0.77\,A$, $0.43\,A$]

18   A factory wiring distribution system uses a cable with resistance $0.03\,\Omega$ per $100\,m$. If a load of $50\,A$ is fed after the first $60\,m$ and an unknown load after a further $80\,m$, calculate the resistance of the unknown load if the combination takes $100\,A$ from a $240\,V$ supply.   [$4.74\,\Omega$]

19   A soldering iron is designed to take $0.45\,A$ from a $110\,V$ supply. Calculate the current taken if two irons are connected in series across a $240\,V$ supply.   [$0.49\,A$]

20   Three relays, each with coil resistance $180\,\Omega$, are connected in parallel and the combination is connected in series with a resistor R_x. Calculate the value of R_x if the relays just operate when the complete network is supplied from 24 V. The current to make each relay just operate is 0.04 A.   [140 Ω]

21   An electric shaver takes 0.5 A from a 110 V supply. Calculate the resistance to be connected in series so that the combination takes the same current from a 240 V supply.   [260 Ω]

22   Two equal-value resistors are connected in series and are supplied from 200 V. A voltmeter of resistance 10 kΩ is connected in parallel with one of them. If the voltmeter reads 80 V, calculate (a) the value of the resistors, (b) the reading on the voltmeter if its resistance was only 5 kΩ.   [5 kΩ; 66.7 V]

23   An ammeter of resistance 0.1 Ω is connected in series with an unknown resistor R_x. If the voltage across the combination is 12 V and the reading on the ammeter is 2.5 A, calculate R_x.   [4.7 Ω]

24   Two loads, of 50 A and 30 A, are supplied via the same cable of resistance 0.02 Ω from a 120 V supply. Calculate the resistances of the two loads. [2.37 Ω; 3.95Ω]

25   Three resistors, with values 5 Ω, 6 Ω, and 7 Ω, are connected in parallel. The combination is connected in series with another parallel combination of 3 Ω and 4 Ω. If the complete circuit is connected across a 20 V supply, calculate (a) the total resistance, (b) the total current, (c) the voltage across the 3 Ω resistor, (d) the current in the 4 Ω resistor.   [3.68 Ω; 5.43 Ω; 9.31 Ω; 2.33 A]

26   Two resistors, of 18 Ω and 12 Ω, are connected in parallel and the combination is connected in series with an unknown resistor R_x. Calculate the value of R_x if the combination of the three resistors takes 0.6 A from a 12 V supply.   [12.8 Ω]

27   Two lathes connected in parallel take 12 A from a 240 V supply. If a milling machine with an electrical resistance of 13.3 Ω is also connected in parallel, calculate (a) the resistance of the total parallel combination, (b) the total current taken from the supply.   [8.0 Ω; 30 A]

28   Three loads, of value 24 A, 8 A, and 12 A, are supplied from a 200 V source. If a motor of resistance 2.4 Ω is also connected across the supply, calculate (a) the total resistance, (b) the total supply current.   [1.57 Ω; 127 A]

29   Two lamps take a total of 2.5 A when they are connected in parallel and fed from a 240 V supply via a 50 Ω resistor. Calculate the resistance to be connected in series if the same current is to be taken by only one lamp from the same supply.   [4 Ω]

30   Four resistors are connected to form a square ABCD. The values of the resistors are 6 Ω between AB, a variable resistor R between BC, a 2 Ω resistor between CD, and a 4 Ω resistor between DA. A 12 V d.c. supply is connected across AC and a high-resistance voltmeter between BD. Draw the circuit and calculate the reading on the voltmeter when R is set at (a) zero, (b) 3 Ω, (c) open circuit.   [4 V; 0 V; 8 V]

31   Two resistors, of values 15 Ω and 5 Ω, are connected in series with an unknown resistor and the combination is fed from a 240 V d.c. supply. If the p.d. across the 5 Ω resistor is 20 V, calculate the value of the unknown

resistor.   [40 Ω]

32   A 200 V 0.5 A lamp is to be connected in series with a resistor across a 240 V supply. Determine the value of the resistor for the lamp to operate at its correct voltage.   [80 Ω]

33   Two resistors, one of 12 Ω and the other 8 Ω, are connected in parallel across the terminals of a battery of e.m.f. 6 V and internal resistance 0.6 Ω. Draw a circuit diagram and calculate the current taken from the battery and the p.d. across the 8 Ω resistor.   [1.11 A; 5.33 V]

34   An electric-cooker element is made up of two resistors, each having a resistance of 18 Ω, which can be connected (a) in series, (b) in parallel, or (c) using one resistance only. Calculate the current taken by the cooker from a 240 V supply for each connection.   [6.67 A; 26.67 A; 13.33 A]

35   When 50 mC of charge are moved across a potential difference, 12 J of energy is used. Calculate the potential difference.   [240 V]

36   A 240 V supply feeds a current of 2 A for 5 hours. Calculate the energy used.   [8.64 MJ]

37   Calculate the supply voltage if 1.5 kJ of energy is used in 30 s when a current of 5 A flows in a resistor.   [10 V]

38   Calculate the energy used in one hour when an 8.3 Ω resistor is supplied from 240 V.   [24.98 MJ]

39   A battery with an e.m.f. of 4 V and an internal resistance of 0.2 Ω supplies a resistive load of 1.8 Ω. Determine (a) the circuit current, (b) the terminal voltage of the battery.   [2 A; 3.6 V]

40   A cell of e.m.f. 2 V and internal resistance 0.1 Ω has a voltmeter connected across its terminals. What will be the reading on the voltmeter (a) when no load is connected across the battery? (b) when a 2.9 Ω resistor is connected across the terminals? Explain why the answers to (a) and (b) are different. [2 V; 1.93 V]

41   An accumulator has a terminal voltage of 1.8 V when supplying a current of 9 A. The terminal voltage rises to 2.02 V when the load is removed. Calculate the internal resistance of the cell.   [0.024 Ω]

42   A voltmeter connected across a car battery reads 12.2 V. When the starter button is pressed the reading falls to 8.4 V. Calculate the starter current if the battery internal resistance is 0.18 Ω.   [21 A]

43   A battery has an open-circuit voltage of 12 V. When it is connected across two 80 Ω bulbs connected in parallel, the current is 0.29 A. Calculate (a) the internal resistance of the battery, (b) the terminal voltage when supplying the lamps.   [1.38 Ω; 11.6 V]

44   Four resistors, values 10 Ω, 20 Ω, 40 Ω, and 40 Ω, are connected in parallel across the terminals of a generator having an e.m.f. of 48 V and an internal resistance of 0.5 Ω. Draw the circuit diagram and calculate (a) the total circuit resistance, (b) the current taken from the generator, (c) the p.d. across each resistor, (d) the current in each resistor.   [5.5 Ω; 8.73 A; 43.6 V; 4.36 A, 2.18 A, 1.09 A, 1.09 A]

45   Determine the p.d. across the 3 Ω resistor in the network shown in fig. 2.24 when the e.m.f. applied to the terminals AB is 11 V.   [2 V]

46   Calculate the voltage across AB in fig. 2.25.   [18.75 V]

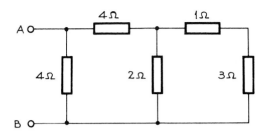

Fig. 2.24

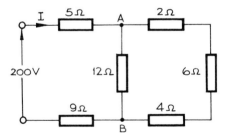

Fig. 2.25

47 For the network shown in fig. 2.26, calculate (a) the resistance of the total circuit, (b) the supply current I, (c) the p.d. between points A and B, (d) the total power dissipated in the circuit, (e) the power dissipated in the 12 Ω resistor. [20 Ω, 10 A; 60 V; 2 kW; 300 W]

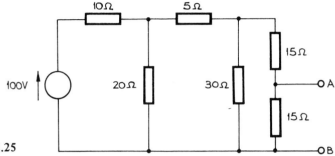

Fig. 2.26

48 A circuit consists of a 15 Ω and a 30 Ω resistor connected in parallel and is fed from a battery with an internal resistance of 2 Ω. If 60 W is dissipated in the 15 Ω resistor, calculate (a) the current in the 30 Ω resistor, (b) the terminal p.d. and the e.m.f. of the battery, (c) the total amount of energy converted in the external circuit in 1 minute, (d) the quantity of electricity that flows through the battery in 1 minute. [1 A; 30 V, 36 V; 5.4 kJ; 180 C]

49 A battery of open-circuit voltage 100 V and internal resistance r is connected to the terminals ab of the circuit shown in fig. 2.27. When switch

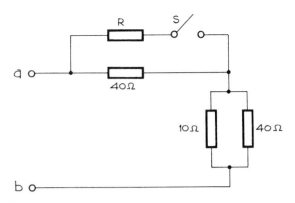

Fig. 2.27

S is open, the current supplied by the battery is 2 A. Find the value of *r* and the terminal voltage of the battery.

When switch S is closed, the voltage across R is twice that across the 10 Ω resistor. Calculate the value of *R* and the voltage across each parallel branch.

50   In the circuit of fig. 2.28, the battery supplies a current of 1 A. Calculate the value of the resistance *R* and the power dissipated by the 10 Ω resistor.   [16 Ω; 1.6 W]

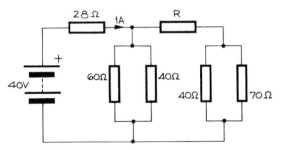

Fig. 2.28

51   In the circuit of fig. 2.29 the current in the resistor R is 2 A. Use Kirchhoff's laws to calculate the value of R.   [5.33 Ω]

52   Use Kirchhoff's laws to determine the magnitude and direction of the current in each branch of the circuit of fig. 2.30.   [2.63 A; −0.42 A; 2.21 A]

53   Calculate the current in the 15 Ω resistor of the circuit shown in fig. 2.31.   [0.73 A]

54   For the circuit shown in fig. 2.32, use Kirchhoff's laws to calculate the current supplied by each battery, the p.d. across the 4 Ω load resistor, and the power dissipated by the load resistor.   [1 A; 0.5 A; 6 V; 9 W]

55   For the circuit of fig. 2.33, use the superposition theorem to calculate the current in the 80 Ω resistor.   [0.588 A]

56   For the circuit of fig. 2.34, use the superposition theorem to calculate the current in the 4 Ω resistor.   [16 mA]

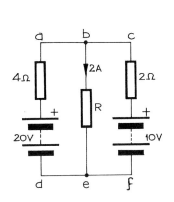

Fig. 2.29

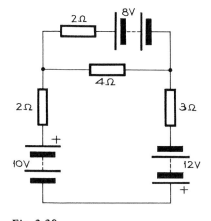

Fig. 2.30

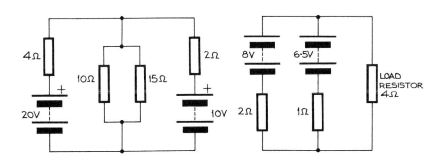

Fig. 2.31

Fig. 2.32

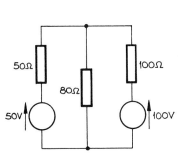

Fig. 2.33

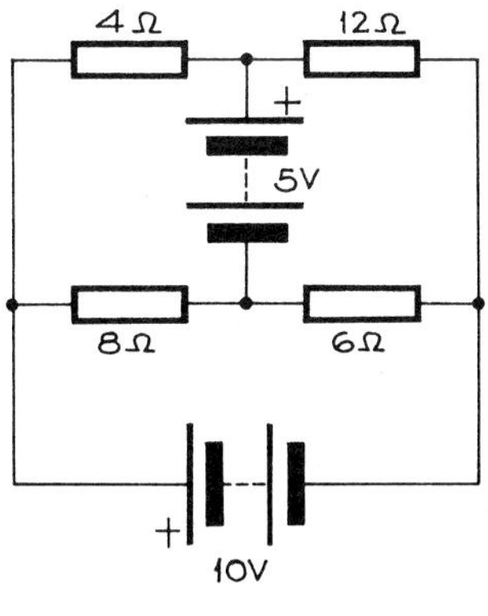

Fig. 2.34

41

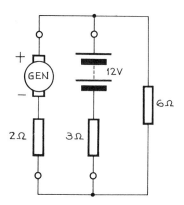

Fig. 2.35

57   Figure 2.35 shows a 12 V battery being charged from a generator such as a car dynamo. If the charging current is 2 A, calculate the terminal p.d. across the battery, the current in the 6 Ω resistor, the generator current, and the generator e.m.f.   [18 V; 3 A; 5 A; 28 V]

58   A circuit consists of two batteries, of 20 V and 24 V, connected in parallel. If the battery internal resistances are 2 Ω and 4 Ω respectively, calculate the current supplied by each battery to a 10 Ω load resistor connected across the combination. Also, calculate the current through and the voltage across the 10 Ω load resistor.   [1.29 A; 0.59 A; 1.88 A; 18.8 V]

3   Capacitors and capacitance

3.1 Electric charge

All bodies are made up of atoms. Atoms consist of a nucleus which has a positive charge and surrounding electrons which have a negative charge. When a body is uncharged it is said to be electrically neutral, and the total negative charge on the electrons is exactly equal to the positive charge on the nucleus. When a body is electrically charged, then it is no longer electrically neutral and it has either an excess of electrons (i.e. a negative charge) or a shortage of electrons (i.e. a positive charge).

The quantity of electric charge on a body is a measure of the number of electrons that the body has above or below the number required to make it electrically neutral. The symbol for electric charge is Q.

The unit of electric charge is the *coulomb* (abbreviation C). 6.28×10^{18} electrons would need to be grouped together to give a charge of one coulomb.

Now   quantity of charge = current × time

or $$Q = It$$

hence   1 coulomb = 1 ampere second

or $$1\,C = 1\,A\,s$$

Example   A uniform current of 10 A flows for 20 s. Calculate the quantity of charge that has flowed past a point in a conductor in this time.

$$Q = It$$

where $I = 10\,A$ and $t = 20\,s$

$\therefore$ $Q = 10\,A \times 20\,s = 200\,C$

i.e. the quantity of charge is 200 C.

Two bodies which are insulated from each other will become charged with opposite polarities when a potential difference (a voltage) is applied across them. This is the effect that occurs in the capacitor, and will be discussed in the following sections.

Force between charged bodies

It is found that there is a force of attraction between oppositely charged bodies. Try charging a balloon by rubbing it with, say, a woollen cloth. It can then be made to stick to the ceiling, due to the force of attraction between opposite charges. The charge on the balloon induces an opposite charge on the ceiling, and there is thus a force of attraction between the two. Conversely, bodies which have the same charge experience a force of repulsion between them.

Unlike charges attract; like charges repel.

The force between charged bodies is small, but is made use of in the electrostatic voltmeter, where the voltage to be measured causes two plates (one fixed, the other free to move) to be forced apart due to the force of repulsion between their charges. A pointer is attached to the moving plate and indicates on a dial the voltage applied across the plates.

3.2 Capacitors and capacitance

A *capacitor* is a device which stores energy in the form of an electric charge. When a voltage is applied across a capacitor, charge is stored in a way analogous to the way in which a bicycle tyre stores air when pumped up to a certain pressure with a bicycle pump. The larger the value of the capacitor, the more charge that it can store from a given voltage.

In its simplest form, a capacitor consists of two metal plates separated by a thin layer of insulating material called the *dielectric*, as shown in fig. 3.1 (a). The dielectric is basically an insulator, but, as will be seen later, the type of

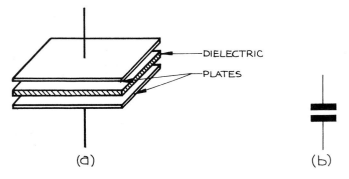

Fig. 3.1 A simple plate capacitor

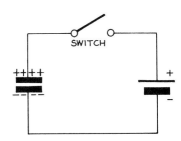

Fig. 3.2 Charging a capacitor

44

dielectric also affects the value and properties of the capacitor. The circuit symbol for a capacitor is shown in fig. 3.1 (b).

When a battery is connected across the capacitor as shown in fig. 3.2, and the switch is closed, electrons flow from the negative side of the battery to the lower plate, which accumulates a negative charge. The upper place accumulates an equal and opposite positive charge by electrons flowing from it to the positive terminal of the battery. The quantity of charge on the capacitor continues to increase until the voltage across the capacitor is equal to the battery e.m.f. The charging current then stops flowing. It should be noticed that, in charging the capacitor, the charge is not manufactured but is simply transferred from one plate to the other via the battery.

For a given capacitor, the total charge Q that is stored is proportional to the applied voltage V. This relationship between charge and voltage is constant for a given capacitor. The ratio is defined as *capacitance* and is given the symbol C:

$$\text{capacitance} = \frac{\text{charge}}{\text{voltage}}$$

or

$$C = \frac{Q}{V}$$

Capacitance is thus defined as the ratio of the charge stored in a capacitor to the applied voltage. The larger the capacitance, the larger will be the charge that is stored from a given voltage. The comparison may be made with the bicycle tyre: the larger the tyre, the larger the quantity of air that it can hold. Notice also that the quantity of stored charge depends on the magnitude of the applied voltage. Similarly, the quantity of air stored in the tyre depends on the pressure to which it is being inflated.

The unit of capacitance is the *farad* (abbreviation F). One farad is that capacitance which will accumulate a charge of one coulomb when connected across a voltage of one volt. This unit is so large that the submultiple which is used in practice is the microfarad (μF):

$$1\ \mu\text{F} = 10^{-6}\ \text{F}$$

Other submultiples of the unit in common use are the nanofarad (nF) and the picofarad (pF):

$$1\ \text{nF} = 10^{-9}\ \text{F}$$

$$1\ \text{pF} = 10^{-12}\ \text{F}$$

Example 1   A capacitor of value 100 μF has 50 V applied across it. Calculate the stored charge.

$$C = Q/V$$

$\therefore$ $Q = CV$

where $C = 100\,\mu\text{F} = 100 \times 10^{-6}\ \text{F}$ and $V = 50\,\text{V}$

$$\therefore \quad Q = 100 \times 10^{-6} \, \text{F} \times 50 \, \text{V}$$

$$= 5000 \times 10^{-6} \, \text{C} = 5 \, \text{mC}$$

i.e. the stored charge is 5 mC.

Example 2 A capacitor stores a charge of $250 \, \mu\text{C}$ when connected across a d.c. supply of 200 V. Calculate its capacitance.

$$C = Q/V$$

where $\quad Q = 250 \, \mu\text{C} = 250 \times 10^{-6} \, \text{C} \quad$ and $\quad V = 200 \, \text{V}$

$$\therefore \quad C = \frac{250 \times 10^{-6} \, \text{C}}{200 \, \text{V}}$$

$$= 1.25 \times 10^{-6} \, \text{F} = 1.25 \, \mu\text{F}$$

i.e. the capacitance is $1.25 \, \mu\text{F}$.

3.3 Electric fields and electric field strength

When a capacitor is charged, one of its plates has an excess of electrons and therefore a negative charge, while the other plate has a shortage of electrons and therefore an equal and opposite positive charge.

These charged plates cause an *electric field* to exist between them in a similar way to that in which a magnetic field exists between the poles of a magnet. An electric field may be defined as a region in which a charged particle will experience electrical forces. In a capacitor, the electric field exists mainly in the dielectric, and the field pattern is shown in fig. 3.3.

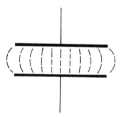

Fig. 3.3 Electric field between charged plates

The electric field is considered to be made up of electric flux (just as the magnetic field consists of magnetic flux, as we shall see in chapter 4). Electric flux has the symbol Ψ (psi) and has the same unit as charge. Electric flux is thus measured in coulombs (abbreviation C).

If the capacitor has a charge of Q coulombs, then the electric flux existing between the plates will be Ψ coulombs, where $\Psi = Q$.

The intensity of the electric field is called the *electric field strength* and has the symbol E. Electric field strength is defined as the voltage V between the plates divided by the thickness d of the dielectric:

$$E = -\frac{V}{d}$$

Notice that a minus sign is included in this expression. This is because electric fields have a direction as well as a magnitude. The direction of the field is defined as the direction in which a positive charge situated in the field would move. A positive charge would move away from the positive plate and towards the negative plate (i.e. unlike charges attract; like charges repel); for this reason the minus sign must be included in the expression for electric field strength. The minus sign will be ignored in the solving of problems, unless the direction is asked for.

The unit of electric field strength is the volt per metre (V/m). Alternative units are the kilovolt per metre (kV/m) and the megavolt per metre (MV/m). The V/mm and V/μm are also used.

The ratio V/d is sometimes called the *potential gradient* through the dielectric.

Example   A dielectric of thickness 20 μm has 250 V applied across it. Calculate the electric field strength in MV/m and V/μm.

$$E = V/d$$

where $V = 250\,\text{V}$ and $d = 20\,\mu\text{m} = 20 \times 10^{-6}\,\text{m}$

$$\therefore \quad E = \frac{250\,\text{V}}{20 \times 10^{-6}\,\text{m}} = 12.5 \times 10^6\,\text{V/m}$$

$$= 12.5\,\text{MV/m} \quad \text{or} \quad 12.5\,\text{V}/\mu\text{m}$$

i.e. the electric field strength is 12.5 MV/m, or 12.5 V/μm.

3.4 Electric flux density
In a capacitor, the electric flux exists in the dielectric, and the electric flux density D is defined as the electric flux Ψ in the dielectric divided by the cross-sectional area A;

i.e. $$D = \frac{\Psi}{A}$$

Since $\Psi = Q$, then

$$D = \frac{Q}{A}$$

The unit of electric flux density is the coulomb per square metre (C/m^2). More convenient units are the mC/m^2 and μC/m^2.

Example   A 200 pF capacitor is made up of two plates of cross-sectional area 100 cm^2. Calculate the charge in the capacitor and the electric flux density when 150 V is applied across the capacitor.

$$Q = CV$$

where $C = 200\,\text{pF} = 200 \times 10^{-12}\,\text{F}$ and $V = 150\,\text{V}$

$\therefore \quad Q = 200 \times 10^{-12}\,\text{F} \times 150\,\text{V}$

$\qquad = 30\,000 \times 10^{-12}\,\text{C} = 30\,\text{nC}$

Now $D = Q/A$

where $A = 100\,\text{cm}^2 = 100 \times 10^{-4}\,\text{m}^2$

$\therefore \quad D = \dfrac{30 \times 10^{-9}\,\text{C}}{100 \times 10^{-4}\,\text{m}^2}$

$\qquad = 3 \times 10^{-6}\,\text{C/m}^2 = 3\,\mu\text{C/m}^2$

i.e. the charge is 30 nC and the electric flux density is $3\,\mu\text{C/m}^2$.

3.5 Factors affecting the capacitance of a capacitor

Consider again the arrangement of fig. 3.1 (a). This shows the capacitor made up of two metal plates separated by a dielectric. The value of the capacitor (i.e. its capacitance) depends on

a) the type of dielectric used between the plates,
b) the area of overlap of the plates (A),
c) the spacing between the plates (d).

Any insulating material may be used as the dielectric, but some materials give a higher capacitance than others and are therefore often preferred. Each type of dielectric has a property called its *absolute permittivity* which has the symbol ϵ (epsilon). Absolute permittivity is a constant for a given material and may be considered as 'the extent to which a dielectric allows itself to be charged from a given voltage when used in a capacitor'.

The capacitance (C) of a capacitor is related to the absolute permittivity and is given by the equation

$$C = \frac{\epsilon A}{d}$$

where ϵ is the absolute permittivity in farads per metre (F/m),

A is the area of overlap of the plates in square metres (m^2),

and d is the distance between the plates in metres (m).

When there is nothing (i.e. a vacuum) between the plates, the permittivity is called the *permittivity of free space* and has the symbol ϵ_0. The value of ϵ_0 is 8.85×10^{-12} F/m, or 8.85 pF/m.

The capacitance of a capacitor with a vacuum between the plates is given by

$$C = \frac{\epsilon_0 A}{d}$$

The absolute permittivity of a dielectric material is normally stated relative to that of a vacuum and is given by

$$\epsilon = \epsilon_0 \epsilon_r$$

where ϵ_r is called the *relative permittivity*. The relative permittivity of a particular dielectric is therefore the ratio of the absolute permittivity of that dielectric to the permittivity of free space:

$$\epsilon_r = \frac{\epsilon}{\epsilon_0}$$

Since relative permittivity is a ratio of like quantities, it has no units.

The more usual form of the equation for capacitance is

$$C = \frac{\epsilon_0 \epsilon_r A}{d}$$

When a capacitor has air between its plates, its capacitance is 1.0006 times the value it would have if instead of air there were a vacuum between the plates. This difference is so small that it is usually ignored, and the relative permittivity of air is taken as 1.0.

Materials used as dielectrics in capacitors include air, mica, oil-impregnated paper, polyester, polycarbonate, polystyrene, and ceramic, as well as aluminium oxide and tantalum oxide which are used as dielectrics in electrolytic capacitors (see section 3.12). Typical relative permittivities of these materials are given in Table 3.1.

Table 3.1 Typical values of relative permittivity of dielectric materials

Dielectric material	Relative permittivity
Dry air	1.0
Polypropylene	2.25
Polystyrene	2.5
Polycarbonate	2.8
Polyester	3.2
Impregnated paper	4–5
Mica	6
Aluminium oxide	7.5
Tantalum oxide	25
High-permittivity ceramic	10 000

Example 1   A plate capacitor with air as the dielectric has a capacitance of 0.01 μF. When a sheet of mica is substituted as the dielectric, the capacitance increases to 0.056 μF. Calculate the relative permittivity of the mica.

Since the relative permittivity of air is approximately 1, we may assume for practical purposes that the relative permittivity of a dielectric means how much greater the permittivity of the dielectric is than that of air. Since the dimensions of the capacitor are the same in both cases, the relative permittivity is given by the ratio of the capacitance values:

$$\epsilon_r = \frac{0.056\ \mu F}{0.01\ \mu F} = 5.6$$

i.e. the relative permittivity of the mica is 5.6.

Example 2   A capacitor is constructed from two sheets of aluminium foil, each of area 200 cm². The plates are separated by a sheet of waxed paper 20 μm thick. Calculate the capacitance of the capacitor if the relative permittivity of the dielectric is 2.5.

$$C = \frac{\epsilon_0\ \epsilon_r\ A}{d}$$

where $\epsilon_0 = 8.85 \times 10^{-12}$ F/m $\epsilon_r = 2.5$

$A = 200\ cm^2 = 200 \times 10^{-4}\ m^2$

and $d = 20\mu m = 20 \times 10^{-6}\ m$

$$\therefore\ C = \frac{8.85 \times 10^{-12}\ F/m \times 2.5 \times 200 \times 10^{-4}\ m^2}{20 \times 10^{-6}\ m}$$

$$= 0.022\ \mu F$$

i.e. the capacitance is 0.022 μF.

Example 3   An electrolytic capacitor is made from two plates of area 400 cm² with an aluminium-oxide dielectric 4 μm thick. If the value of the capacitor is 0.68 μF, calculate the absolute and relative permittivities of the dielectric.

$$C = \epsilon A/d$$

$$\therefore\quad \epsilon = Cd/A$$

where $C = 0.68\ \mu F = 0.68 \times 10^{-6}$ F $d = 4\mu m = 4 \times 10^{-6}\ m$

and $A = 400\ cm^2 = 400 \times 10^{-4}\ m^2$

$$\therefore\quad \epsilon = \frac{0.68 \times 10^{-6}\ F \times 4 \times 10^{-6}\ m}{400 \times 10^{-4}\ m^2}$$

$$= 68 \times 10^{-12}\ F/m = 68\ pF/m$$

The relative permittivity is given by

$$\epsilon_r = \epsilon/\epsilon_0$$

$$= \frac{68\,\text{pF/m}}{8.85\,\text{pF/m}} = 7.68$$

i.e. the absolute and relative permittivities of aluminium oxide are 68 pF/m and 7.68 respectively.

3.6 Relationship between ϵ, D, and E.

The ratio of electric flux density D to electric field strength E is the absolute permittivity ϵ of a dielectric material:

$$\epsilon = \frac{D}{E}$$

This is in fact the definition of permittivity, and gives a convenient means of deriving the equation for the capacitance of a plate capacitor given in section 3.5.

$$D = \frac{Q}{A} \quad \text{and} \quad E = \frac{V}{d}$$

$$\therefore \quad \epsilon = \frac{Q/A}{V/d} = \frac{Qd}{VA}$$

But $\quad Q = CV$

$$\therefore \quad \epsilon = \frac{CVd}{VA} = \frac{Cd}{A}$$

$$\therefore \quad C = \frac{\epsilon A}{d}$$

This is the equation for the capacitance of a plate capacitor with plate area A, dielectric thickness d, and absolute dielectric permittivity ϵ.

Example A capacitor is made up of two metal plates, each having an area of 0.02 m^2 and spaced 2.5 mm apart. A potential difference of 250 V across the plates establishes a charge of 50 nC. Calculate (a) the electric field strength, (b) the electric flux density, (c) the absolute permittivity of the dielectric, (d) the relative permittivity of the dielectric.

a) $E = V/d$

where $V = 250\,\text{V}$ and $d = 2.5\,\text{mm} = 2.5 \times 10^{-3}\,\text{m}$

$$\therefore \quad E = \frac{250\,\text{V}}{2.5 \times 10^{-3}}$$

$$= 100 \times 10^{3}\,\text{V/m} = 100\,\text{V/mm}$$

b) $D = Q/A$

where $Q = 50\,\text{nC} = 50 \times 10^{-9}\,\text{C}$ and $A = 0.02\,\text{m}^2$

$\therefore \quad D = \dfrac{50 \times 10^{-9}\,\text{C}}{0.02\,\text{m}^2}$

$\qquad = 2.5 \times 10^{-6}\,\text{C/m}^2 = 2.5\,\mu\text{C/m}^2$

c) $\epsilon = \dfrac{D}{E} = \dfrac{2.5 \times 10^{-6}\,\text{C/m}^2}{100 \times 10^3\,\text{V/m}}$

$\qquad = 25 \times 10^{-12}\,(\text{C/V})/\text{m} = 25\,\text{pF/m}$

d) $\epsilon_r = \dfrac{\epsilon}{\epsilon_0} = \dfrac{25 \times 10^{-12}\,\text{F/m}}{8.85 \times 10^{-12}\,\text{F/m}}$

$\qquad = 2.82$

i.e. the electric field strength is $100\,\text{V/mm}$, the electric flux density is $2.5\,\mu\text{C/m}^2$, the absolute permittivity is $25\,\text{pF/m}$, and the relative permittivity is 2.82.

3.7 Capacitors in parallel
When capacitors are connected in parallel, as shown in fig. 3.4, their resultant capacitance (C_T) is equal to the sum of their separate values,

i.e. $C_T = C_1 + C_2 + C_3$

This is just the opposite to the case for resistors in parallel. The proof of the equation is as follows.

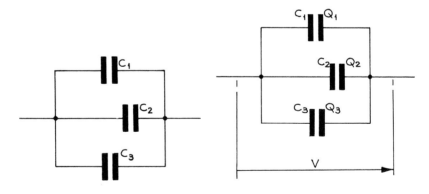

Fig. 3.4 Capacitors in parallel   **Fig. 3.5**

Consider the three capacitors connected in parallel as shown in fig. 3.5. When the switch is closed, the same voltage appears across each capacitor, and the charging current which flows into each capacitor is determined by the capacitance of that capacitor. The single capacitance which is equivalent to that of the three capacitors in parallel is given by C_T, where

$$Q = C_T V$$

But $\quad Q = Q_1 + Q_2 + Q_3$

$\therefore \quad C_T V = C_1 V + C_2 V + C_3 V$

$\therefore \quad C_T = C_1 + C_2 + C_3$

Example Two capacitors, of values $2\,\mu\text{F}$ and $6\,\mu\text{F}$, are connected in parallel across a d.c. supply of 40 V. Calculate (a) the total capacitance, (b) the charge on each capacitor, (c) the total charge stored by the combination.

a) $\quad C_T = C_1 + C_2$

$\quad\quad = 2\,\mu\text{F} + 6\,\mu\text{F} = 8\,\mu\text{F}$

b) $\quad Q = CV$

$\therefore \quad Q_1 = C_1 V = 2\,\mu\text{F} \times 40\,\text{V} = 80\,\mu\text{C}$

$\quad\quad Q_2 = C_2 V = 6\,\mu\text{F} \times 40\,\text{V} = 240\,\mu\text{C}$

c) $\quad$ Total charge $= 80\,\mu\text{C} + 240\,\mu\text{C}$

$\quad\quad\quad\quad = 320\,\mu\text{C}$

i.e. the total capacitance is $8\,\mu\text{F}$, the charges on the capacitors are $80\,\mu\text{C}$ and $240\,\mu\text{C}$, and the total charge is $320\,\mu\text{C}$.

3.8 Capacitors in series

When capacitors are connected in series, as shown in fig. 3.6, their resultant capacitance (C_T) is given by the equation

$$\frac{1}{C_T} = \frac{1}{C_1} + \frac{1}{C_2} + \frac{1}{C_3}$$

The proof of the equation is as follows.

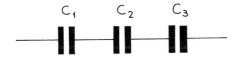

Fig. 3.6 Capacitors in series

Consider three capacitors connected in series as shown in fig. 3.7. When the switch is closed, the same charging current must flow into each capacitor for the same length of time, and therefore the charge $(Q = It)$ given to each capacitor must be the same. The voltages across the capacitors are thus given by:

53

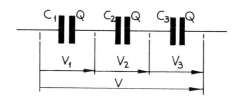

Fig. 3.7

$$V_1 = \frac{Q}{C_1} \qquad V_2 = \frac{Q}{C_2} \quad \text{and} \quad V_3 = \frac{Q}{C_3}$$

The single capacitance which is equivalent to that of the three capacitors in series is given by C_T, where

$$V = \frac{Q}{C_T}$$

But $\quad V = V_1 + V_2 + V_3$

$$\therefore \quad \frac{Q}{C_T} = \frac{Q}{C_1} + \frac{Q}{C_2} + \frac{Q}{C_3}$$

$$\therefore \quad \frac{1}{C_T} = \frac{1}{C_1} + \frac{1}{C_2} + \frac{1}{C_3}$$

Example Two capacitors, of values $2\,\mu F$ and $6\,\mu F$, are connected in series across a d.c. supply of 50 V. Calculate (a) the total capacitance, (b) the total charge stored by the combination, (c) the charge on each capacitor, (d) the voltage across each capacitor.

a) $\quad \dfrac{1}{C_T} = \dfrac{1}{C_1} + \dfrac{1}{C_2}$

$$= \frac{1}{2\,\mu F} + \frac{1}{6\,\mu F} = \frac{3+1}{6\,\mu F} = \frac{4}{6\,\mu F}$$

$\therefore \quad C_T = 6\,\mu F/4 = 1.5\,\mu F$

b) $\quad Q = CV$

where $\quad C = 1.5\,\mu F \quad$ and $\quad V = 50\,V$

$\therefore \qquad Q = 1.5\,\mu F \times 50\,V = 75\,\mu C$

c) The charge on each capacitor is equal to the charge on the equivalent single capacitor:

$$Q_1 = Q_2 = 75\,\mu C$$

54

d) $V_1 = \dfrac{Q_1}{C_1} = \dfrac{75\,\mu C}{2\,\mu F} = 37.5\,V$

$V_2 = \dfrac{Q_2}{C_2} = \dfrac{75\,\mu C}{6\,\mu F} = 12.5\,V$

i.e. the total capacitance is $1.5\,\mu F$, the total stored charge is $75\,\mu C$, the charge on each capacitor is $75\,\mu C$, and the voltage across the capacitors are $37.5\,V$ and $12.5\,V$.

Notice that the individual voltages add up to the total applied voltage. Notice also that the charge on each capacitor is the same and is equal to the charge on the equivalent single capacitor.

3.9 Capacitors in series–parallel combinations

Capacitors are often connected in combinations more complex than those just discussed, and the method of performing calculations in such cases is best demonstrated by some examples. In these examples we shall limit the number of capacitors to three.

Example 1   A capacitor network is made up as shown in fig. 3.8, and a 100 V d.c. supply is connected across AC. Calculate (a) the total capacitance, (b) the total charge stored, (c) the voltage across each capacitor.

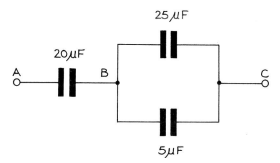

Fig. 3.8

a) The equivalent capacitance of $25\,\mu F$ and $5\,\mu F$ in parallel is given by

$$C_{BC} = 25\,\mu F + 5\,\mu F = 30\,\mu F$$

The equivalent capacitance of C_{AB} and C_{BC} in series is given by

$$\frac{1}{C_{AC}} = \frac{1}{C_{AB}} + \frac{1}{C_{BC}}$$

$$= \frac{1}{20\,\mu F} + \frac{1}{30\,\mu F} = \frac{3+2}{60\,\mu F}$$

$\therefore$ $C_{AC} = 60\,\mu F/5 = 12\,\mu F$

b) The total charge stored is given by

$$Q = C_{AC} \, V$$
$$= 12 \, \mu F \times 100 \, V = 1200 \, \mu C$$

c) The voltages across AB and BC are given by

$$V_{AB} = \frac{Q}{C_{AB}} = \frac{1200 \, \mu C}{20 \, \mu F} = 60 \, V$$

$$V_{BC} = \frac{Q}{C_{BC}} = \frac{1200 \, \mu C}{30 \, \mu F} = 40 \, V$$

i.e. the total capacitance is $12 \, \mu F$, the total charge stored is $1200 \, \mu C$, and the voltages across the capacitors are 60 V and 40 V.

Example 2   If in the series capacitor network shown in fig. 3.9 the voltage across AB is required to be exactly one third of the voltage across BC, show where an additional capacitor would need to be connected and calculate its value.

Fig. 3.9

We require that $V_{AB} = \frac{1}{3} V_{BC}$

Now $V = Q/C$; i.e. in a series capacitor combination, the voltage across a capacitor is inversely proportional to the value of the capacitor. To make $V_{AB} = \frac{1}{3} V_{BC}$ requires that

$$C_{AB} = 3 \, C_{BC}$$

But $C_{BC} = 5 \, \mu F$

$\therefore$ $C_{AB} = 15 \, \mu F$

i.e the additional capacitor is $10 \, \mu F$ across AB.

Example 3   The variable capacitance C_v in the network shown in fig. 3.10 is adjusted to $4 \, \mu F$, and a 500 V d.c. supply is connected across terminals AC. Calculate (a) the total capacitance, (b) the charge on the $6 \, \mu F$ capacitor, (c) the value of C_v required to produce a voltage of 100 V across the $6 \, \mu F$ capacitor.

a) The equivalent capacitance (C_s) of $4 \, \mu F$ and $6 \, \mu F$ in series is given by

$$\frac{1}{C_s} = \frac{1}{4 \, \mu F} + \frac{1}{6 \, \mu F} = \frac{3 + 2}{12 \, \mu F}$$

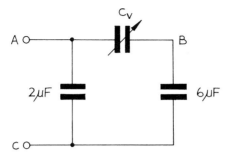

Fig. 3.10

∴ $C_s = 12\,\mu F/5 = 2.4\,\mu F$

∴ total capacitance $C_{AC} = 2\,\mu F + 2.4\,\mu F$

$$= 4.4\,\mu F$$

b) The charge on C_s is given by

$$Q_s = C_s V$$

$$= 2.4\,\mu F \times 500\,V = 1200\,\mu C$$

Since the $4\,\mu F$ and $6\,\mu F$ capacitors are in series, the charge on each of them is also $1200\,\mu C$.

c) If C_v is now varied such that the voltage across the $6\,\mu F$ capacitor is $100\,V$, then the new value of Q_s is

$$Q_s = CV$$

where $C = 6\,\mu F$ and $V = 100\,V$

∴ $Q_s = 600\,\mu C$

Now $C_v = Q_s/V_{AB}$

where $Q_s = 600\,\mu C$ and $V_{AB} = 500\,V - 100\,V = 400\,V$

∴ $C_v = \dfrac{600\,\mu C}{400\,V} = 1.5\,\mu F$

i.e. the total capacitance is $4.4\,\mu F$, the charge on the $6\,\mu F$ capacitor is $1200\,\mu C$, and the new value of C_v required is $1.5\,\mu F$.

Example 4   An unknown capacitance C_x is connected in a network as shown in fig. 3.11, and a d.c. voltage of $100\,V$ is applied across the terminals AC. Calculate (a) the value of C_x given that the total capacitance is $30\,pF$, (b) the electric field strength in V/mm across capacitor C_x if its dielectric is $2\,mm$ thick.

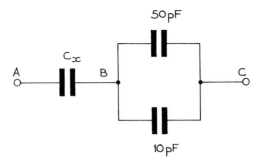

Fig. 3.11

a) $C_{BC} = 50\,\text{pF} + 10\,\text{pF} = 60\,\text{pF}$

$$\frac{1}{C_{AC}} = \frac{1}{C_{AB}} + \frac{1}{C_{BC}}$$

$\therefore \quad \dfrac{1}{C_{AB}} = \dfrac{1}{C_{AC}} - \dfrac{1}{C_{BC}}$

$$= \frac{1}{30\,\text{pF}} - \frac{1}{60\,\text{pF}} = \frac{2-1}{60\,\text{pF}}$$

$\therefore \quad C_{AB} = 60\,\text{pF} = C_x$

b) To calculate the electric field strength, we need to know the voltage across the capacitor.

Since $C_{AB} = C_{BC} = 60\,\text{pF}$, then the voltage across AB is exactly half of the voltage across AC.

$\therefore \quad V_{AB} = 50\,\text{V}$

$\therefore \quad$ electric field strength $= \dfrac{50\,\text{V}}{2\,\text{mm}} = 25\,\text{V/mm}$

i.e. the value of C_x is 60 pF and the electric field strength is 25 V/mm.

3.10 Dielectric strength

When an insulator breaks down, it suddenly becomes a low resistance and passes a larger than normal current. (All insulators pass some leakage current, although this is normally very small – in the order of microamperes.) Dielectric strength relates to the voltage that a dielectric can withstand without break-down occurring. It is measured in volts per metre (V/m), and the thicker the dielectric the greater is its ability to withstand breakdown.

If a dielectric of thickness d can withstand voltages up to a maximum level V, then

$$\text{dielectric strength} = \frac{V}{d}$$

Alternatively, the maximum voltage V that a dielectric can withstand is given by

$$V = \text{dielectric strength} \times d$$

For a given capacitor, the thickness of the dielectric is fixed, and the maximum voltage that the capacitor can withstand is defined as the maximum working voltage.

Capacitors available commercially are normally marked with their capacitance and their maximum working voltage. The voltage may be stated as 'd.c. wkg' (i.e. d.c. working voltage) or as 'a.c. r.m.s.' (i.e. root-mean-square working voltage). For example, a capacitor marked 0.015/400 is a 0.015 μF capacitor with a maximum d.c. working voltage of 400 V and may be used at any voltage up to this value. When used on a.c., the peak voltage should not exceed the d.c. rating of the capacitor.

Example 1   A ceramic capacitor has a dielectric of thickness 0.005 mm and is rated at 60 V d.c. wkg. Calculate the dielectric strength in V/μm.

Dielectric strength = V/d

where $V = 60\,\text{V}$ and $d = 0.005\,\text{mm} = 5\,\mu\text{m}$

$\therefore$ dielectric strength = $\dfrac{60\,\text{V}}{5\,\mu\text{m}}$ = $12\,\text{V}/\mu\text{m}$

i.e. the dielectric strength is 12 V/μm.

Example 2   Aluminium oxide is the dielectric in one type of electrolytic capacitor and has a dielectric strength of 1000 V/μm. Calculate the voltage rating of a capacitor whose dielectric is 0.005 mm thick.

V = dielectric strength $\times d$

where   dielectric strength = $1000\,\text{V}/\mu\text{m}$

and $d = 0.005\,\text{mm} = 5\,\mu\text{m}$

$\therefore$ $V = 1000\,\text{V}/\mu\text{m} \times 5\,\mu\text{m}$

$= 5000\,\text{V} = 5\,\text{kV}$

i.e. the capacitor is rated at 5 kV.

3.11 Energy stored in a capacitor

When a voltage is applied across the terminals of a capacitor, energy is stored in the form of an electric field. The quantity of stored energy is given by the equation

$$\text{energy} = \tfrac{1}{2}CV^2$$

where energy is, of course, measured in joules. This equation may be proved as follows.

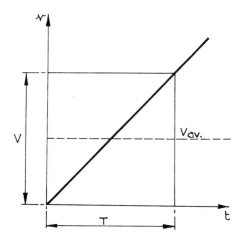

Fig. 3.12 Variation of voltage across a capacitor with a constant charging current

Consider the voltage v across a capacitor to be uniformly increasing with time t as shown in fig. 3.12. In a time T seconds the voltage has increased to V volts and the capacitor (value C) has become charged with Q coulombs, where

$$Q = CV$$

The charging current flowing into the capacitor during time T is constant at

$$I = \frac{Q}{T} = \frac{CV}{T}$$

The average voltage across the capacitor over the period T is

$$V_{av.} = V/2$$

Therefore the average rate of energy conversion by the capacitor during this period is given by

$$\text{average power} = I \times V_{av.}$$
$$= \frac{CV}{T} \times \frac{V}{2} = \frac{CV^2}{2T}$$

60

Therefore the energy W stored in the capacitor during this time is given by

$$W = \text{average power} \times \text{time}$$

$$= \frac{CV^2}{2T} \times T$$

$$= \tfrac{1}{2}CV^2$$

Example Calculate the energy stored by a capacitor of $1000\,\mu\text{F}$ which has been charged to 250 V d.c. If this energy could be discharged at a constant rate into a 60 W lamp, calculate the time for which the lamp would be illuminated.

$$W = \tfrac{1}{2}CV^2$$

where $C = 1000\,\mu\text{F} = 1000 \times 10^{-6}\,\text{F}$ and $V = 250\,\text{V}$

$\therefore$ $W = \tfrac{1}{2} \times 1000 \times 10^{-6}\,\text{F} \times (250\,\text{V})^2$

$= 31.25\,\text{J}$

Now   energy = power $\times$ time

$\therefore$ $\text{time} = \dfrac{\text{energy}}{\text{power}}$

where   energy = $31.25\,\text{J}$ and   power = 60 W

$\therefore$ $\text{time} = \dfrac{31.25\,\text{J}}{60\,\text{W}} \approx 0.5\,\text{second}$

i.e. the energy stored is 31.25 J and the 60 W lamp would be lit for about 0.5 second.

3.12 Dielectric materials in capacitors

Capacitors are made using a variety of dielectric materials. The factors which affect the choice of the best capacitor for a particular application are complex, and each dielectric has its own particular characteristics.

The parameters (features) with which the user is normally concerned are the capacitance (the capacitor value), the working voltage (the voltage that the capacitor can withstand without breaking down), the tolerance (the percentage deviation from a specified value), and the stability (the total change of capacitance during the life of the capacitor or during a change of environmental condition), as well as the size and price. Other parameters of concern are the insulation resistance (or the leakage resistance across the dielectric) and the temperature coefficient (the percentage change of capacitance value with change of temperature).

The simplest capacitors consist of two sheets of aluminium foil separated by a layer of flexible dielectric which is then rolled into a tubular shape as shown in fig. 3.13. This forms a compact device for insertion into printed-

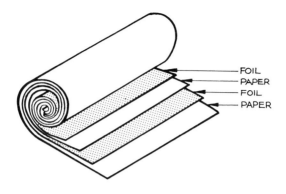

Fig. 3.13 One form of capacitor construction

circuit boards, and the tubular shape is sometimes flattened to take up less room. Most plastics- and paper-dielectric capacitors are made using this construction. Electrolytic capacitors of the aluminium-oxide type, are made by rolling long sheets of aluminium foil and paper into a tubular shape after an oxide layer has been formed on the aluminium foil.

The different types of dielectric material in common use in capacitors, together with their particular features, are listed below.

Polyester
This dielectric material gives a compact capacitor with good electrical and temperature characteristics. Polyester capacitors are cheap and typically range from 0.001 μF to 10 μF, with working voltages up to 750 V d.c. wkg. Typical tolerances are ± 20%. They are not suitable for high-frequency use.

Polycarbonate
This material has better electrical characteristics than polyester, particularly with regard to its insulation resistance and temperature coefficient. These advantages make polycarbonate capacitors suitable for use in timing and other high-stability applications. Values typically range from 0.01 μF to 10 μF, with voltages up to 630 V d.c wkg and tolerances of ± 20%.

Silvered mica
The most accurate and reliable capacitors use a dielectric made of mica. They are well suited for applications where high stability is required, such as in tuned circuits, filters, etc. They consist of a thin sheet of mica which is coated with a silver compound, fired, made up into a capacitor, adjusted, and then finally encased. They have values which typically range from 2 pF to 10 000 pF at voltages up to 350 V d.c. wkg. Their tolerance is typically ± 1%, and they are rather expensive.

62

Mixed dielectric

This is made from paper impregnated with polyester and assembled as a tubular foil construction. Mixed-dielectric capacitors are physically larger than metallised-film types (e.g silvered mica) but are good general-purpose types suitable for mains applications such as suppression circuits etc. Typical values range from $0.001\,\mu F$ to $1\,\mu F$, with working voltages up to $1000\,V$ d.c. and tolerances of $\pm\,20\%$.

*Polystyrene

Polystyrene dielectric gives a high insulation resistance with good electrical properties. Its maximum operating temperature ($85\,^\circ C$) is lower than that for polyester ($125\,^\circ C$) and polycarbonate ($125\,^\circ C$) types. Polystyrene-dielectric capacitors are physically smaller than mica types and typically range from $10\,pF$ to $10\,000\,pF$, with working voltages up to $160\,V$ d.c. wkg and typical tolerances of $\pm\,2\frac{1}{2}\%$.

Polypropylene

This is a low-loss dielectric suitable for continuous use at high a.c. voltages. It will withstand high voltage and fast-rise time pulses and has good high-frequency performance. Polypropylene-dielectric capacitors have a smaller physical size and better electrical performance than mixed-dielectric types. Typical values range from $0.01\,\mu F$ to $0.1\,\mu F$, with working voltages up to $1250\,V$ d.c. wkg and typical tolerances of $\pm\,20\%$.

High-capacity paper

This dielectric is made of paper impregnated with wax or oil and is rather bulky. It has poor stability but is frequently used in power-factor-correction and suppression circuits, where a high-capacity, high-voltage, non-polarised capacitor is required. Typical capacitor values range from $1\,\mu F$ to $10\,\mu F$, with working voltages up to $600\,V$ d.c. wkg and tolerances of $\pm\,20\%$.

Plate ceramic

Plate-ceramic capacitors consist of metallic coatings on the opposite faces of a thin disc of ceramic material. They are mainly used in high-frequency circuits subject to wide variation of temperature and have close tolerance, high stability, and low loss. Typical values range from $2.2\,pF$ to $0.1\,\mu F$, with working voltages up to $750\,V$ d.c. wkg and tolerances of $\pm\,2\%$.

Electrolytic

Electrolytic capacitors are used where a large capacitance is required together with a small physical size. They have either an aluminium-oxide-film or a tantalum-oxide dielectric and capacitances up to about $100\,000\,\mu F$. The most common type consists of two sheets of aluminium foil separated by paper impregnated with a conducting electrolyte. When a charging current flows, a thin oxide film is formed on one of the foils, and this film is the dielectric. The high capacitance with small volume derives from the extreme thinness of the dielectric coupled with a high dielectric strength.

Electrolytic capacitors depend on the applied voltage to maintain the oxide film electrolytically, and disuse or reverse polarity may cause this film to degenerate. For this reason, electrolytic capacitors must have the correct voltage polarity connected across them and should not be reversed, or else they are liable to explode.

Electrolytic capacitors also have a relatively high leakage current. This is due to current leakage through the dielectric, which happens in any dielectric to a greater or lesser extent. Electrolytic capacitors are thus unsuitable for oscillators or tuned circuits where a high insulation resistance is required.

Typical capacitances range from $0.1\,\mu F$ to $10\,000\,\mu F$, with working voltages up to 450 V d.c. wkg and tolerances of $+100\%$ and -25%.

Air
Air is commonly used as the dielectric in variable capacitors. These are constructed as shown in fig. 3.14, with two sets of interleaving plates insulated from each other by air. The capacitance is varied by rotating the spindle to change the area of overlap of the plates. They are most frequently used as the tuning capacitor in radio receivers.

Fig. 3.14 Variable air-dielectric capacitor

Various types of capacitor are shown in fig. 3.15, and typical relative permittivities of a variety of dielectrics were given in Table 3.1.

3.13 Applications of capacitors
Some of the uses of capacitors are as follows:
a) to store charge in direct-current circuits where they are used as a charge reservoir, such as the reservoir capacitor in a d.c. power-supply circuit;
b) to act as a coupling capacitor in alternating-current circuits, where they allow the a.c. voltage on one side of the capacitor to appear on the other side while acting as a block to d.c. voltage, such as the coupling capacitor between two a.c. amplifiers;
c) to provide a timing circuit, where the charging time of the capacitor may be varied by variation of the charging resistor;
d) when coupled with an inductor, to provide a frequency-tuned circuit such that the combined circuit resonates (oscillates most easily) at one particular frequency;

SINGLE – ENDED
ELECTROLYTIC CAPACITOR

RECTANGULAR POLYESTER
CAPACITOR

DOUBLE – ENDED
ELECTROLYTIC CAPACITOR

SOLID – TANTALUM
ELECTROLYTIC CAPACITOR

POLYCARBONATE CAPACITOR

TUBULAR POLYESTER
CAPACITORS

POLYSTYRENE CAPACITORS

MIXED – DIELECTRIC
CAPACITOR

SILVERED – MICA
CAPACITOR

Fig. 3.15 Various types of capacitor

65

e) to prevent arcing in switching circuits, such as across the contact breaker on the distributor of a motor car;

f) to provide power-factor correction for inductive loads such as induction motors and fluorescent-lamp circuits;

g) to act as a decoupling capacitor across d.c. supply-voltage rails so that voltage ripple is reduced.

Example　State the type of capacitor which would be preferred for each of the following applications:

a) a variable tuning capacitor for use as a radio tuner,
b) a large reservoir capacitor,
c) connection across an inductor to provide a very stable tuned circuit,
d) a cheap coupling capacitor,
e) a large-value capacitor for power-factor correction.

The preferred type of capacitor would be: (a) a variable air capacitor; (b) an electrolytic capacitor; (c) a silvered-mica or possibly a plate-ceramic or polystyrene capacitor; (d) a polyester capacitor, although other types would do equally well; (e) a high-capacity paper capacitor.

Exercises on chapter 3

1　State briefly the main applications of a capacitor, and explain what happens when a d.c. voltage is applied across an uncharged capacitor.

2　A 100 μF capacitor has 400 V d.c. applied across it. Calculate the total charge accumulated.　[40 mC]

3　A human body with a capacitance of 200 pF is charged to 1.2 kV when removing a nylon coat. Calculate the stored charge.　[240 nC]

4　A reservoir capacitor holds a total charge of 0.2 C when 240 V is applied across it. Calculate the capacitance value.　[833.3 μF]

5　A 47 μF capacitor stores a charge of 8 mC when connected to a d.c. supply. Calculate the supply value.　[170.2 V]

6　A capacitor consists of two plates, each of area 500 cm^2, spaced 3 mm apart. If the dielectric has a relative permittivity of 5, calculate the value of the capacitor.　[737 pF]

7　A variable air capacitor has a capacitance of 260 pF. If the plates are adjusted so that this value is halved, and a material of relative permittivity 6.5 is substituted as the dielectric, calculate the new capacitance.　[845 pF]

8　A capacitor charges to 25 μC when it has an applied voltage of 400 V. Calculate the capacitance and the charge when it has an applied voltage of 240 V.　[62.5 nF; 15 μC]

9　Explain the basic construction of a capacitor. Explain why current will flow for a short time when a d.c. voltage is applied across a capacitor.

10　State the factors which determine the value of a capacitor. Explain how a variation in each of these factors will influence the value of the capacitor.

Calculate the value of a capacitor with two parallel plates separated by a mica sheet 0.2 mm thick. The area of each plate is 400 cm^2 and the relative permittivity of mica is 5.0.　[8.85 nF]

11   Draw the outline of a capacitor suitable for
a) $100\,\mu$F + 50% − 25% 25 V d.c. wkg,
b) a silvered mica 200 pF ± 1% 500 V d.c. wkg,
c) a polystyrene 470 pF ± 2.5% 250 V d.c. wkg,
e) a disc ceramic 0.001 μF + 50% − 25% 750 V d.c. wkg,
f) a variable air capacitor of 400 pF.

12   Suggest the type of capacitor suitable for (a) tuning in to different frequencies in a radio tuner, (b) smoothing a rectified voltage supply, (c) a low-tolerance capacitor which changes little with temperature, (d) a coupling capacitor, (e) a radio-frequency tuned circuit.

13   State two reasons why electrolytic capacitors should not have reverse voltage applied across them. State two materials which are used as dielectrics in electrolytic capacitors.

14   Describe, with the aid of a sketch, the construction of a small paper capacitor. State one practical application of such a capacitor.

15   State the type and approximate value of the capacitor you would expect to use in each of the following applications: (a) a power-supply reservoir capacitor, (b) an oscillator tuning capacitor for a frequency of 0.5 MHz to 1.5 MHz, (c) a cathode bypass capacitor for a valve radio-frequency amplifier (approximately 1 MHz).

16   State the type of dielectric which would be used in capacitors performing the following functions: (a) a 100 pF to 500 pF tuning capacitor in a radio receiver, (b) a 0.05 μF low-frequency interstage coupling capacitor, (c) a 100 pF fixed capacitor in a high-frequency (1 MHz) amplifier circuit.

17   State, giving reasons, which of the following 0.01 μF capacitors should be selected for a circuit in which stability and limited size is essential: (a) 0.01 μF mica dielectric, (b) 0.01 μF impregnated paper, (c) 0.01 μF air dielectric.

18   Explain the meaning of the terms 'electric flux density' and 'potential gradient' as applied to a capacitor, and state the units in which each is measured.

19   A capacitor is made up of two metal plates, each having an area of $0.01\,\text{m}^2$ and spaced 2 mm apart. When a p.d. of 100 V establishes a charge of $40\,\mu$C, calculate (a) the potential gradient in the dielectric, (b) the electric flux density, (c) the capacitance.   [50 V/mm; $0.4\,\mu\text{C/m}^2$, 0.4 μF]

20   Explain what are meant by 'potential gradient' and 'electric flux density' and state the relationship between them.

A 100 pF air-dielectric capacitor is made up of two plates each of cross-sectional area $2.5 \times 10^{-2}\,\text{m}^2$. Calculate the distance between the plates and the maximum permissible p.d. that may be applied across them if the potential gradient in the dielectric is not to exceed 1.5 MV/m. Calculate the total charge stored under these conditions.   [2.2 mm; 3.3 kV; 330 nC]

21   A capacitor consists of two plates, each of effective area $500\,\text{cm}^2$, spaced 1 mm apart in air. If the capacitor is connected to a 400 V d.c. supply, calculate the capacitance, the charge stored, and the potential gradient in the dielectric.

If the arrangement is immersed in oil and the capacitance changes to $0.0025\,\mu$F, calculate the relative permittivity of the oil and the electric flux density if a p.d. of 200 V is applied between the plates. [442 pF; 177 nC; 400 V/mm; 5.65; 10 μC/m^2]

22 Explain briefly why electrolytic capacitors can be made with a smaller volume than paper-type capacitors of the same value. Why is it necessary for electrolytic capacitors to be connected with a given d.c. polarity?

23 Three capacitors, each of 42 μF, are connected first in series and then in parallel. Calculate the effective capacitance in each case. [14 μF; 126 μF]

24 A capacitor A is made up of two plates with effective cross-sectional area 2 × 10^3 mm^2. Calculate the capacitance if the dielectric is 1.5 mm thick and has a relative permittivity of 4.24.

If the capacitor is connected in series with a second capacitor, B, of 30 pF and is charged from a constant voltage, it is found that the smallest voltage is 300 V. Calculate the source voltage and the potential gradient and electric flux density for capacitor A. [50 pF; 800 V; 200 V/mm; 7.5 μC/m^2]

25 In the circuit of fig. 3.16 the variable capacitor C is set to 60 μF. Find the voltage across this capacitor if a 500 V d.c. supply is connected across ab. Calculate the total capacitance, the charge on the 14 μF capacitor, and the value of C required to produce a voltage of 100 V across the 14 μF capacitor. [200 V; 50 μF; 12 mC; 10 μF]

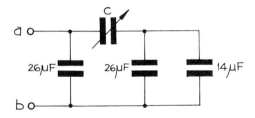

Fig. 3.16

26 A 50 pF capacitor is made up of two plates separated by a dielectric 2 mm thick and of relative permittivity 1.4. Calculate the effective plate area.

The capacitor is connected as shown in the circuit of fig. 3.17 and 100 V is applied across AB. Calculate the value of the capacitor C if the total capacitance is 16 pF. Find also the potential gradient in the 50 pF capacitor and the charge on the 10 pF capacitor. [80.7 cm^2; 48 pF; 13.3 V/mm; 266.7 μC]

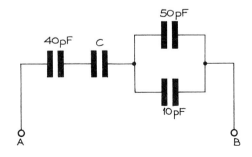

Fig. 3.17

27 The capacitor network shown in fig. 3.18 has 100 V d.c. applied across AC. Calculate the voltage across and the charge on each capacitor. An additional capacitor is connected in the circuit such that the voltage across AB is equal to that across BC. Show where the capacitor is connected and calculate its value. [840 μC, 840 μC, 540 μC, 300 μC; 42 V, 28 V, 30 V, 30 V; 16 μF across AB]

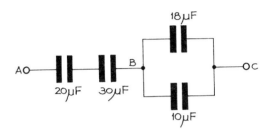

Fig. 3.18

28 Three capacitors, of 6 μF, 8 μF, and 10 μF respectively, are connected in parallel across a 60 V d.c. supply. Calculate (a) the total capacitance, (b) the charge stored in the 8 μF capacitor, (c) the total charge stored. [24 μF; 480 μC; 1.44 mC]

29 Explain what is meant by 'the electric field strength of a capacitor' and state the unit in which it is measured. State briefly why it is essential that the electric field strength must not be exceeded for a given insulating material.

State the effect on the capacitance of a parallel-plate capacitor if (a) the thickness of the dielectric is doubled, (b) the effective plate area is halved.

30 Two capacitors, one of 3 μF and the other of 6 μF, are connected in series across a 150 V d.c. supply. Calculate (a) the total capacitance, (b) the total charge, (c) the p.d. across each capacitor, (d) the energy stored in each capacitor. [2 μF; 300 μC; 100 V, 50 V; 15 mJ, 7.5 mJ]

31 A parallel-plate capacitor has two plates, each of area 400 cm² and spaced 4 mm apart. The relative permittivity of the dielectric is 5. If the p.d. between the plates is 100 V, calculate (a) the capacitance in picofarads, (b) the charge in microcoulombs, (c) the electric field strength, (d) the electric flux density. [442 pF; 0.044 μC; 25 V/mm; 1.1 μC/m²]

32 Two capacitors, of 10 μF and 40 μF, are connected in parallel. What is the value of the third capacitor required to give a total capacitance of 20 μF, and how is it connected? [33.3 μF]

4　The magnetic field

4.1. Introduction

Magnetism plays a major role in the operation of a wide range of electrical systems, such as motors, generators, transformers, contactors, solenoids, relays, loudspeakers, measuring instruments, and computer memory systems.

To design and maintain these types of system, it is necessary to understand the laws relating to magnetic fields and to be able to apply these laws to the solution of magnetic-circuit problems. It must be said at the outset that we do not know what magnetism is, and we may investigate magnetism usefully only by considering its effects. These effects may be described by a number of laws which provide a clearer understanding of the subject, and it is with these laws and the basic concepts of the magnetic circuit that this chapter is concerned.

4.2 Magnetic flux and magnetic circuits

A magnet affects the space around it such that other magnets placed in this space experience forces. The space in which this occurs is known as a magnetic field. The presence of a magnetic field surrounding a magnet may be demonstrated by sprinkling iron filings on to a sheet of thin card on top of the magnet. The pattern shown in fig. 4.1 is obtained. Michael Faraday referred to the apparent lines as *lines of magnetic flux*, and, although the flux does not exist as a number of separate lines, the concept is a very useful one since it provides a basis for explaining the various magnetic effects. For example, where the flux is more intense, then the lines are closer together, and where the flux is weaker then the lines are more widely spaced apart.

Magnetic flux has the following properties:

a) the direction of each apparent line of flux is defined as being from north to south at any point outside the magnet;
b) lines of magnetic flux form complete closed paths, as in fig. 4.1 (the paths which do not close around the magnet join those of the earth's magnetic field such that the continuity is still maintained);
c) lines of magnetic flux never intersect, although they may become very distorted.

Magnetic flux may be regarded as being like electric current in that it exists only in 'circuits'. The complete closed path in which the magnetic flux exists is referred to as a *magnetic circuit*. An example of a magnetic circuit is the horseshoe magnet shown in fig. 4.2. The magnetic flux exists in the iron and in the air gap, which together form a closed magnetic circuit. In most electrical machines, the flux exists partly in the iron of the machine

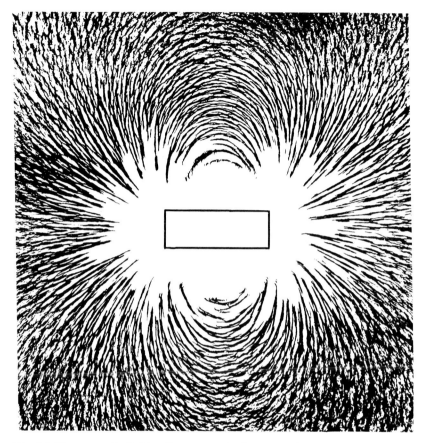

Fig. 4.1 The magnetic-field pattern around a bar magnet

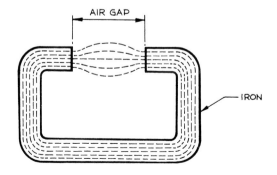

Fig. 4.2 A magnetic circuit

71

and partly in the air gap. In a rotating machine, the air gap is the mechanical clearance between the fixed and moving parts.

The symbol for magnetic flux is Φ (phi) and the unit is the *weber* (abbreviation Wb). The formal definition of magnetic flux, in terms of the e.m.f. induced in a coil situated in a magnetic field, will be given in section 5.3.

4.3 Magnetic flux density

Magnetic flux density is usually a more important quantity to the engineer than the total amount of flux, and is a measure of the amount of flux (Φ) existing within an area (A) perpendicular to the direction of the flux.

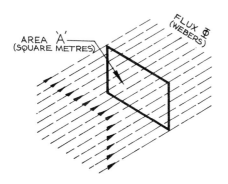

Fig. 4.3 Cross-section through a uniform magnetic flux

The symbol for flux density is *B* and the unit is the *tesla* (abbreviation T). By reference to fig. 4.3 it may be seen that

$$B = \frac{\Phi}{A}$$

and $\quad$ 1 tesla $= \dfrac{1 \text{ weber}}{1 \text{ square metre}}$

or $\quad$ 1 T = 1 Wb/m²

Example Calculate the flux density existing in an area of 400 mm² if a uniform magnetic flux of 300 μWb exists at right angles to that area.

$$B = \Phi/A$$

where $\quad \Phi = 300\,\mu\text{Wb} = 300 \times 10^{-6} \text{ Wb}$

and $\quad A = 400 \text{ mm}^2 = 400 \times 10^{-6} \text{ m}^2$

$$\therefore \quad B = \frac{300 \times 10^{-6} \text{ Wb}}{400 \times 10^{-6} \text{ m}^2} = 0.75 \text{ T}$$

i.e. the flux density is 0.75 T.

4.4 Magnetic flux produced by an electric current

A phenomenon which is extremely important in electrical engineering is that an electric current flowing in a wire sets up a magnetic field around the wire. This effect is fundamental to electrical machines, but it should be realised that it is not understood how the effect occurs. The magnetic field surrounds the conductor like a continuous jacket and, using the concept of lines of flux, it may be thought of as a series of concentric circles as shown in fig. 4.4.

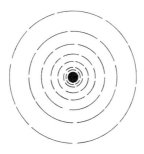

Fig. 4.4 Magnetic-field pattern around a current-carrying conductor

Notice that the flux is most intense closest to the conductor, and this is represented by the lines being closer together in this region. Further away from the conductor, the flux becomes weaker, and therefore the lines are more widely spaced apart.

The direction of the flux may be found by using the right-hand screw rule. This rule is shown in fig. 4.5 and states that, if the direction of the current in a conductor is considered to be the direction of travel of a screw, then the direction of the lines of flux will be the direction of rotation of the screw.

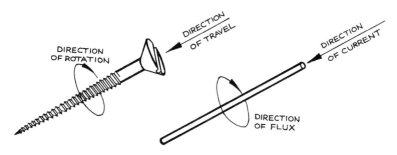

Fig. 4.5 Right-hand screw rule

Example   The convention that is used to show the direction of the current in a conductor is that a current flowing into the paper is shown by the flight of an arrow, while a current flowing out of the paper is shown by the point

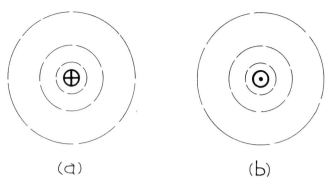

(a)   (b)

Fig. 4.6

of an arrow, as shown in fig. 4.6. Using the right-hand screw rule, state the direction of the flux in fig. 4.6 (a) and (b).

The direction of the flux is (a) clockwise, (b) anticlockwise.

If the conductor is wound into the shape of a coil, it is then referred to as a *solenoid*, and the magnetic-flux pattern produced has the shape shown in fig. 4.7 (a). There are various conventions which are used to find the direction of the magnetic flux produced by the solenoid, and the one described here is called the 'grip rule'. The grip rule states that, if the right hand grips the solenoid such that the fingers point in the same direction as the current, then the thumb points in the direction of the magnetic flux, as shown in fig. 4.7 (b).

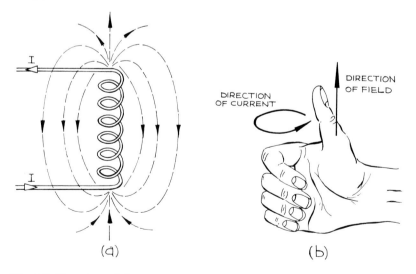

(a)   (b)

Fig. 4.7 Direction of the magnetic flux produced by a solenoid – the grip rule

74

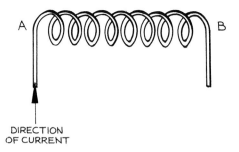

DIRECTION
OF CURRENT

Fig. 4.8 A solenoid

Example In the coil of fig. 4.8, the current has the direction shown. Using the grip rule, state which end of the coil would appear as a north pole and which end as a south pole.

End B would appear as a north pole, since the flux travels from this end, and end A as a south pole.

4.5 Magnetomotive force (m.m.f.)

Magnetomotive force causes flux to exist in a magnetic circuit in a way analogous to that in which an electromotive force (e.m.f.) causes current to exist in an electrical circuit.

The magnitude of the m.m.f. depends on the number of turns of the coil (N) and on the current in the coil (I), and is given the symbol F_m:

$$\text{m.m.f.} = F_m = NI$$

i.e. magnetomotive force is defined as the product of the current and the number of turns of the coil.

Since m.m.f. is equal to NI, the unit of m.m.f. is the ampere-turn (abbreviation A t). However, the number of turns has no units, and an alternative unit for m.m.f. is simply the ampere (abbreviation A).

The flux density around a permanent magnet is relatively small. In electrical machines, a flux much larger than can be provided by a permanent magnet is required, and this flux is produced by a current flowing in a coil, i.e. by the m.m.f.

Example Calculate the m.m.f. produced by a current of 1.5 A flowing in a 300-turn coil.

$$F_m = NI$$

where $N = 300$ and $I = 1.5$ A

$\therefore$ $F_m = 300 \times 1.5 \text{ A} = 450 \text{ A t}$

i.e. the m.m.f. is 450 A t.

4.6 Magnetic field strength

An alternative quantity to express the magnetic 'force' produced by a current in a coil is *magnetic field strength*. This is the magnetomotive force per unit length of the magnetic circuit and is given the symbol H.

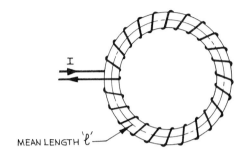

Fig. 4.9 A simple magnetic circuit

Consider the simple magnetic circuit of fig. 4.9, where a coil of N turns is uniformly wound around a ring of uniform cross-sectional area. If l is the length of the magnetic circuit, then the magnetic field strength is given by

$$H = \frac{F_m}{l} = \frac{NI}{l}$$

(Notice that l is the length of the flux path inside the coil and is *not* the length of the wire.)

The unit of magnetic field strength is the ampere per metre (abbreviation A/m).

Example   A current of 2.3 A flows in a coil of 500 turns which is wound on a ring of mean circumference 25 cm. Calculate (a) the magnetomotive force, (b) the magnetic field strength.

a) $F_m = NI$

where $N = 500$ and $I = 2.3$ A

$\therefore$ $F_m = 500 \times 2.3$ A $= 1150$ A t

b) $H = F_m/l$

where $F_m = 1150$ A t   and $l = 25$ cm $= 0.25$ m

$\therefore$ $H = \dfrac{1150 \text{ A t}}{0.25 \text{ m}} = 4600$ A/m

i.e. the magnetomotive force is 1150 A t and the magnetic field strength is 4600 A/m.

If the coil is not uniformly wound (as for example in the arrangement of fig. 4.13 (a)), then the magnetic field strength is not quite uniform around the whole length of the ring, and some of the flux exists in the surrounding air. This is referred to as *magnetic leakage* and occurs to some extent in all magnetic circuits. In the magnetic circuits considered in this chapter, the magnetic leakage will be assumed to be negligible.

4.7 Permeability

The magnetic flux density (B) inside a current-carrying coil is obviously related to the magnetic field strength (H), since one exists as a result of the other. The ratio of these two quantities is referred to as *permeability* and is given the symbol μ (mu),

i.e. $\quad \mu = \dfrac{B}{H}$

Permeability is a constant and may be expressed as 'the ease with which a magnetic flux is set up within a magnetic circuit.'

The unit of permeability is the henry per metre (abbreviation H/m). (The henry is the unit of inductance and is considered in chapter 5.)

The magnitude of the permeability depends on the material which is present inside the coil. When there is nothing inside the coil (i.e. a vacuum), the permeability is referred to as the *permeability of free space* and is given the symbol μ_0. This is a constant and has the value

$$\mu_0 = 4\pi \times 10^{-7} \text{ H/m}$$

Since it makes negligible difference if air (or any non-magnetic material) rather than a vacuum is inside the coil, then μ_0 is frequently used as the permeability of air.

Example   Calculate the flux density produced inside an air-cored coil with a magnetic field strength of 4600 A/m.

$$B = \mu_0 H$$

where $\quad \mu_0 = 4\pi \times 10^{-7} \text{ H/m} \quad$ and $\quad H = 4600 \text{ A/m}$

$\therefore \quad B = 4\pi \times 10^{-7} \text{ H/m} \times 4600 \text{ A/m}$

$\qquad = 5.8 \times 10^{-3} \text{ T} = 5.8 \text{ mT}$

i.e. the flux density is 5.8 mT (i.e. 5.8 millitesla).

4.8 Ferromagnetic materials

The flux density produced inside an air-cored coil is very weak, since the permeability of air is very small. Without some means of significantly increasing this flux density, the development of useful electrical machines would not have been possible. Certain materials, when placed inside a coil, have the property of greatly increasing the magnetic flux density, by as much as 1000 times (i.e. they have a large permeability). These materials are referred to as *ferromagnetic*. This property occurs in iron and steel and their alloys, as well as in cobalt, nickel, and tungsten, but it is only very very slight in other materials.

Consideration of the characteristics of ferromagnetic materials plays a major role in the design of electrical machines, and these materials will be discussed further in the section on magnetic materials (section 4.16).

4.9 Magnetisation curves and μ-H curves

The usefulness of a ferromagnetic material will depend on its particular magnetic properties, and these can be recorded on a *magnetisation curve*. This is a graph of flux density (B) plotted against magnetic field strength (H). It is sometimes referred to as a *B-H* curve. A typical magnetisation curve for a ferromagnetic material is shown in fig. 4.10. Notice that B is displayed vertically and H horizontally. The magnetisation characteristic for air is also shown for comparison.

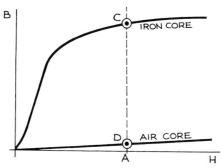

Fig. 4.10 Magnetisation curves of iron and air

It is evident that the slope of the magnetisation curve for a ferromagnetic material is not constant but varies with the degree of magnetisation. The curve starts with a small rate of rise (exaggerated in this case), then rises more steeply, and finally levels off. Notice that the magnetisation characteristic for air has a constant slope which is very much smaller than that for iron.

The magnetisation curves for a variety of ferromagnetic materials are shown in fig. 4.11. It can be seen from these curves that these materials have somewhat different properties, and their applications with regard to these properties will be considered later (section 4.16).

Since the slope of the magnetisation curve for a ferromagnetic material is not constant, then the permeability ($\mu = B/H$) must also vary with the magnetic field strength. The permeability is largest when the magnetisation curve is rising at its steepest rate, and begins to fall off as saturation occurs.

The permeability (μ) may be plotted against magnetic field strength (H) by taking points from the magnetisation curve. The resulting curves give useful information to the design engineer in his choice of magnetic materials. They are called *μ-H curves* and a variety are shown in fig. 4.12, corresponding to the *B-H* curves of fig. 4.11.

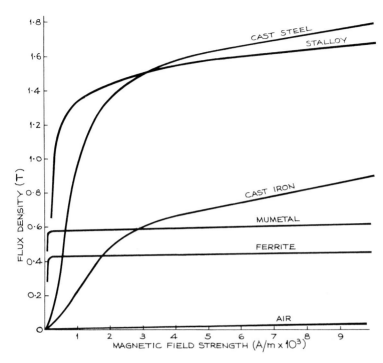

Fig. 4.11 Magnetisation curves for a variety of ferromagnetic materials (*B–H* curves)

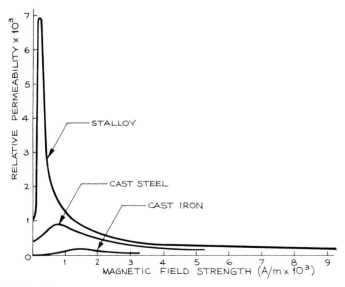

Fig. 4.12 μ–H curves

4.10 Relative permeability

We have seen that, if the non-magnetic core of a coil is replaced by an iron core, then the flux density produced from a given magnetic field strength is greatly increased. The ratio of the flux density produced when the iron core is present to that produced if the iron core is removed (or, more precisely, in a vacuum) is called the *relative permeability*. This is a measure of the number of times that the permeability of, say, iron is greater than that of a vacuum. We thus use μ_0 as a reference by which to compare the permeability of other materials. Relative permeability has the symbol μ_r and has no units, since it is a ratio of like quantities.

The relative permeability of a material may be derived from fig. 4.10 as follows.

If AC represents the flux density produced in a magnetic circuit using an iron core at some value of H, and AD represents the flux density produced using an air core at the same value of H, then

$$\mu_r = \frac{\text{flux density with iron core}}{\text{flux density with air core}}$$

$$= \frac{AC}{AD}$$

The absolute permeability (μ) of a ferromagnetic material is given by

$$\mu = \mu_0 \mu_r = \frac{B}{H}$$

Example Calculate the flux density produced in an iron ring of relative permeability 1600, if it is uniformly wound with a coil which produces a magnetic field strength of 500 A/m.

$$B = \mu H = \mu_0 \mu_r H$$

where $\mu_0 = 4\pi \times 10^{-7}$ H/m $\mu_r = 1600$ and $H = 500$ A/m

$\therefore$ $B = 4\pi \times 10^{-7}$ H/m $\times 1600 \times 500$ A/m

$= 1.005$ T

i.e. the flux density is 1.005 T.

4.11 Reluctance and magnetic circuits

In the magnetic circuit of fig. 4.13 (a), the flux density existing in the iron ring is affected by the properties of the iron from which the ring is made. We have already considered these properties in terms of the permeability of the material. We shall now introduce a new term called *reluctance* (symbol S). This is the ratio of the m.m.f. (F_m) to the flux in the iron (Φ) and may be thought of as magnetic resistance:

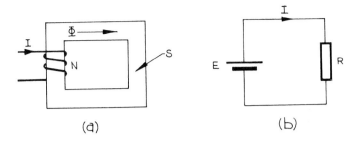

(a)　　　　　　　　　(b)

Fig. 4.13 A magnetic circuit

$$\text{reluctance} = \frac{\text{m.m.f.}}{\text{flux}}$$

or
$$S = \frac{F_m}{\Phi}$$

Reluctance has the unit ampere per weber (abbreviation A/Wb).

It is a useful exercise to compare the magnetic circuit of fig. 4.13(a) and the electric circuit of fig. 4.13(b).

In the electric circuit, the e.m.f. E causes the current I to flow through the resistance R. We have the relationship

$$E = IR$$

In the magnetic circuit it is the m.m.f. F_m which causes the flux Φ to exist in the magnetic circuit of reluctance S. The relationship is

$$F_m = \Phi S$$

This analogy is a useful one when performing calculations on magnetic circuits. It should be noted that, although flux may be compared to current in the analogy, it is *not* a continuous flow like current but simply exists as a result of the m.m.f.

Example 1　Figure 4.13 (a) shows an iron ring of reluctance 15×10^6 A/Wb wound with a coil of 100 turns. Calculate the current required in the coil to maintain a flux of $20\,\mu$Wb in the iron.

$$F_m = NI = \Phi S$$

where　$\Phi = 20\,\mu\text{Wb} = 20 \times 10^{-6}$ Wb　$S = 15 \times 10^6$ A/Wb
and　$N = 100$

$$\therefore \quad I = \frac{20 \times 10^{-6} \text{ Wb} \times 15 \times 10^6 \text{ A/Wb}}{100}$$

$$= 3.0 \text{ A}$$

i.e. the required current is 3.0 A.

Since reluctance and permeability both describe the magnetic properties of ferromagnetic materials, they are obviously related. The relationship between reluctance S and permeability μ may be shown as follows.

The greater the length l of a magnetic circuit, the greater is the reluctance. The greater the cross-sectional area A of a magnetic circuit, the smaller is the reluctance.

By definition, we have

$$S = \frac{\text{m.m.f.}}{\text{flux}} = \frac{F_m}{\Phi}$$

where $F_m = Hl$ and $\Phi = BA$

$$\therefore \quad S = \frac{Hl}{BA}$$

but $\dfrac{H}{B} = \dfrac{1}{\mu} = \dfrac{1}{\mu_0 \mu_r}$

$$\therefore \quad S = \frac{l}{\mu_0 \mu_r A}$$

From this equation it can be seen that, for a magnetic circuit to have a low reluctance, it should be short and fat, and be made of a material with a high relative permeability (μ_r).

Example 2 A magnetic circuit made of armature iron of relative permeability 1500 has a mean length of 80 cm and a cross-sectional area of 400 mm^2. Calculate the reluctance of the circuit.

$$S = \frac{l}{\mu_0 \mu_r A}$$

where $l = 80\,\text{cm} = 0.8\,\text{m}$ $\qquad \mu_0 = 4\pi \times 10^{-7}\,\text{H/m}$ $\qquad \mu_r = 1500$

and $A = 400\,\text{mm}^2 = 400 \times 10^{-6}\,\text{m}^2$

$$\therefore \quad S = \frac{0.8\,\text{m}}{4\pi \times 10^{-7}\,\text{H/m} \times 1500 \times 400 \times 10^{-6}\,\text{m}^2}$$

$$= 1.06 \times 10^6\,\text{A/Wb}$$

i.e. the reluctance of the circuit is 1.06×10^6 A/Wb.

4.12 Series and parallel magnetic circuits

In practice, magnetic circuits are often poorly defined, due to the spread of the magnetic flux. The magnetic circuit of fig. 4.14, for example, shows the flux paths that exist within the fixed stator (yoke and poles) and the moving rotor of a d.c. motor. As well as the magnetic circuit consisting of different types of ferromagnetic materials, and having an air gap, there is a

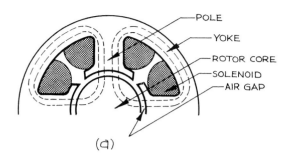

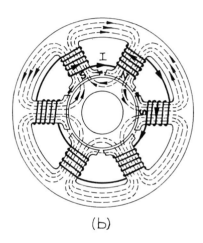

Fig. 4.14 Magnetic flux paths in a d.c. motor

small proportion of the flux which exists in the surrounding air (magnetic leakage). In the discussions that follow, we shall be simplifying the circuits so that they are more easily defined. A more complex analysis may be considered at a later stage, if required.

Series magnetic circuits
Figure 4.15 (a) shows a simple series magnetic circuit consisting of an iron ring with an air gap. Neglecting magnetic leakage, we may say that the same flux (Φ) exists both in the iron ring and in the air gap. The air gap has a large effect on the magnitude of the flux that exists in the circuit. If S_i is the reluctance of the iron path and S_a the reluctance of the air gap, then the magnetomotive force required to maintain the flux is given by

$$F_m = \Phi S_i + \Phi S_a$$

This may be compared to the series electric circuit of fig. 4.15 (b), where the electromotive force is given by

$$E = IR_1 + IR_2$$

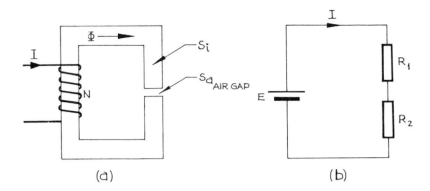

(a)   (b)

Fig. 4.15 Series magnetic circuit

Example 1   Figure 4.16 shows an iron ring of mean circumference 40 cm and cross-sectional area 25 mm² with a relative permeability of 800. It has a coil of 100 turns wound around it and a 1 mm air gap cut radially through it. Calculate the current in the coil to maintain a flux of 10.5 μWb in the iron ring and in the air gap.

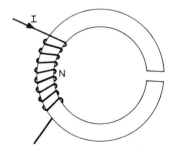

Fig. 4.16 Iron ring with air gap

$$F_m = NI = \Phi S_i + \Phi S_a$$

where $\Phi = 10.5\,\mu\text{Wb} = 10.5 \times 10^{-6}\,\text{Wb}$ and $N = 100$

The reluctance of the iron ring is given by

$$S_i = \frac{l_i}{\mu_0 \mu_r A}$$

where $l_i = 40\,\text{cm} = 0.4\,\text{m}$ $\mu_0 = 4\pi \times 10^{-7}\,\text{H/m}$ $\mu_r = 800$

and $A = 25\,\text{mm}^2 = 25 \times 10^{-6}\,\text{m}^2$

$$\therefore \quad S_i = \frac{0.4\,\text{m}}{4\pi \times 10^{-7}\,\text{H/m} \times 800 \times 25 \times 10^{-6}\,\text{m}^2}$$

$$= 15.9 \times 10^6 \ \text{A/Wb}$$

The reluctance of the air gap is given by

$$S_a = \frac{l_a}{\mu_0 A}$$

where $\quad l_a = 1\,\text{mm} = 0.001\,\text{m} \qquad \mu_0 = 4\pi \times 10^{-7}\,\text{H/m}$

and $\quad A = 25\,\text{mm}^2 = 25 \times 10^{-6}\,\text{m}^2$

$$\therefore \quad S_a = \frac{0.001\,\text{m}}{4\pi \times 10^{-7}\,\text{H/m} \times 25 \times 10^{-6}\,\text{m}^2}$$

$$= 31.8 \times 10^6 \ \text{A/Wb}$$

Substituting in the original equation,

$$100 \times I = (10.5 \times 10^{-6}\,\text{Wb} \times 15.9 \times 10^6\,\text{A/Wb})$$
$$+ (10.5 \times 10^{-6}\,\text{Wb} \times 31.8 \times 10^6\,\text{A/Wb})$$
$$= 500.85\,\text{A}$$

$$\therefore \qquad I = \frac{500.85\,\text{A}}{100} = 5.01\,\text{A}$$

i.e. the required current is 5.01 A.

It should be noticed that without the 1 mm air gap the required current to maintain the same flux would be 1.67 A; i.e. considerably less.

Example 2 Figure 4.17 shows an iron ring of relative permeability 500 which consists of two sections. There is a thin section of length 2 m and cross-sectional area 400 mm^2 and a thick section of length 1 m and cross-sectional area 900 mm^2. If a coil wound on the ring carries a current of 2 A, calculate the number of turns required to produce a flux density of 0.25 T in the thicker section.

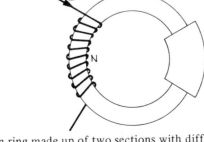

Fig. 4.17 Iron ring made up of two sections with different cross-sectional areas

This is a series magnetic circuit where the same flux exists in both sections of the circuit. However, the flux density in each section will not be the same, due to the different cross-sectional areas.

$$F_m = NI = \Phi S_1 + \Phi S_2$$

where I = 2 A $\quad\Phi$ = flux

$\qquad S_1$ = reluctance of thin section

and $\qquad S_2$ = reluctance of thick section

The flux is found from

$$\Phi = BA_2$$

where flux density in thick section (B) = 0.25 T

and cross-sectional area of thick section (A_2) = 900 mm²

$$= 900 \times 10^{-6} \text{ m}^2$$

$\therefore \quad \Phi = 0.25 \text{ T} \times 900 \times 10^{-6} \text{ m}^2$

$\qquad = 225 \times 10^{-6} \text{ Wb} = 225\,\mu\text{Wb}$

The reluctance of the thin section is found from

$$S_1 = \frac{l_1}{\mu_0 \mu_r A_1}$$

where l_1 = 2 m $\qquad \mu_0 = 4\pi \times 10^{-7}$ H/m $\qquad \mu_r$ = 500

and $\qquad A_1$ = 400 mm² = 400×10^{-6} m²

$\therefore \quad S_1 = \dfrac{2 \text{ m}}{4\pi \times 10^{-7} \text{ H/m} \times 500 \times 400 \times 10^{-6} \text{ m}^2}$

$\qquad = 7.96 \times 10^6$ A/Wb

The reluctance of the thick section is found from

$$S_2 = \frac{l_2}{\mu_0 \mu_r A_2}$$

where l_2 = 1 m and A_2 = 900 mm² = 900×10^{-6} m²

$\therefore \quad S_2 = \dfrac{1 \text{ m}}{4\pi \times 10^{-7} \text{ H/m} \times 500 \times 900 \times 10^{-6} \text{ m}^2}$

$\qquad = 1.77 \times 10^6$ A/Wb

$\therefore \quad N \times 2 \text{ A} = (225 \times 10^{-6} \text{ Wb} \times 7.96 \times 10^6 \text{ A/Wb})$

$\qquad\qquad + (225 \times 10^{-6} \text{ Wb} \times 1.77 \times 10^6 \text{ A/Wb})$

$\qquad\qquad = 2189 \text{ A t}$

$$\therefore \quad N = \frac{2189 \text{ At}}{2 \text{ A}} = 1095$$

i.e. the required number of turns is 1095.

Parallel magnetic circuits

Figure 4.18(a) shows a symmetrical parallel magnetic circuit such as is used in a shell-type transformer. The flux Φ that exists in the centre limb splits evenly between the two outer limbs so that each carries half the flux, $\frac{1}{2}\Phi$. Taking S_c as the reluctance of the centre limb and S_o as the reluctance of each outer limb, then, by considering only one of the magnetic circuits, the magnetomotive force is given by

$$F_m = \Phi S_c + \tfrac{1}{2}\Phi S_o$$

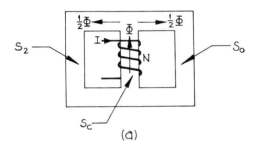

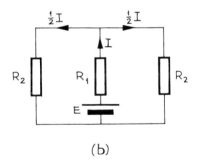

Fig. 4.18 Symmetrical parallel magnetic and electrical circuits

This equation should be compared with that for the symmetrical electrical circuit of fig. 4.18(b). Using Kirchoff's law and considering one of the loops, we have

$$E = IR_1 + \tfrac{1}{2}IR_2$$

Example 3   The contactor shown in fig. 4.19 consists of two E-shaped cores: a fixed (lower) one wound with a coil of 500 turns and a movable

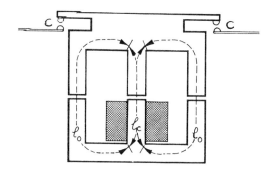

Fig. 4.19 A contactor made up of two E-shaped cores

(upper) one which carries the contacts (C). When the coil is energised, the upper core is attracted towards the lower one, thus closing the contacts at C. The cross-sectional area of each of the three limbs is $100 \, \text{mm}^2$, and the centre limb has a length (l_c) of 30 mm while each outer limb has a length (l_o) of 90 mm. Calculate the flux in the centre limb for a current of 1.5 A in the coil *when the contacts are closed* (i.e. no air gap). Assume the relative permeability of the core is 1000.

$$F_m = NI = \Phi S_c + \tfrac{1}{2}\Phi S_o$$

where $N = 500$ and $I = 1.5 \, \text{A}$

The reluctance of the centre limb is found from

$$S_c = \frac{l_c}{\mu_0 \mu_r A}$$

where $l_c = 30 \, \text{mm} = 0.03 \, \text{m}$ $\mu_0 = 4\pi \times 10^{-7} \, \text{H/m}$ $\mu_r = 1000$

and $A = 100 \, \text{mm}^2 = 100 \times 10^{-6} \, \text{m}^2$

$$\therefore \quad S_c = \frac{0.03 \, \text{m}}{4\pi \times 10^{-7} \, \text{H/m} \times 1000 \times 100 \times 10^{-6} \, \text{m}^2}$$

$$= 0.24 \times 10^6 \, \text{A/Wb}$$

The reluctance of each outer limb is found from

$$S_o = \frac{l_o}{\mu_0 \mu_r A}$$

where $l_o = 90 \, \text{mm} = 0.09 \, \text{m}$

$$\therefore \quad S_o = \frac{0.09 \, \text{m}}{4\pi \times 10^{-7} \, \text{H/m} \times 1000 \times 100 \times 10^{-6} \, \text{m}^2}$$

$$= 0.72 \times 10^6 \, \text{A/Wb}$$

$$\therefore \quad 500 \times 1.5 \text{ A} = (\Phi \times 0.24 \times 10^6 \text{ A/Wb})$$
$$+ (\tfrac{1}{2}\Phi \times 0.72 \times 10^6 \text{ A/Wb})$$
$$= \Phi \times (0.24 + 0.36) \times 10^6 \text{ A/Wb}$$
$$= \Phi \times 0.6 \times 10^6 \text{ A/Wb}$$

$$\therefore \quad \Phi = \frac{500 \times 1.5 \text{ A}}{0.6 \times 10^6 \text{ A/Wb}} = 1250 \times 10^{-6} \text{ Wb}$$

$$= 1250 \, \mu\text{Wb} \quad \text{or} \quad 1.25 \, \text{mWb}$$

i.e. the flux in the centre limb is 1.25 mWb.

4.13 Calculations involving B-H curves

The examples considered so far assume a fixed value of relative permeability (μ_r). As we have seen, μ_r is not constant but varies with the degree of magnetisation. An alternative method of performing calculations on magnetic circuits makes use of the B-H curve for each particular material. This requires the use of a different equation which describes the m.m.f. (F_m) in terms of the magnetic field strength (H) and the length of the magnetic circuit (l). The equation for magnetic field strength ($H = F_m/l$) may be rearranged to give the equation

$$F_m = Hl \quad \text{(see section 4.6)}$$

The general form of the equation for a magnetic circuit with two elements is

$$F_m = H_1 l_1 + H_2 l_2$$

Provided that B is known, then H_1 and H_2 may be derived from the respective B-H curves. A few examples will clarify the method.

Example 1   Figure 4.20 shows a simplified representation of a relay which has two components, one being the fixed yoke and the other the movable armature. The total length of the magnetic circuit is 120 mm. Assuming that

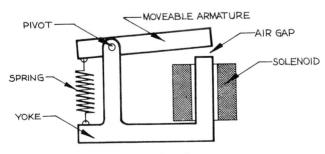

Fig. 4.20 Simplified representation of a relay

the air gap is 2 mm when the relay is open, calculate the current required in the coil of 1000 turns to produce a flux of $12\,\mu$Wb in the armature, yoke, and air gap. Assume that both components are made of cast iron with a B-H characteristic as shown in fig. 4.11 and that the cross-sectional area of the yoke, armature, and air gap is 24 mm^2 in each case.

$$NI = H_i l_i + H_a l_a$$

where   length of iron path (l_i) = 120 mm = 0.12 m

          length of air gap (l_a) = 2 mm = 0.002 m

and N = 1000

    Flux density $B = \Phi/A$

where Φ = $12\,\mu$Wb = 12×10^{-6} Wb   and A = 24 mm^2 = 24×10^{-6} m

$$\therefore \quad B = \frac{12 \times 10^{-6}\ \text{Wb}}{24 \times 10^{-6}\ \text{m}^2} = 0.5\ \text{T}$$

From the B-H curve for cast iron, fig. 4.11, when B = 0.5 T then H_i = 2000 A/m.

    H_a is found from

$$H_a = B/\mu_0 = \frac{0.5\ \text{T}}{4\pi \times 10^{-7}\ \text{H/m}} = 0.40 \times 10^6\ \text{A/m}$$

$\therefore$ $1000 \times I$ = 2000 A/m $\times$ 0.12 m + 0.40×10^6 A/m $\times$ 0.002 m

                = 240 A t + 800 A t

                = 1040 A t

$$\therefore \qquad I = \frac{1040\ \text{A t}}{1000} = 1.04\ \text{A}$$

i.e. the current in the coil is 1.04 A.

Example 2   A lifting electromagnet, shown in fig. 4.21, has one section made of cast steel and a detachable section made of cast iron. The mean length of the steel section is 2.5 m and that of the iron section 0.8 m. Both sections have the same cross-sectional area, and the two coils aid each other. Calculate the total number of turns on both coils to produce a flux density of 0.8 T in each section if the current available is 20 A. You may assume that the two sections are joined together with no air gap. The B-H curves are shown in fig. 4.11.

$$NI = H_s l_s + H_i l_i$$

where   length of steel section (l_s) = 2.5 m

          length of iron section (l_i) = 0.8 m

and I = 20 A

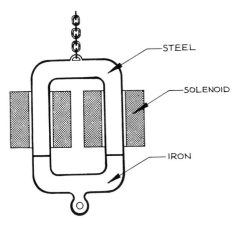

Fig. 4.21 A lifting electromagnet made up of two sections

A lightweight electromagnet handling swarf

From the curves of fig. 4.11 with a flux density B of 0.8 T,

magnetic field strength for steel (H_s) = 800 A/m

magnetic field strength for iron (H_i) = 7200 A/m

$$\therefore \quad N \times 20\,\text{A} = 800\,\text{A/m} \times 2.5\,\text{m} + 7200\,\text{A/m} \times 0.8\,\text{m}$$

$$= 2000\,\text{A t} + 5760\,\text{A t}$$

$$= 7760\,\text{A t}$$

$$\therefore \quad N = \frac{7760\,\text{A t}}{20\,\text{A}} = 388$$

i.e the number of turns is 388.

Example 3 Figure 4.22 shows a shell-type transformer with the coil wound on the centre limb. The centre limb has a length of 60 mm and a cross-sectional area of 300 mm^2. The outer limb has a length of 140 mm and a cross-sectional area of 200 mm^2. Calculate the m.m.f. to produce a flux density of 0.4 T in the centre limb. Assume that the transformer core is made of cast iron with a B–H curve as shown in fig. 4.11.

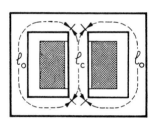

Fig. 4.22 A shell-type transformer

$$F_m = H_c l_c + H_o l_o$$

where   length of centre limb (l_c) = 60 mm = 0.06 m

and   length of outer limb (l_o) = 140 mm = 0.14 m

The flux (Φ) in the centre limb is found from

$$\Phi = B_c A_c$$

where B_c = flux density in centre limb = 0.4 T

and A_c = 300 mm^2 = 300 $\times$ 10^{-6} m^2

$$\therefore \quad \Phi = 0.4\,\text{T} \times 300 \times 10^{-6}\,\text{m}^2$$

$$= 120 \times 10^{-6}\,\text{Wb} = 120\,\mu\text{Wb}$$

Flux in outer limb $= \frac{1}{2}\Phi = 60\,\mu\text{Wb}$

The flux density in the outer limb is found from

$$B_o = \frac{\Phi/2}{A_o}$$

where $\quad \Phi/2 = 60\,\mu\text{Wb} = 60 \times 10^{-6}\,\text{Wb}$

and $\quad A_o = 200\,\text{mm}^2 = 200 \times 10^{-6}\,\text{m}^2$

$$\therefore \quad B_o = \frac{60 \times 10^{-6}\,\text{Wb}}{200 \times 10^{-6}\,\text{m}^2} = 0.3\,\text{T}$$

From the $B\text{-}H$ curve for cast iron in fig. 4.11,

when $\quad B_c = 0.4\,\text{T} \quad$ then $\quad H_c = 1500\,\text{A/m}$

when $\quad B_o = 0.3\,\text{T} \quad$ then $\quad H_o = 1100\,\text{A/m}$

Inserting these values into the original equation,

$$F_m = 1500\,\text{A/m} \times 0.06\,\text{m} + 1100\,\text{A/m} \times 0.14\,\text{m}$$

$$= 90\,\text{At} + 154\,\text{At}$$

$$= 244\,\text{At}$$

i.e. the required m.m.f. is 244 At.

4.14 Magnetic screening

In a magnetic circuit, the magnetic flux will exist in the path of least reluctance. If a soft-iron ring is placed in a magnetic field, then the pattern of the magnetic flux will be as shown in fig. 4.23: almost no flux exists in the air space inside the ring. This effect may be used to advantage in *magnetic screening*, since a body placed inside this space would be screened from the surrounding magnetic field. Magnetic screening is used to protect cathode-ray tubes and instruments such as moving-iron ammeters and voltmeters from external magnetic fields.

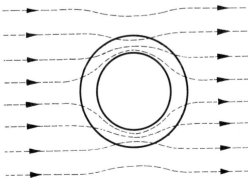

Fig. 4.23 Magnetic screening using a soft-iron ring

4.15 Hysteresis

The magnetisation characteristics for various magnetic materials have already been discussed in section 4.9, and the curve OA in fig. 4.24 represents one such magnetisation characteristic. However, when the magnetic field strength (H) is reduced to zero, ferromagnetic materials retain some of their magnetisation, which is referred to as the *remanent flux density* and is represented by OB in fig. 4.24.

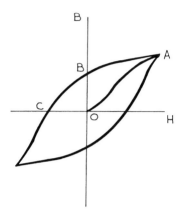

Fig. 4.24 Hysteresis loop (*B–H* loop) for a ferromagnetic material

If the magnetic field strength is now reversed, then the flux density (B) will eventually be reduced to zero. The magnetic field strength at this point is referred to as the *coercive force* and is represented by OC in fig 4.24. If the magnetic field strength continues to be reversed, then the material will become magnetised in the opposite direction.

When the magnetic field strength is increased and decreased, first in one direction and then in the other, the values of B and H describe a loop which is referred to as the *hysteresis loop* (or *B–H* loop) for the material. *Magnetic saturation* is the point on the characteristic when an increase in the magnetic field strength will produce no further increase in the flux density. When the hysteresis loop is obtained for a material which is magnetised to saturation, OB and OC are referred to as the *remanence* and *coercivity* for the material.

When a material is subjected to alternations of magnetic flux, some energy is lost as work is done in magnetising and demagnetising the material. This loss is referred to as *hysteresis loss*. It may be shown that the energy loss per cycle is proportional to the area of the hysteresis loop. In the iron core of a motor or generator, for example, such a loss occurs due to the rotor passing first under a north pole, then under a south pole, and thus experiencing alternations of magnetic flux. It also occurs in transformers, due to the flux increasing and decreasing in the iron core.

94

Another form of energy loss which occurs in magnetic circuits is caused by the e.m.f. which is induced in the iron or steel core due to the changing magnetic flux produced by the winding. (Electromagnetic induction is explained in chapter 5.) This induced e.m.f. causes a current to flow in the core, and heat is produced. Induced currents produced in this way in a block of material are called *eddy currents*, and the energy loss associated with them is known as *eddy-current loss*. Eddy-current loss is kept to a minimum by assembling the core from sheet-steel laminates (thin strips of sheet steel). This increases the resistance of the core to the flow of eddy currents and therefore reduces the loss for a given induced e.m.f. However it is sometimes necessary to use a solid casting to provide strength, such as in the manufacture of the yoke of a d.c. machine. In this case, cast steel is generally preferred.

4.16 Magnetic materials

One of the most important developments in electrical engineering has been in the production of ferromagnetic materials. The properties of remanence, coercivity, saturation, hysteresis loss, and permeability must all be taken into consideration when choosing a ferromagnetic material for a particular application. Although the ratio of remanence to saturation flux density does not vary very much from one material to another, the coercivities of different materials vary enormously.

Magnetic materials can broadly be divided into two classes:

a) those which magnetise easily but readily lose their magnetism after removal of the magnetomotive force,

b) those which are comparatively difficult to magnetise but strongly retain their magnetism.

Class (a) includes the 'soft' magnetic materials used for the rotor and field cores of electric motors and generators and for transformer cores. They have a small coercivity and therefore a small hysteresis loss, which is essential for these applications. Examples of such materials are soft iron and Stalloy (a silicon–iron alloy), with a hysteresis loop similar to that shown in fig. 4.25 (a).

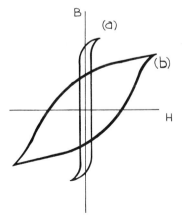

Fig. 4.25 Hysteresis loop for (a) a 'soft' magnetic material, (b) a 'hard' magnetic material

Materials of type (b) are classed as magnetically 'hard' and are used for permanent magnets. These should not be easily demagnetised, and therefore a material with a high coercivity is required. Examples of such materials are hard steel and Alcomax (an alloy of iron, aluminium, nickel, cobalt, and copper), with a hysteresis loop similar to that shown in fig. 4.25 (b).

Some important groups of ferromagnetic materials, used in electronics, have a hysteresis loop which is almost square, as shown in fig. 4.26. In these materials, the remanent flux density is nearly equal to the saturation flux density, and the sides of the loop have steep slopes as a small change in H causes a large change in B. One such group is the *ferrites*, which are made from powdered iron oxide with part of the iron replaced by nickel or manganese. Ferrite cores are made in a variety of shapes by a sintering process. (Sintering means to make solid from a powder by heating.) They have a very low hysteresis loss and low coercive force. They are used as memory cores in digital computers and as cores in inductors for use at high frequencies.

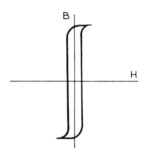

Fig. 4.26 Hysteresis loop for a ferrite

4.17 Summary of important equations

Flux density:	$B = \Phi/A$
Magnetomotive force:	$F_m = NI$
Magnetic field strength:	$H = NI/l$
Permeability:	$\mu = B/H = \mu_0 \mu_r$
Reluctance:	$S = F/\Phi = l/\mu_0 \mu_r A$

Laws for magnetic circuits:

at any junction the summation of the flux is zero,

i.e. $\Sigma \Phi = 0$

for a complete magnetic circuit,

$$\Sigma F_m = \Sigma \Phi S$$

also $\Sigma F_m = \Sigma H l$

Exercises on chapter 4

1 Describe how the magnetic field of a bar magnet could be shown using a bar magnet, a sheet of cardboard, and iron filings. Make a sketch of the field which should result.

2 Figure 4.27 shows a solenoid through which a current is flowing. Sketch the magnetic field and indicate the polarity.

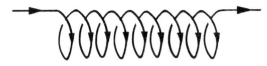

Fig. 4.27

3 With the aid of a sketch, show how a magnetic compass can be used to plot the paths of the lines of force surrounding a bar magnet. Sketch the lines of force to indicate the resultant field produced by the two current-carrying conductors shown in fig. 4.28.

Fig. 4.28

4 State one practical application for a permanent magnet and one for an electromagnet.

  Indicate the magnetic polarity of the electromagnet shown in fig. 4.29.

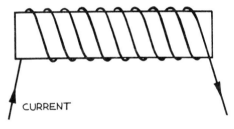

CURRENT

Fig. 4.29

5 Calculate the flux density if a total flux of 20 mWb passes through an area of 200 mm^2.   [100 T]

6 Calculate the total flux from a pole of a magnet if the flux density is 0.25 T and the magnet pole face has dimensions 20 mm × 5 mm.   [25 μWb]

7 On clearly labelled axes, sketch a typical hysteresis loop for a soft-iron material specimen. Mark the following points on the loop: (a) coercive force, (b) residual flux density.

8 Sketch a typical hysteresis loop for a sample of iron. Indicate on the loop and discuss the relative importance of (a) coercive force, (b) residual flux density, (c) maximum flux density, and (d) loop area.

9 On clearly labelled axes, sketch a B–H curve for (a) a non-magnetic material, (b) silicon steel.

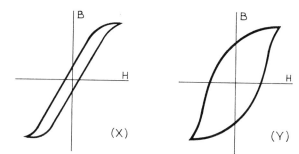

Fig. 4.30

10   Figure 4.30 shows two hysteresis loops, to the same scale, for two samples of steel. State (a) which sample saturates more readily, (b) which sample has the greater loss per cycle, (c) which sample has the greater coercive force, (d) which sample has the greater remanence, (e) which sample would make the better permanent magnet.

11   State any two advantages obtained by the use of ferrite-cored inductors.

12   Explain the meaning of the terms (a) magnetic flux density, (b) magnetic flux, (c) absolute permeability, (d) permeability of free space, (e) relative permeability as applied to a magnetic material and state the units in which each is measured.

13   An iron ring of mean length 90 cm and cross-sectional area 6 cm² is uniformly wound with 900 turns of insulated wire having a resistance of 60 Ω. Calculate the magnetic flux in the ring when a 240 V d.c. supply is applied to the winding. (μ_r = 500)   [1.5 mWb]

14   An iron ring has a diameter of 8 cm and a cross-sectional area of 4 cm². At the working flux density the relative permeability of the material is 800. Calculate the reluctance of the magnetic circuit.   [625×10^3 A/Wb]

15   A magnetic circuit having a length of 0.5 m and a cross-sectional area of 4×10^{-4} m² is made of iron having a relative permeability of 1000. Calculate the reluctance of the circuit and the flux density produced if the circuit is uniformly wound with a 200-turn coil carrying a current of 1 A. [99.5×10^3 A/Wb; 0.5 T]

16   The reluctance of a steel magnetic circuit is 10^8 A/Wb. Calculate the flux produced by a coil of 1000 turns wound on the steel when a current of 1 A flows in the coil. If the cross-sectional area of the steel is 4×10^{-3} m², find the value of the flux density.   [10 μWb; 2.5 mT]

17   A magnetising winding of 500 turns is uniformly wound on a closed magnetic circuit having a cross-sectional area of 300 mm² and a mean length of magnetic path of 600 mm. The magnetic flux in the core is 360 μWb and the relative permeability of the core material under these conditions is 1000. Find (a) the flux density in the core, (b) the current in the winding.   [1.2 T; 1.146 A]

18   Explain the term 'reluctance' as applied to a magnetic circuit. Sketch a typical *B–H* curve for a sample of magnetic material.

A closed magnetic circuit has a cross-sectional area of 200 mm² and a mean length of magnetic path of 400 mm. Calculate (a) the flux density produced by a current of 0.5 A flowing in a 500-turn magnetising winding, (b) the reluctance of the circuit under this condition. (The relative permeability of the core material under these conditions is 1500.)   [1.18 T; 1.06 × 10⁶ A/Wb]

19   Explain the meaning of the terms 'reluctance' and 'magnetomotive force' as applied to a magnetic circuit.

A closed magnetic circuit has a cross-sectional area of 100 mm² and is wound with a 1000-turn magnetising winding. The current in the winding is adjusted until the magnetic flux in the core is 100 µWb. Given that the reluctance of the magnetic circuit under this condition is 10 MA/Wb and the relative permeability of the core material is 1000, calculate the magnetising current and the mean length of the magnetic path of the core.

The magnetising current is now increased by 50% of its initial value, and it is found that the flux density in the core is 1.25 T. Find the corresponding value of relative permeability.   [1 A; 1.256 m; 833]

20   Explain the meaning of 'magnetomotive force' and 'reluctance' as applied to a magnetic circuit. State the relationship between these two quantities.

A direct current of 4 A flows in a magnetising winding and produces a magnetic flux of 200 µWb. The magnetic circuit has a reluctance of 10⁷ A/Wb, a cross-sectional area of 160 mm², and a mean length of magnetic path of 2.5 m. Calculate (a) the number of turns on the winding, (b) the flux density, (c) the magnetic field strength.   [500; 1.25 T; 800 A/m]

21   A steel ring of mean length 0.4 m and uniform cross-sectional area 10 cm² is uniformly wound with 250 turns of insulated wire. Using the values given below for the steel, determine the total flux produced when a current of 5.6 A flows in the coil.   [1.5 mWb]

B (T)	1.0	1.2	1.3	1.4	1.45	1.5	1.55	1.6
H (A/m)	1000	1500	2000	2500	3000	3500	4000	4900

22   A steel ring of mean length 0.3 m and cross-sectional area 300 mm² is wound uniformly with 252 turns of wire. The values of flux density, B tesla, against magnetising force, H amperes/metre, for the steel are given in the following table. Draw a B–H curve for the values given and, using your graph, determine the total flux produced in the steel when the coil takes a current of 5 A from the supply. Calculate the reluctance of the magnetic path.   [45 mWb; 28 × 10³ A/Wb]

H (A/m)	1000	1500	2000	2500	3000	3500	4000	4500	5000
B (T)	0.9	1.15	1.3	1.38	1.43	1.46	1.49	1.51	1.53

23   A magnetising winding has 500 turns and is uniformly wound on a Stalloy ring having mean diameter 200 mm and a cross-sectional area 150 mm². A radial air gap 0.5 mm wide is cut in the ring. Calculate (a) the direct current required in the coil in order to produce a flux of 160 µWb in the air gap, (b) the relative permeability of the core under these conditions. Values of B and H for Stalloy are as follows:

B (T)	0.95	1.0	1.05	1.10
H (A/m)	100	150	210	275

[1.146 A; 3600]

24 Explain what are meant by 'magnetic field strength' and 'magnetic flux density'. State the relationship between them.

A laminated iron core shown in fig. 4.31 is constructed from a magnetic material, the relevant part of the magnetisation characteristic for which is shown in fig. 4.32. A magnetising winding of 500 turns is wound on the core. Calculate the current required to produce a flux density of 1.1 T in the air gap. (The effects of magnetic leakage and fringing are to be ignored.)
[3.18 A]

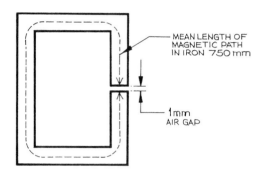

Fig. 4.31

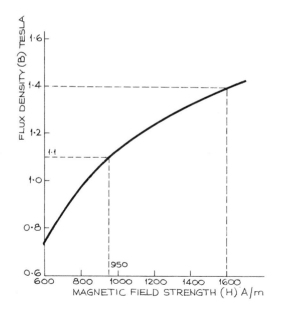

Fig. 4.32

25 A steel ring with mean diameter 0.8 m and cross-sectional area 700 mm²
has a radial air gap of width 2 mm. The magnetic characteristic of the iron is
given below. Calculate the current which must flow in a coil of 3000 turns to
produce a flux of 0.6 mWb in the air gap. Neglect the effects of magnetic
leakage and fringing.   [1.1 A]

B (T)	0.1	0.3	0.6	0.9	1.08	1.18	1.25
H (A/m)	200	400	600	800	1000	1200	1400

26 A magnetic circuit has the form shown in fig. 4.33. The centre limb has
a cross-sectional area of 2000 mm², and each outer limb has a cross-sectional
area of 1500 mm². Calculate the current which must flow in a coil of 1800
turns wound on the centre limb to produce a flux of 2.6 mWb in the air gap.
The magnetic characteristic of the iron is given in the table below. Neglect
the effects of magnetic leakage and fringing.   [0.21 A]

H (A/m)	400	800	1200	1600	2000
B (T)	0.95	1.27	1.4	1.47	1.5

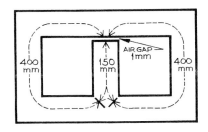

Fig. 4.33

27 A magnetic circuit consists of a ring-shaped iron core having a mean
length of 200 mm and a cross-sectional area of 4 cm². There is an air gap
1 mm wide cut in the core. A coil of 500 turns is wound around the core,
and a direct current of 2 A is passed through the winding. If 60% of the
total m.m.f. is required for the air gap, calculate (a) the flux density in the
air gap, (b) the relative permeability of the iron, (c) the self-inductance of
the winding at this flux density.   [0.75 T; 298; 188 mH]

28 A magnetic circuit has the form shown in fig. 4.34. The centre limb
has a cross-sectional area of 800 mm² and the outer limbs have cross-sectional
area 500 mm². Calculate the current which must flow in a coil of 1500 turns
wound on the centre limb to produce a flux of 0.9 mWb in the centre limb.
Neglect effects of magnetic leakage and assume μ_r = 800.   [0.69 A]

29 A wrought-iron magnetic circuit has the dimensions shown in fig. 4.35.
The cross-sectional area of the centre limb is 10 cm², and each of the side
limbs has a cross-sectional area of 6 cm². A coil of 500 turns is wound on each
side limb, and the two coils are connected in series aiding (i.e. their m.m.f.'s
act in the same direction around the circuit). Calculate the current required

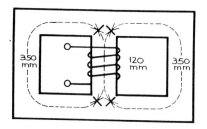

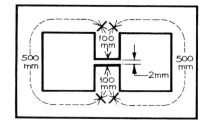

Fig. 4.34

Fig. 4.35

in the coils to establish a flux density of 1.4 T in the air gap. The magnetic data for the iron is given in the table below.   [5.42 A]

H (A/m)	250	500	750	1000	1250	1500	1750
B (T)	1.05	1.22	1.3	1.35	1.38	1.42	1.45

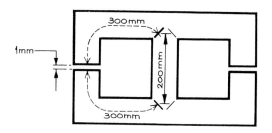

Fig. 4.36

30   Figure 4.36 represents the iron core of an inductor with an air gap in each side limb. The core is symmetrical about its centre line. The cross-sectional area of the centre limb is 30 cm^2, and that of each side limb is 20 cm^2. A coil of 500 turns is wound on the centre limb. Calculate the current required in the coil to maintain a flux density of 1.0 T in the centre limb. Neglect the effects of magnetic leakage and fringing at the edges of the air gaps. The B-H data for the iron is as follows:

B (T)	0.40	0.67	0.94	1.07	1.15	1.20
H (A/m)	100	200	400	600	800	1000

[1.68 A]

5   Electromagnetic induction

5.1 Introduction
Electromagnetic induction is the basis of many electrical machines, such as
the d.c. motor, d.c. generator, induction motor, synchronous motor, and the
transformer. Since these are the most frequently used machines in the electrical engineering industry, it is important that the laws of electromagnetic
induction are clearly understood.

5.2 Electromagnetic induction
The phenomenon of electromagnetic induction is the inducing of an e.m.f.
in a coil by a *changing* magnetic flux. Michael Faraday discovered this important effect, which may be stated as follows: 'A coil situated in a magnetic field
will have an e.m.f. induced in it if the magnetic flux linking with the coil
changes.' This is often referred to as Faraday's first law of electromagnetic
induction. It is important to realise that an e.m.f. is induced only while the
flux is changing.

The student should be aware that the reason why this phenomenon
occurs is not known; however, it is with the effects that the electrical
engineer is concerned in practice. The following is a useful experiment by
which the effects may be investigated.

Figure 5.1 shows two coils, A and B, with a current flowing in coil A
such that it produces a magnetic flux which surrounds the coil, as discussed
in chapter 4. If the coils are sufficiently close together, then this magnetic
flux links with the windings of coil B, which has a sensitive galvanometer
connected across its ends. When the magnetic flux linking with coil B changes,
then an e.m.f. is induced in coil B and is shown as a deflection on the galvano-

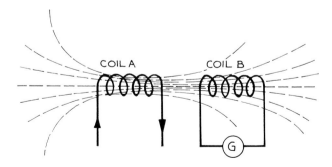

Fig. 5.1 Magnetic flux linking two coils

103

meter. There are two means by which the magnetic flux linking with coil B may be changed:

a) by increasing or decreasing the current in coil A, and thus changing the *amount* of flux linking with coil B. This effect is referred to as *mutual induction* and is the effect used in the transformer.
b) by moving one coil relative to the other and thus causing coil B to *cut through* the magnetic flux produced by coil A. This effect is referred to as *induction by motion* and is the effect used in the generator.

These two effects form the basis of electromagnetic machines and we shall consider them separately in the following two sections.

5.3 Induction by change of flux

Referring to fig. 5.1, when the magnetic flux Φ changes due to a change of current in coil A, then we have seen that an e.m.f. is induced in coil B. It is found that the faster the magnetic flux changes, then the greater is the e.m.f. induced in the coil. We may say that the magnitude of the e.m.f. is proportional to the rate of change of magnetic flux, $d\Phi/dt$. It is also found to be proportional to the number of turns of the coil, N. This is referred to as Faraday's second law of electromagnetic induction and may be expressed in equation form as follows:

$$e = -N\frac{d\Phi}{dt}$$

(The minus sign is due to Lenz's law, which will be explained later, and is included to show that the direction of the e.m.f. opposes the flux change that is producing it. It will be ignored in the solving of problems unless the direction of the induced e.m.f. is asked for.)

If the magnetic flux linking with a coil of N turns changes uniformly from Φ_1 webers to Φ_2 webers in t seconds, then the average e.m.f. that is induced in the coil is given by

$$e = -N\frac{\Phi_2 - \Phi_1}{t}$$

If the change of flux $\Phi_2 - \Phi_1$ is given simply as $\Delta\Phi$ and the change of time as Δt, then the equation becomes

$$e = -N\frac{\Delta\Phi}{\Delta t}$$

This is the usual way of expressing Faraday's second law in equation form if the rate of change of flux can be assumed to be uniform.

Example   In a transformer, the secondary coil has 100 turns and the flux linking with this coil changes uniformly from 1 mWb to 3 mWb in 0.02 s. Calculate the e.m.f. induced in the coil during the period of the change.

Ignoring the minus sign,

$$e = N(\Delta\Phi/\Delta t)$$

where $N = 100$

$\Delta\Phi = \Phi_2 - \Phi_1 = 3\,\text{mWb} - 1\,\text{mWb} = 2\,\text{mWb} = 0.002\,\text{Wb}$

and $\Delta t = 0.02\,\text{s}$

$\therefore \quad e = 100 \times \dfrac{0.002\,\text{Wb}}{0.02\,\text{s}} = 10\,\text{V}$

i.e. the induced e.m.f. is 10 V.

We can measure the induced e.m.f. produced by a changing magnetic flux, and the electromagnetic effect thus provides a convenient means of defining the unit of magnetic flux.

The unit of magnetic flux, called the weber, is the flux which, linking a circuit of one turn, produces in it an electromotive force of one volt as the flux is reduced to zero at a uniform rate in one second;

i.e.   1 weber = 1 volt × 1 second

or   1 Wb = 1 V s

5.4 Induction by motion.

Referring to fig. 5.1, we have seen that an e.m.f. is induced in coil B when one of the coils *moves* relative to the other. It is found that, the faster coil B moves across the magnetic flux, then the greater is the e.m.f. induced in that coil. We may say that the magnitude of the induced e.m.f. is proportional to the rate at which the coil cuts (or is cut by) the magnetic flux.

Consider the arrangement of fig. 5.2 where a conductor of length l metres is at right angles to and moving through a magnetic field of uniform flux density B tesla. The lines of magnetic flux are shown passing into the paper. Remember that the conductor must cut through the lines of flux for an

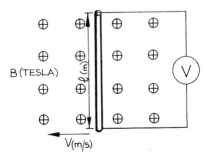

Fig. 5.2 E.m.f. induced in a conductor cutting through a magnetic flux

e.m.f. to be induced. If a voltmeter is connected across the ends of the conductor, then a complete closed circuit is formed. As the conductor cuts through the magnetic field, the reading on the voltmeter will be the e.m.f. induced in the circuit formed by the conductor and voltmeter leads. We can ensure that the induced e.m.f. is due solely to the movement of the conductor by arranging that the voltmeter leads do not cut any flux.

If the conductor is moving through the magnetic field with velocity v m/s, then the area that the conductor moves through in one second is $lv\,\mathrm{m}^2$. Since the induced e.m.f. depends on the flux 'cut' by the conductor, then the magnitude of the e.m.f. induced in the conductor is given by

$$e = -Blv$$

(Again, the minus sign is due to Lenz's law and may be ignored in the solving of problems unless the direction of the induced e.m.f. is asked for.)

Example 1   Calculated the e.m.f. induced in a conductor of length 25 cm which is moving through a magnetic field of flux density 0.45 T at a velocity of 30 m/s.

Ignoring the minus sign,

$$e = Blv$$

where $B = 0.45\,\mathrm{T}$ $l = 25\,\mathrm{cm} = 0.25\,\mathrm{m}$ and $v = 30\,\mathrm{m/s}$

$\therefore$ $e = 0.45\,\mathrm{T} \times 0.25\,\mathrm{m} \times 30\,\mathrm{m/s} = 3.375\,\mathrm{V}$

i.e. the induced e.m.f. is 3.375 V.

Example 2   Figure 5.3 shows part of a d.c. generator where the armature has a radius of 0.5 m and is rotating at a speed of 1000 rev/min. Calculate the e.m.f. induced in one of the conductors of the armature which has a length of 0.15 m and is moving under a pole which produces a uniform radial flux density of 0.45 T.

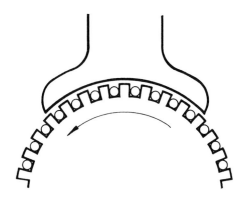

Fig. 5.3

$$\text{Velocity at rotor periphery} = \text{radius} \times \text{angular velocity}$$

where   angular velocity $= 2\pi \times \text{rotation speed}$

$$= 2\pi \times 1000 \text{ rad/min}$$

$$= \frac{2\pi}{60} \times 1000 \text{ rad/s}$$

$\therefore$ velocity $v = r \times \dfrac{2\pi}{60} \times \text{rotation speed}$

$$= 0.5 \text{ m} \times \frac{2\pi}{60} \times 1000 \text{ rad/s}$$

$$= 52.33 \text{ m/s}$$

Now $e = Blv$

where $B = 0.45 \text{ T}$ $l = 0.15 \text{ m}$ and $v = 52.33 \text{ m/s}$

$\therefore$ $e = 0.45 \text{ T} \times 0.15 \text{ m} \times 52.33 \text{ m/s}$

$$= 3.53 \text{ V}$$

i.e. the induced e.m.f. is 3.53 V.

5.5 Lenz's law

Consider the arrangement of fig. 5.1. We have seen that, when the flux changes, an e.m.f. is induced in coil B. Since the coil has a galvanometer connected across its ends, a complete electric circuit is formed and a current will flow around the circuit. We have already seen in chapter 4 that whenever a current flows in a conductor a magnetic field is set up around it. It is found by experiment that the direction of this magnetic field is always such that it opposes the effect which is producing it. If, for example, the induced e.m.f. is produced by increasing or decreasing the flux, then the resulting current flow will produce a flux which opposes that change. If the induced e.m.f. is produced by relative movement of the two coils, then the resulting current will produce a flux which opposes this movement. The result of these effects is that, to induce an e.m.f. in a coil, some work must be done against this opposing flux. It may be seen as the old problem that 'you can't get something for nothing'. Lenz stated this in a law as follows:

'When an e.m.f. is induced in a coil by electromagnetic induction, the direction of the induced e.m.f. is always such as to set up a current which opposes the motion or change of flux responsible for inducing that e.m.f.'

The following experiment can be used to demonstrate Lenz's law.

Consider the arrangement of fig. 5.4. As the bar magnet is pushed into the coil, it experiences an opposing force which tends to resist its motion. This may be explained as follows. As the magnet moves into the coil, the magnetic flux linking with the coil changes, thus inducing an e.m.f. in the coil by

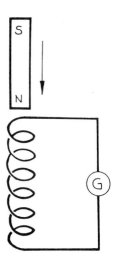

Fig. 5.4 Bar magnet being pushed into a coil

electromagnetic induction. The direction of the induced e.m.f. is such that the resulting current in the coil produces a north pole at the top of the coil and, since like poles repel, this opposes the movement of the magnet into the coil.

Conversely, if the magnet is drawn out of the coil, then the direction of the current is such that it produces a south pole at the top of the coil and, since unlike poles attract, this opposes the movement of the magnet out of the coil.

Example 1 Figure 5.5(a) shows a coil with an ammeter connected across its ends situated in a magnetic field with the direction of the flux as shown. If the flux is suddenly reduced to zero, what will be the direction of the current in the coil due to the change of flux?

By Lenz's law, the direction of the current will be such that it attempts to oppose the change of flux. It will therefore attempt to maintain the existence of flux by producing a flux in the same direction. By using the grip rule explained in chapter 4, the direction of the current must be as shown in fig. 5.5(b) and (c). Notice that the current will exist only for a short period and will quickly decay to zero.

Example 2 Predict the direction of the current in the coil in the arrangement of fig 5.6(a), if the magnet is being moved out of the coil.

Moving the magnet out of the coil must produce a south pole at the top of the coil, since this would oppose the motion of the magnet. The bottom of the coil must therefore act as a north pole.

Using the grip rule, the direction of the current is as shown in fig 5.6(b).

108

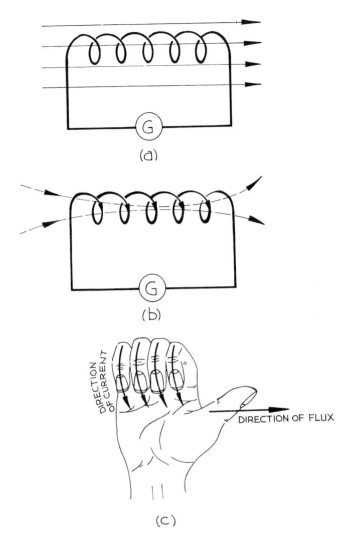

(a)

(b)

DIRECTION OF CURRENT

DIRECTION OF FLUX

(c)

Fig. 5.5 E.m.f. induced in a coil by a change of magnetic flux

An alternative means of finding the direction of the induced e.m.f. in a conductor cutting through a magnetic field is to use Fleming's right-hand rule.

5.6 Fleming's right-hand rule
This rule is stated for a straight conductor rather than a coil. It states that, when a conductor cuts across a magnetic flux as shown in fig. 5.7(a), then the direction of the induced e.m.f. and therefore of the current may be found by holding the fingers of the right hand at right angles to each other as shown in fig 5.7(b). The forefinger then represents the direction of the

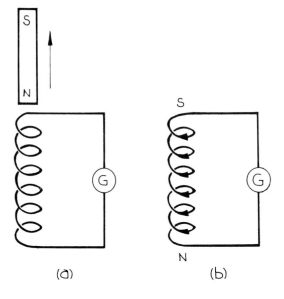

Fig. 5.6 E.m.f. induced in a coil by withdrawing a magnet

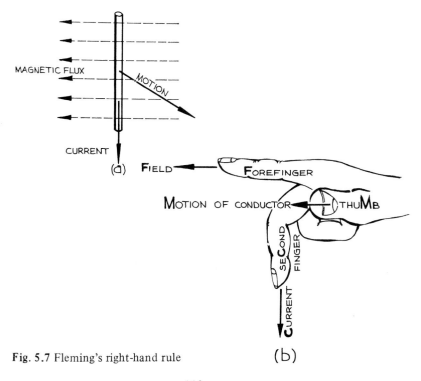

Fig. 5.7 Fleming's right-hand rule

magnetic flux, the thumb represents the direction of motion of the conductor relative to the field, and the second finger represents the direction of the current.

Example 1 Use Fleming's right-hand rule to find the direction of the current in the conductor shown in fig. 5.8.

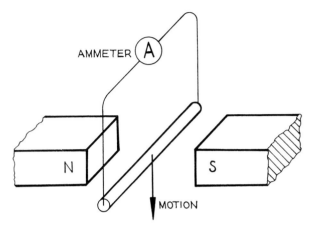

Fig. 5.8 A conductor moving through a magnetic field

The flux is from north to south, the motion is downwards, and the current is therefore out of the paper. Notice that a closed circuit must be provided if current is to flow.

Example 2 In fig. 5.9, the horseshoe magnet is moving downwards while the conductor remains stationary. Use Fleming's right-hand rule to find the direction of the induced e.m.f. and therefore of the current in the conductor during the motion.

The direction of the current is into the paper. Notice that the direction of the motion in Fleming's right-hand rule is that of the conductor relative to the field. Moving the magnet downwards has the same effect as keeping the magnet fixed and moving the conductor upwards.

Example 3 Use Fleming's right-hand rule to find the direction of the induced e.m.f. and therefore of the current in the arrangement of fig. 5.10. Assume that the magnet is being pushed into the coil.

Remember that in Fleming's right-hand rule the direction of motion is that of the conductors relative to the field. Consider the upper part of the coil. It is the component of the field which is at right angles to the motion which produces the induced e.m.f. Since the magnet is being pushed into the coil, the motion of the conductor relative to the field is from right to left. The direction of the magnetic field is upwards. By Fleming's right-hand rule,

111

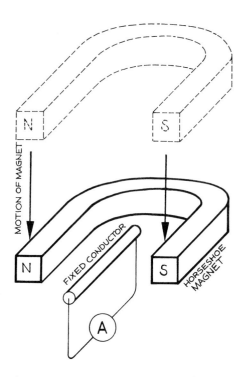

Fig. 5.9 A horseshoe magnet moving past a conductor

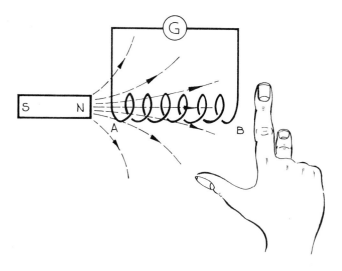

Fig. 5.10 Direction of e.m.f. induced in a coil by inserting a magnet

the direction of the e.m.f. and therefore of the current is into the paper. The current in the coil would thus flow from A to B.

5.7 Self-inductance
Referring back to fig. 5.1, when the current in coil A changes, an opposing e.m.f. is induced in coil A itself, due to the changing magnetic flux. This effect is also due to electromagnetic induction and is known as *self-induction*. The coil is said to be inductive and to posses *self-inductance*.

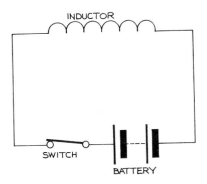

Fig. 5.11 Circuit containing an inductor

Consider the circuit of fig. 5.11. When the switch is opened, the current rapidly reduces to zero which causes the magnetic field to decay rapidly. This changing magnetic field induces an e.m.f. in the coil, which, by Lenz's law, must oppose the decay of magnetic flux and therefore opposes the reducing current. For this reason the self-induced e.m.f. is sometimes referred to as a back e.m.f. The magnitude of the back e.m.f. is found to be proportional to the rate at which the current changes. In this case, since the current reduces rapidly to zero when the switch is opened, the back e.m.f. will be very large.

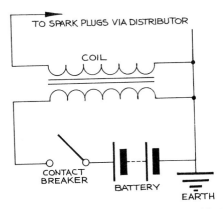

Fig. 5.12 Motor-car ignition coil, contact breaker, and battery

It is this e.m.f. which gives rise to the spark across the switch when an electrical appliance, such as a kettle, is switched off. It is also this effect which is used in a motor-car ignition system to produce the high voltage which is fed to the spark plugs. In this case, a contact breaker and coil are used to produce a high voltage from a 12 volt battery, as shown in fig. 5.12.

Consider a coil in which the current changes uniformly by ΔI amperes in a time Δt seconds. Since the magnitude of the induced e.m.f. is proportional to the rate of change of current, we may say

$$e \propto -\frac{\Delta I}{\Delta t}$$

or $\quad e = -\text{constant} \times \frac{\Delta I}{\Delta t}$

(The minus sign is due to Lenz's law and will be ignored in the solving of problems unless the direction of the induced e.m.f. is asked for.) The constant in this expression is given the name *inductance* and has the symbol L,

$$\therefore \quad e = -L\frac{\Delta I}{\Delta t}$$

Notice that the change of current with time is assumed to be uniform; if this is not the case, then the equation must be expressed by differential calculus in the form

$$e = -L\frac{\mathrm{d}I}{\mathrm{d}t}$$

The unit of inductance is the henry (abbreviation H). One henry is the inductance of a coil which has an e.m.f. of one volt induced in it by a uniform rate of change of current of one ampere per second in the coil,

i.e. $\quad 1 \text{ henry} = \dfrac{1 \text{ volt}}{1 \text{ ampere per second}}$

or $\qquad 1 \text{ H} = 1 \text{ V s/A}$

A submultiple of the unit which is frequently used is the millihenry (mH):

$$1 \text{ mH} = 10^{-3} \text{ H}$$

Example 1   The current in a coil changes uniformly from 0 to 0.5 A in 0.2 s. If the induced e.m.f. in the coil is 15 V, calculate the inductance of the coil.

Ignoring the minus sign,

$$L = \frac{E}{\Delta I/\Delta t}$$

where $\quad E = 15 \text{ V} \qquad \Delta I = 0.5 \text{ A} \quad$ and $\quad \Delta t = 0.2 \text{ s}$

$$\therefore \quad \frac{\Delta I}{\Delta t} = \frac{0.5 \text{ A}}{0.2 \text{ s}} = 2.5 \text{ A/s}$$

$$\therefore \quad L = \frac{15 \text{ V}}{2.5 \text{ A/s}} = 6 \text{ H}$$

i.e. the inductance of the coil is 6 H.

Example 2   Calculate the induced e.m.f. in a motor-car ignition coil which has an inductance of 2 H. Assume that, when the contacts open, the current of 0.5 A is uniformly reduced to zero in 2.5 ms.

Ignoring the minus sign,

$$E = L \frac{\Delta I}{\Delta t}$$

where $L = 2 \text{ H}$ $\Delta I = 0.5 \text{ A}$ and $\Delta t = 2.5 \text{ ms} = 0.0025 \text{ s}$

$$\therefore \quad E = 2 \text{ H} \times \frac{0.5 \text{ A}}{0.0025 \text{ s}}$$

$$= 400 \text{ V}$$

i.e. the induced e.m.f. is 400 V.

5.8 Relationship between the inductance of a coil and the number of turns

Consider the two equations which express the value of the induced e.m.f. in a coil due to a change of flux. They are

$$e = -N \frac{\Delta \Phi}{\Delta t}$$

and $$e = -L \frac{\Delta I}{\Delta t}$$

From these two equations we may say

$$N \frac{\Delta \Phi}{\Delta t} = L \frac{\Delta I}{\Delta t}$$

Rearranging to make L the subject of the equation gives

$$L = N \frac{\Delta \Phi}{\Delta I} \tag{i}$$

Now we know from chapter 4 that

$$NI = \Phi S$$

i.e.   m.m.f. = flux × reluctance

115

Rearranging gives

$$\Phi = \frac{NI}{S}$$

$$\therefore \quad \Delta\Phi = \frac{N\,\Delta I}{S}$$

Substituting this into equation (i) gives

$$L = N\frac{N\,\Delta I/S}{\Delta I} = \frac{N^2}{S}$$

i.e. the inductance of a coil is proportional to the square of the number of turns of the coil.

Example Calculate the inductance of an air-cored coil of 1500 turns if a current of 2 A in the coil produces a magnetic flux of $6\,\mu\text{Wb}$.

$$NI = \Phi S$$

$$\therefore \quad S = NI/\Phi$$

where $N = 1500$ $I = 2\,\text{A}$ and $\Phi = 6\,\mu\text{Wb} = 6 \times 10^{-6}\,\text{Wb}$

$$\therefore \quad S = \frac{1500 \times 2\,\text{A}}{6 \times 10^{-6}\,\text{Wb}}$$

$$= 500 \times 10^6\,\text{A/Wb}$$

$$L = N^2/S$$

where $N = 1500$ and $S = 500 \times 10^6\,\text{A/Wb}$

$$\therefore \quad L = \frac{1500^2}{500 \times 10^6\,\text{A/Wb}}$$

$$= 0.0045\,\text{H} \quad\text{or}\quad 4.5\,\text{mH}$$

i.e. the inductance of the coil is 4.5 mH.

5.9 Energy stored in an inductor

When a current flows through a coil, energy is stored in the form of a magnetic field in the area around the coil. This energy is accumulated when the switch completing the circuit is closed and the current is allowed to flow in the coil. The energy is released when the circuit is broken. The quantity of energy stored may be calculated as follows.

Consider a circuit which is completed such that the current builds up uniformly to a steady value I in time T seconds, as shown in fig. 5.13. The average current during this time period is given by

$$I_{av.} = I/2$$

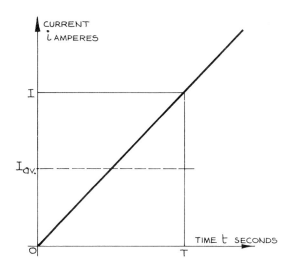

Fig. 5.13 A uniformly increasing current in a coil

The *magnitude* of the e.m.f. induced in the coil by the build-up of current is given by

$$e = L \frac{\Delta I}{\Delta t}$$

where $\Delta I = I$ and $\Delta t = T$

$$\therefore \quad e = L \frac{I}{T}$$

Thus the average power input to the coil during this time period is given by

$$\text{average power} = e \times I_{av.}$$

$$= L \frac{I}{T} \times \frac{I}{2}$$

$$= L \frac{I^2}{2T}$$

The energy stored in the inductor during this time period is given by

$$\text{energy stored} = \text{average power} \times \text{time}$$

$$= L \frac{I^2}{2T} \times T$$

$$= \tfrac{1}{2} L I^2$$

This energy is measured in joules (abbreviation J).

Example Calculate the energy stored in a 10 mH inductor which carries a current of 0.5 A.

$$\text{Energy} = \tfrac{1}{2}LI^2$$

where $L = 10\,\text{mH} = 0.01\,\text{H}$ and $I = 0.5\,\text{A}$

$\therefore$ energy $= \tfrac{1}{2} \times 0.01\,\text{H} \times (0.5\,\text{A})^2$

$\qquad\qquad = 1.25\,\text{mJ}$

i.e. the energy stored in the inductor is 1.25 mJ.

5.10 Mutual inductance

Consider the two coils A and B of fig 5.14. Mutual induction is the generation of an e.m.f. in coil B (the secondary coil) due to a change of current in coil A (the primary coil). Since the changing magnetic flux links with both coils, there is a self-induced e.m.f. in coil A and a mutually induced e.m.f. in coil B. The directions of both these e.m.f.'s are such as to produce a current which oppposes the original current change. The two coils are said to possess *mutual inductance*.

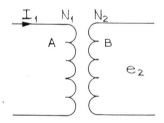

Fig. 5.14 Two coils side by side

The magnitude of the e.m.f. in the secondary coil (e_2) is found to be proportional to the rate of change of current in the primary coil. Suppose that the current in the primary coil changes uniformly by ΔI_1 amperes in a time Δt seconds, then the secondary e.m.f. is given by

$$e_2 \propto -\frac{\Delta I_1}{\Delta t}$$

or $\quad e_2 = -\text{constant} \times \dfrac{\Delta I_1}{\Delta t}$

(The minus sign is due to Lenz's law and will be ignored in the solving of problems unless the direction of the induced e.m.f. is asked for.) The constant in this expression is called mutual inductance and has the symbol M,

$$\therefore \quad e_2 = -M\frac{\Delta I_1}{\Delta t}$$

Notice that the rate of change of current is assumed to be uniform. If this is not the case, then the equation must be expressed by differential calculus in the form

$$e_2 = -M\frac{di_1}{dt}$$

The unit of mutual inductance is the henry (i.e. the same as for self inductance). Two coils are said to have a mutual inductance of 1 henry if a uniform current change of 1 ampere per second in one of the coils induces an e.m.f. of 1 volt in the other coil.

Example   Two coils have a mutual inductance of 2 H. Calculate the induced e.m.f. in the secondary coil if the current in the primary coil changes uniformly by 0.75 A in 20 ms.

Ignoring the minus sign,

$$e_2 = M\frac{\Delta I_1}{\Delta t}$$

where $M = 2\,\text{H}$ $\Delta I_1 = 0.75\,\text{A}$ and $\Delta t = 20\,\text{ms} = 0.02\,\text{s}$

$$\therefore\quad e_2 = 2\,\text{H} \times \frac{0.75\,\text{A}}{0.02\,\text{s}}$$

$$= 75\,\text{V}$$

i.e. the induced e.m.f. is 75 V.

5.11 Relationship between mutual inductance and number of turns

In the circuit of fig 5.14, if the flux linking with the secondary coil of N_2 turns changes uniformly by an amount $\Delta\Phi_2$ in a time t seconds, then, by Faraday's second law, the secondary e.m.f. is given by

$$e_2 = -N_2\frac{\Delta\Phi_2}{\Delta t}$$

We also have an equation for the secondary e.m.f. in terms of the mutual inductance:

$$e_2 = -M\frac{\Delta I_1}{\Delta t}$$

From these two equations we may say

$$M\frac{\Delta I_1}{\Delta t} = N_2\frac{\Delta\Phi_2}{\Delta t}$$

$$\therefore \quad M = N_2 \frac{\Delta\Phi_2}{\Delta I_1}$$

i.e. the mutual inductance is proportional to the number of turns of the secondary coil and to the rate of change of secondary flux with primary current.

Example   Two coils are wound on the same core such that they both experience the same change of flux. If a change of current of 2 A in the primary coil produces a change of flux of 7.5 mWb in the core, calculate the mutual inductance between the primary and secondary coils if the number of turns of the secondary coil is 100.

$$M = N_2 (\Delta\Phi_2 / \Delta I_1)$$

where $N_2 = 100$ $\Delta\Phi_2 = 7.5 \, \text{mWb} = 0.0075 \, \text{Wb}$ and $\Delta I_1 = 2 \, \text{A}$

$$\therefore \quad M = 100 \times \frac{0.0075 \, \text{Wb}}{2 \, \text{A}} = 0.375 \, \text{H}$$

i.e. the mutual inductance is 0.375 H.

5.12 The transformer

Transformers are used for converting alternating voltages from one value to another (see chapter 6 for a description of the properties of alternating voltage and current). The transformation may be to either a higher or a lower voltage. A most important application of the transformer is in stepping voltages up to a very high voltage ready for transmission along overhead lines and, after transmission, in stepping the voltages down again ready for distribution to the consumer. Transmission at high voltage is more economical, since the transmission current may then be kept small and the power loss in the cable is therefore much reduced. Transformers are used in a wide variety of other applications, such as transforming voltages down from 240 V mains to say 20 V for use in record players and radios etc. They are also used extensively as instrument transformers for transforming a current or voltage to a suitable level for measurement.

The symbol for a transformer is shown in fig. 5.15. Notice the parallel lines drawn between the coils which indicate that the coils are wound on a soft-iron core. The usual form of construction of a low-power transformer is shown in fig. 5.16, with the primary and secondary coils both wound around the centre limb. This is referred to as a 'shell-type' or 'double-wound' transformer.

Transformers are very efficient, and very little power is lost in transformation. Small energy losses do exist in transformers, and these consist mainly of hysteresis losses and eddy-current losses in the core. To keep these losses to a minimum, the core is made of soft iron with a high permeability and a low hysteresis loss. Also, the iron core is made up of laminates (thin slices) to reduce eddy-current loss.

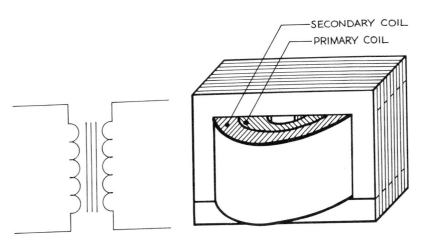

Fig. 5.15 Transformer symbol

Fig. 5.16 Transformer construction (low-power)

5.13 Transformer operation

The operation of the transformer depends on a changing voltage across the primary winding causing a changing flux in the core, which in turn induces a changing e.m.f. in the secondary winding. As shown in fig. 5.17, a sinusoidal alternating voltage V is applied to the primary winding and causes an alternating current I_1 to flow. This current produces an alternating magnetic flux in the core of the transformer. Due to this changing magnetic flux, alternating e.m.f.'s E_1 and E_2 are induced in the primary and secondary windings respectively. Notice that E_1 is in opposition to the applied voltage V and in an ideal transformer E_1 is equal to V. E_2 is in the same direction as E_1. If a resistor is connected across the secondary winding, then the secondary circuit of the transformer is completed, and alternating currents I_1 and I_2 will flow in the primary and secondary circuits.

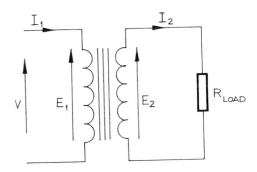

Fig. 5.17 E.m.f.'s induced in transformer coils with an alternating voltage applied to the primary

121

A 300 MVA 762 kV single-phase auto transformer. Three of these could supply the electrical needs of a city the size of Liverpool.

5.14 Transformer turns ratio, voltage ratio and current ratio

In a transformer, the e.m.f. induced in each winding is proportional to the number of turns on that winding. If the primary and secondary turns are N_1 and N_2 respectively, then

122

$$E_1 \propto N_1$$
$$E_2 \propto N_2$$

and $\dfrac{E_1}{E_2} = \dfrac{N_1}{N_2}$

E_1/E_2 is called the voltage ratio and N_1/N_2 is called the turns ratio. Ignoring losses, the voltage ratio is equal to the turns ratio. The current ratio is I_2/I_1, where

$$\frac{I_2}{I_1} = \frac{N_1}{N_2}$$

The ratio of the voltage across one of the windings of the transformer to the number of turns of that winding is called the volts per turn. Notice that the volts per turn of the primary is equal to the volts per turn of the secondary:

$$\frac{E_1}{N_1} = \frac{E_2}{N_2}$$

Example 1 A transformer has a turns ratio of 20 : 1. Assuming that the primary induced e.m.f. (E_1) is equal to the primary applied voltage of 240 V, calculate the secondary e.m.f. (E_2).

$E_1/E_2 = N_1/N_2$

∴ $E_2 = E_1 \times N_2/N_1$

where $N_1/N_2 = 20$ and thus $N_2/N_1 = 1/20$ and $E_1 = 240$ V

∴ $E_2 = 240$ V $\times 1/20$

    $= 12$ V

i.e. the secondary e.m.f. is 12 V.

Example 2 An ideal 50 kVA, 1000 V/250 V, 50 Hz single-phase transformer has 500 turns on the primary. Determine (a) the number of secondary turns, (b) the primary and secondary full-load currents, (c) the volts per turn on both the primary and secondary windings.

a) $N_2 = N_1 \times E_2/E_1$

where $E_1 = 1000$ V $E_2 = 250$ V and $N_1 = 500$

∴ $N_2 = 500 \times 250$ V$/1000$ V

    $= 125$

b) The transformer input power is given by

    input power $= V_1 \times I_1$

where $V_1 = E_1 = 1000$ V for an ideal transformer

But we are given that

input power $= 50\,\text{kVA} = 50\,000\,\text{VA}$

$\therefore \quad V_1 I_1 = 50\,000\,\text{VA}$

$\therefore \quad I_1 = \dfrac{50\,000\,\text{VA}}{1000\,\text{V}}$

$\qquad = 50\,\text{A}$

In an ideal transformer, the losses are assumed to be negligible

$\therefore \quad$ output power $=$ input power $= 50\,\text{kVA}$

$\therefore \qquad\qquad E_2 I_2 = 50\,000\,\text{VA}$

$\therefore \qquad\qquad I_2 = \dfrac{50\,000\,\text{VA}}{250\,\text{V}} = 200\,\text{A}$

c)   Primary volts per turn $= E_1/N_1$

$\qquad\qquad\qquad\qquad\qquad = 1000\,\text{V}/500$

$\qquad\qquad\qquad\qquad\qquad = 2\,\text{V/turn}$

Also,   secondary volts per turn $= 2\,\text{V/turn}$

i.e. the number of secondary turns is 125, the primary and secondary full-load currents are 50 A and 200 A, and the volts per turn on both the primary and secondary are 2 V/turn.

5.15 Magnetic induction

By now the reader should be clear that electromagnetic machines operate by the inducing of an e.m.f. in a coil by a change of the magnetic flux linking with the coil. This is the case in the transformer and in the generator. However, there is a range of machines which do not require the magnetic flux to *change* for their operation. This type of machine is referred to as operating by *magnetic induction*. This is the inducing of magnetic polarity in a ferromagnetic material when it is situated in a magnetic field.

Consider the relay shown in fig 5.18(a). When a current passes through the stator solenoid, the stator core takes on a magnetic polarity of north and south as shown. The armature does the same, and presents a south pole adjacent to the north pole of the stator. This causes the armature to be attracted towards the stator, and thus operates the contacts as shown in fig 5.18(b). When the current is removed, the armature moves back to its normal position, thus opening the contacts. It should be noticed that the relay does not depend on the inducing of an e.m.f. in the armature; nor does it require the flux to change.

There are many devices used in industry which operate by magnetic induction, examples being the relay, solenoid valve, lifting magnet, electric bell, and vibrator. A selection of relays is shown in fig. 5.19.

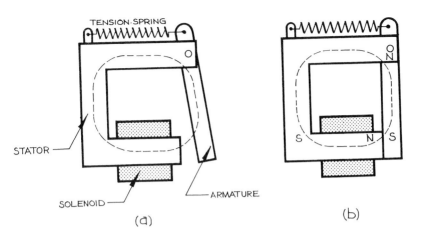

Fig. 5.18 Simplified representation of a relay

Fig. 5.19 A selection of relays

5.16 The electric-motor principle

When a current passes through a conductor situated in a magnetic field, then a force acts on the conductor tending to move it out of the field, as shown in fig. 5.20. This effect is the basis of the electric motor (which is considered later in the chapter), and also of the moving-coil instrument (which is considered in chapter 8).

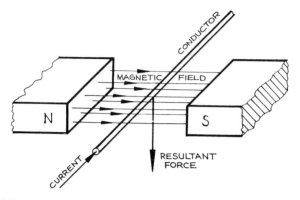

Fig. 5.20 Force on a current-carrying conductor in a magnetic field

One method of finding the direction of the force is to consider the force as being due to the interaction of two magnetic fields. It was stated in chapter 4 that, when a current flows through a wire, a magnetic field is set up around the wire. The direction of the lines of magnetic flux are found by using the right-hand screw rule, and are as shown in fig. 5.21 (b). If the conductor is now placed in the uniform magnetic field of fig. 5.21 (a) then the two fields interact to form the pattern shown in fig. 5.21 (c). Notice that above the conductor both of the flux directions are the same and the total flux is increased, while below the conductor the two flux directions are in opposition and the total flux is reduced. The flux pattern is stressed, rather like a web of elastic bands would be if a bar were pushed into it, and the result is that the conductor experiences a downward force.

Fig. 5.21 Force on a current-carrying conductor in a magnetic field

An alternative method of finding the direction of the force is to use Fleming's left-hand rule.

5.17 Fleming's left-hand rule

This rule states that, when a current and a magnetic field react together to produce a force, the direction of the force may be found by holding the thumb, first, and second fingers of the left hand perpendicular to each other as shown in fig. 5.22. The forefinger then represents the direction of the flux (north to south), the second finger represents the direction of the current, and the thumb represents the direction of the motion produced by the force.

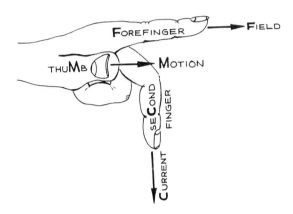

Fig. 5.22 Fleming's left-hand rule

Example 1   Using Fleming's left-hand rule, what would be the direction of motion of the conductor shown in fig. 5.23?

Answer   Upwards.

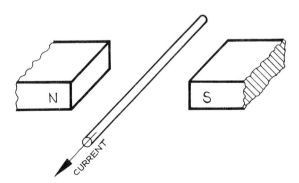

Fig. 5.23 Force on a current-carrying conductor in a magnetic field

Example 2   A horseshoe magnet is placed around a freely suspended conductor connected via a switch to a battery as shown in fig. 5.24. When the switch is closed, the reaction of the current with the magnetic field produces a force on the wire which causes it to flick out of the bowl of mercury. In which direction will the wire move?

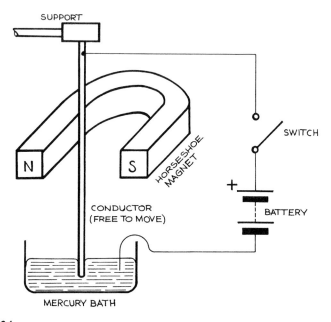

Fig. 5.24

Answer   When the switch is closed, the direction of the current is downwards. The direction of the magnetic field is from left to right. The motion will therefore be *out of the paper*. This experiment is frequently used to demonstrate the effect.

5.18 Factors affecting the force on a conductor in a magnetic field
From the experiment described in the last example, it is reasonable to assume that the size of the force (F) on the conductor will depend upon:

a) the intensity of the magnetic field (i.e. the flux density B),
b) the magnitude of the current (I), and
c) the length of the conductor in the magnetic field (l).

The relationship between these factors is shown in fig. 5.25. The magnitude of the force (F) on the conductor is given by:

$$F = BIl$$

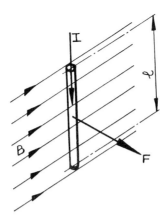

Fig. 5.25 Force on a current-carrying conductor in a magnetic field

where F = force on conductor (newtons)

         B = flux density (teslas)

         I = current (amperes)

and l = length of conductor in the magnetic field and at right angles to it (metres)

Example 1   A conductor carrying a current of 4 A is placed at right angles in a magnetic field of flux density 0.6 T. If 20 cm of the wire is in the field, calculate the force on the conductor.

$$F = BIl$$

where B = 0.6 T I = 4 A   and l = 20 cm = 0.2 m

$\therefore$ F = 0.6 T × 4 A × 0.2 m

      = 0.48 N

i.e. the force on the conductor is 0.48 N.

The expression 'at right angles' used above needs some explanation. Consider the arrangement of fig. 5.26(a). In this case the conductor is in line with the magnetic field and no force is exerted on the conductor. To produce a force, the direction of the current must *cut across* the lines of magnetic flux. It need not do so at right angles, but the force produced is a maximum when this is the case.

In fig. 5.26(b), the component of the conductor at right angles to the flux is $l \cos \theta$. The complete expression for the force is then

$$F = BIl \cos \theta$$

where θ is the angle between the conductor and the perpendicular to the flux.

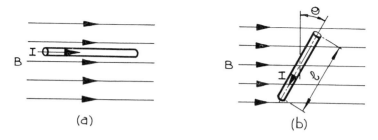

Fig. 5.26 Force on a current-carrying conductor in a magnetic field

Example 2 A conductor carrying a current of 200 mA is placed in a magnetic field, at 30° to the perpendicular to the flux. The field has a flux density of 0.4 T and 50 cm of the conductor is in the field. Calculate the force on the conductor.

$$F = BIl \cos \theta$$

where $B = 0.4\,\text{T}$ $I = 200\,\text{mA} = 0.2\,\text{A}$ $l = 50\,\text{cm} = 0.5\,\text{m}$

and $\theta = 30°$

$\therefore$ $F = 0.4\,\text{T} \times 0.2\,\text{A} \times 0.5\,\text{m} \times \cos 30°$

$= 0.04\,\text{N} \times 0.866 = 0.0346\,\text{N}$

i.e. the force on the conductor is 0.0346 N.

5.19 How rotary motion is produced
A single-turn coil of wire which is free to rotate about the dotted centre line is shown in fig. 5.27. The coil is situated in a magnetic field. Consider first the left-hand side of the coil. With the directions of current and magnetic

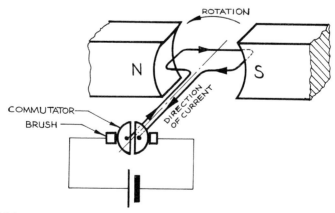

Fig. 5.27 A simple d.c. motor

130

flux shown, by Fleming's left-hand rule a downwards force is produced on this side of the coil. Now consider the right-hand side of the coil. This side of the coil has an upwards force produced on it. The result of the forces on both coil sides is to produce a torque or turning moment in an anticlockwise direction, and thus produce rotary motion. To produce continuous motion the direction of the current in the coil must be reversed every time the coil passes through the vertical, otherwise the coil would stop in a vertical position. This reversal is achieved by using a *split-ring commutator* as shown in fig. 5.27. This acts like a switch and changes the direction of the current once every revolution.

This is the basic principle of the d.c. electric motor.

Example 1 A single-turn coil of length 4 cm and breadth 2 cm is placed in a magnetic field of flux density 0.25 T as shown in fig. 5.28. If the coil is at right angles to the flux and carries a current of 200 mA, calculate (a) the force on each coil side, (b) the total torque produced. (Torque is given by force multiplied by the distance of the force from the point about which it produces rotation.)

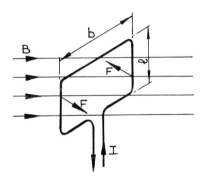

Fig. 5.28 Single-turn current-carrying coil in a magnetic field

$$B = 0.25\,\text{T} \qquad I = 200\,\text{mA} = 0.2\,\text{A}$$
$$l = 4\,\text{cm} = 0.04\,\text{m} \qquad b = 2\,\text{cm} = 0.02\,\text{m}$$

a) Force on each coil side is given by

$$F = BIl = 0.25\,\text{T} \times 0.2\,\text{A} \times 0.04\,\text{m}$$
$$= 0.002\,\text{N}$$

i.e. the force on each coil side is 0.002 N.

b) Torque due to one coil side = force × distance from centre of rotation
$$= F \times b/2 = 0.002\,\text{N} \times (0.02\,\text{m})/2$$
$$= 0.002\,\text{N} \times 0.01\,\text{m} = 20 \times 10^{-6}\,\text{N\,m}$$

Torque due to both sides of coil $= 2 \times F \times b/2 = 2 \times 20 \times 10^{-6}$ N m

$$= 40 \times 10^{-6} \text{ N m}$$

i.e. the total torque produced is $40\,\mu$N m.

The equation for the torque produced by an N-turn current-carrying coil situated in a magnetic field is derived as follows.

Consider a coil of N turns, each of length l metres and breadth b metres. If the flux may be assumed to be of uniform flux density B tesla, and the current in the coil is I amperes, then the force F on each coil side is given by

$F = BIlN$ newtons

The torque T' due to each coil side is found by multiplying the force F by the distance from the centre of rotation $(b/2)$:

$T' = BIlNb/2$

But, since there are two coil sides producing torque, the total torque T is

$T = BIlbN$ newton metres

Now $l \times b = A =$ cross-sectional area of coil

$\therefore \quad T = BAIN$ newton metres

Example 2 A coil of 20 turns has a cross-sectional area of $18\,\text{cm}^2$ and is suspended in a magnetic field of flux density 0.45 T. Calculate the current required in the coil to produce a torque of $10\,\mu$N m.

$$I = \frac{T}{BAN} \text{ - amperes}$$

where $T = 10\,\mu\text{N m} = 10 \times 10^{-6}$ N m $\qquad A = 18\,\text{cm}^2 = 18 \times 10^{-4}\,\text{m}^2$

$N = 20 \quad$ and $\quad B = 0.45$ T

$$\therefore \quad I = \frac{10 \times 10^{-6} \text{ N m}}{0.45 \text{ T} \times 18 \times 10^{-4} \text{ m}^2 \times 20}$$

$$= 617 \times 10^{-6} \text{ A} = 617\,\mu\text{A}$$

i.e. the current required in the coil is $617\,\mu$A.

5.20 Motor–generator duality

It is important to realise that d.c. electrical machines may be run either as motors or as generators. If the cell in fig. 5.27 is replaced by a galvanometer and the coil is made to rotate by an externally applied torque, then an e.m.f. will be generated and a current will flow in the galvanometer.

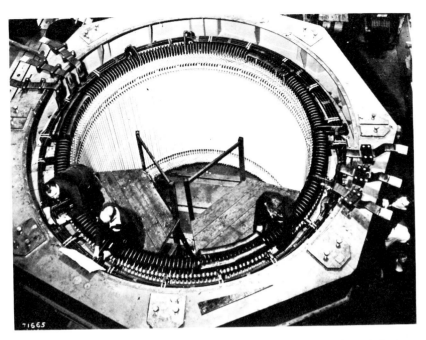

Alternator winding of a high-speed pump-storage motor–generator rated at 95 MVA

When the machine is run as a motor, it may be regarded as a device for converting electrical energy into mechanical energy. When it is run as a generator, it converts mechanical energy into electrical energy.

Exercises on chapter 5

1 The flux linking with a 500-turn coil changes from 100 mWb to 50 mWb in 100 ms. Calculate the average induced e.m.f. in the coil.   [250 V]

2 An average e.m.f. of 400 V is induced in a 1000-turn coil when the flux changes by 200 μWb. Calculate the time taken for the change of flux. [0.5 ms]

3 A flux of 2 mWb, linking with a 250-turn coil, is reversed in 0.02 s. Calculate the average value of the induced e.m.f.   [50 V]

4 State Faraday's first law of electromagnetic induction and draw sketches to illustrate the law, using (a) a permanent magnet moving into a coil; (b) two coils, one inside the other, with an alternating current supplied to one of the coils.

5 State why the induced e.m.f. produced when a circuit is broken could be very dangerous.

A coil of 2000 turns is linked by a magnetic flux of 300 μWb. Calculate the e.m.f. induced in the coil when (a) the flux is reversed in 0.05 s, (b) the flux is reduced to zero in 0.15 s.   [24 V; 4 V]

6   When a flux linking with a coil changes, an e.m.f. is induced. What determines (a) the magnitude of the e.m.f.? (b) the direction of the e.m.f.?

7   Describe the phenomenon of self-induction. Why can the current not reach its final value instantaneously, and how is this effect made use of in a 'choke'? Give a practical example where an inductive coil is used to advantage.

8   State Lenz's law in connection with an induced e.m.f.

9   If an e.m.f. of 400 V is induced in an inductive circuit having an inductance of 0.2 H, calculate the rate of change of the current.   [2000 A/s]

10   A coil of self-inductance 0.05 H has a resistance of 20 Ω. Calculate the energy stored in the inductor when the coil is connected to a 200 V d.c. supply.   [2.5 J]

11   What d.c. voltage is required to raise the current in a circuit uniformly from 10 A to 20 A in 2 seconds if the circuit inductance is 0.1 H and the resistance negligible?   [0.5 V]

12   Explain why a d.c. current rises more slowly in an inductive circuit than in a purely resistive circuit. Why is there a sudden voltage surge at the terminals when an inductive circuit is broken?

13   Explain what is meant by 'self-inductance' and state the unit in which it is measured. The current flowing through a constant inductance of 2 H is increased uniformly from 0 to 5 A in 0.5 s, maintained constant at 5 A for 0.1 s, and then reduced uniformly to zero in 0.2 s. Draw, to scale, graphs representing the variation of current and induced e.m.f. with respect to time.

14   A current flowing in a 50-turn air-cored coil produces a flux of 2 mWb. Calculate the average value of the e.m.f. induced in the coil when the current is completely reversed in 1 ms.   [200 V]

15   When a current of 0.5 A is passed through a coil of 200 turns, a flux of 0.025 Wb is produced. Calculate the coil inductance.   [10 H]

16   State Faraday's first law of electromagnetic induction and describe, with the aid of suitable diagrams, how this law may be demonstrated.

A straight conductor is moved with uniform velocity 10 m/s at right angles to its length and to a uniform magnetic field of flux density 1.5 T. Given that the e.m.f. induced in the conductor is 6 V, calculate the length of the conductor. If the conductor forms part of a closed circuit and the force acting on the conductor is 0.3 N, find the resistance of the circuit.   [0.4 m; 12 Ω]

17   Two coils are placed side by side. If a d.c. supply voltage is suddenly switched across one coil, state what happens in the other coil and explain why.

18   Describe the phenomenon of mutual induction. Explain how this effect is made use of in a car ignition coil.

19   When the current in a coil changes from 2 A to 10 A in 0.1 s, the e.m.f. induced in an adjacent coil is 6 V. Calculate the mutual inductance between the coils.   [75 mH]

20   Explain the terms 'self-inductance' and 'mutual inductance'. The mutual inductance between two coils is 0.2 H. Find the e.m.f. induced in one coil when the current in the other changes uniformly from 5 A to 3 A in 10 ms. [40 V]

21   A coil of 500 turns is uniformly wound on a magnetic core having a cross-sectional area of 100 cm^2 and a mean circumference of 1 m. A secondary winding of 100 turns is wound over the primary. If a direct current of 4 A is passed through the primary winding, calculate

a) the self-inductance of the primary winding, given that the relative permeability of the core material under these conditions is 1500;
b) the mutual inductance between the primary and secondary windings if all the primary flux links with every turn of the secondary winding;
c) the average e.m.f. induced in the secondary winding if interruption of the primary current causes the magnetic flux in the core to decay to zero in 0.05 s.

[0.47 H; 94.2 mH; 7.54 V]

22   Explain briefly how a voltage appears on the secondary winding of a double-wound transformer when the primary winding is connected to an a.c. supply.

23   Give two practical examples of mutual inductance.

A coil of 15 000 turns is required to produce an e.m.f. of 15 kV for ignition purposes. Calculate the rate of change of flux required to provide this e.m.f. [1 Wb/s]

24   The mutual inductance between the two windings of an ignition coil is 5 H. Calculate the average value of the e.m.f. induced in the secondary winding when a current of 2.5 A in the primary winding is reduced to zero in 1 ms. [12.5 kV]

25   Two coils, A and B, are mounted on a common core. When the current in coil B is changed from 16 A to 20 A in 0.4 s an average e.m.f. of 40 V is induced in coil A. Determine the mutual inductance between the two coils. [4 H]

26   Two air-cored coils, A and B, are wound with 100 and 500 turns respectively and lie in parallel planes such that 80% of the magnetic flux produced by A links with every turn on B. A steady current of 5 A in A produces a flux of 10 μWb. Given that all this flux links every turn in A, calculate (a) the self-inductance of coil A, (b) the mutual inductance between the two coils, (c) the average e.m.f. induced in each coil if the current A is now reversed in 10 ms. [0.2 mH; 0.8 mH; 0.2 V, 0.8 V]

27   Two identical coils, A and B, are placed adjacent to each other. An e.m.f. of 0.25 V is induced in A when the flux linking the coil changes at a rate of 1.2×10^{-3} Wb/s. A current of 1.8 A in B causes a flux of 1.2×10^{-5} Wb to link A. Calculate the mutual inductance of the circuit.   [1.39 mH]

28   Explain the operation of the transformer and draw the transformer symbol. State why the transformer has a soft-iron core and why this is made up of laminations.

29   Make a sketch to show the construction of a two-winding transformer and clearly label each part. Explain how the secondary voltage is obtained.

30   A transformer with a turns ratio of 30 : 1 has 240 V applied to the primary. Calculate the secondary voltage.   [8 V]

31   Calculate the secondary current and voltage of a 4:1 voltage-step-down transformer with a primary voltage of 110 V and a primary current of 100 mA.   [27.5 V; 400 mA]

32 A transformer has a primary applied voltage of 200 V and a secondary current of 2.5 A. If the secondary resistance is 10 Ω, calculate the turns ratio of the transformer.   [8:1]

33 A transformer has a voltage ratio of 1000 : 240. Calculate the secondary voltage when the primary applied voltage is 250 V.   [60 V]

34 A current transformer with a current ratio of 5:100 has a primary current of 40 A. Calculate the secondary current.   [2 A]

35 A double-wound transformer has 400 primary turns and 80 secondary turns. When the primary is supplied with 240 V, calculate (a) the secondary voltage, (b) the primary current when the secondary load current is 25 A. [48 V; 5 A]

36 Explain briefly how a voltage appears on the secondary winding of a double-wound transformer when an alternating voltage is connected to the primary. State two practical applications of a transformer.

The turns ratio of a voltage-step-down transformer is 4:1. If the primary voltage is 1200 V, calculate the secondary voltage.   [300 V]

37 A transformer has 200 primary turns. Calculate the number of turns required on the secondary winding to produce a voltage of 65% of that of the primary.

If the secondary winding is tapped to give an alternative choice of output voltage of 10% of that of the primary, how many turns would there be between this tapping and the common output terminal?   [130; 20]

38 State Faraday's first law of electromagnetic induction.

A straight conductor 0.8 cm long is moved with constant velocity at right angles both to its length and to a uniform magnetic field. Given that the e.m.f. induced in the conductor is 4 V and the velocity is 10 m/s, calculate the flux density of the magnetic field. If the conductor forms part of a closed circuit of total resistance 5 Ω, calculate the force on the conductor.   [0.5 T; 0.32 N]

39 A conductor has a length of 0.25 m and moves at right angles through a magnetic field of flux density 0.7 T at a velocity of 10 m/s. Calculate the e.m.f. induced in the conductor.   [1.75 V]

40 A coil has 100 turns and an effective coil-side length of 2 cm. If the coil is rotated at 20 m/s between two poles of uniform flux density 0.8 T, calculate the maximum e.m.f. generated in the coil.   [64 V]

41 A 100-turn coil is square with 200 mm sides and is arranged to rotate at a constant speed of 240 rev/min in a uniform magnetic field of intensity 1 T. Calculate the e.m.f. induced in the coil when its plane is (a) parallel to the direction of the field, (b) at right angles to it.   [0 V; 100.5 V]

42 a) Figure 5.29 shows two conductors of a d.c. generator armature. Assuming that the loop rotates in a clockwise direction, as indicated, show the direction of the e.m.f. in each conductor.

b) If the arrangement were to be used as a motor, with the rotation in the direction shown, show the direction in which the supply current would need to flow.

43 a) When a current-carrying conductor is situated in a magnetic field, a force is produced on the conductor. State the factors which affect this force and derive the equation for the force.

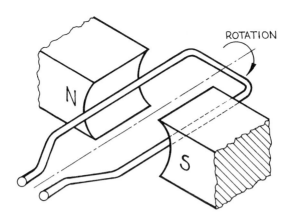

ROTATION

N

S

Fig. 5.29

b) Hence state how rotary motion is produced and sketch a simple d.c. motor. What is the purpose of a commutator in a d.c. motor?

44 A conductor of length 0.6 m is placed at right angles in a magnetic field of flux density 0.45 T. Calculate the force exerted on the conductor if it carries a current of 5 A.   [1.35 N]

45 State three things which determine the force on a current-carrying conductor in a magnetic field.

46 A conductor of length 1.5 m is placed at right angles in a magnetic field of flux density 0.25 T. Calculate the current in the conductor if the force on it is 0.75 N.   [2 A]

47 A conductor carrying a current of 200 mA experiences a force of 0.02 N when placed in a magnetic field of flux density 0.7 T. Calculate the length of the conductor.   [143 mm]

48 A coil has a height of 2 cm and is situated in a magnetic field of flux density 0.65 T. Calculate the current in the coil side if the force is 50 μN.   [3.85 mA]

49 a) Figure 5.30 shows a single-turn coil connected to a d.c. supply and situated in the magnetic field of a two-pole d.c. motor. Show, by means of a simple diagram, the resulting magnetic field and indicate the direction in which the coil will tend to move. Mark on the diagram the polarity of the poles.

b) A conductor 0.4 m long lies at right angles to a magnetic field of flux density 0.5 T and carries a current of 30 A. Determine the force exerted on the conductor.   [6 N]

50 A conductor of length 0.2 m and carrying a current of 50 A is placed in and at right angles to a magnetic field of flux density 0.6 T. Calculate the force on the conductor.   [6 N]

51 A conductor 20 mm long carrying a current of 40 A lies in and at right angles to a magnetic field. If the force on the conductor is 0.4 N, calculate the density of the magnetic field.   [0.5 T]

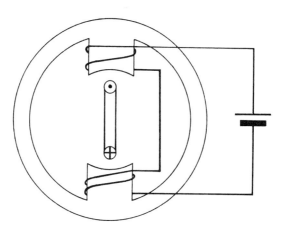

Fig. 5.30

52 A current-carrying conductor situated in a magnetic field experiences a force of 0.2 N. What will be the force (a) if the current is doubled? (b) if the magnetic flux is halved? (c) if the conductor has five turns instead of one? (d) if the length of the conductor is increased by 50%?   [0.4 N; 0.1 N; 1 N; 0.3 N]

53 The coil of a moving-coil meter has a height of 2 cm and carries a current of 5 A. The flux density at right angles to the coil is 0.4 T. Calculate the force on the coil side if the coil has (a) one turn, (b) 200 turns.   [0.04 N; 8 N]

54 The coil of a moving-coil instrument is wound with 70 turns on a former having an effective length of 2.5 cm and width 2 cm. The former rotates at right angles to a magnetic field of flux density 0.5 T. Calculate the torque produced on the coil when it carries a current of 0.2 A.   [3.5 mN m]

55 The coil of a moving-coil instrument is pivoted between the poles of a permanent magnet. Given that the flux density in the air gap is 0.2 T, the mean width of the coil is 15 mm, the active length of each coil side is 22.5 mm, the current in the coil is 25 mA, and the coil is wound with 96.5 turns, calculate (a) the force acting on each side of the coil, (b) the total torque exerted on the coil. (Assume the air-gap flux density to be uniform.)   [2.4 mN; 18 μN m]

56 When a p.d. is applied to a coil of self-inductance 0.5 H, a current of 200 mA flows. Calculate the energy stored. If the current is reduced to 50% of its original value, determine the new value of energy stored.   [0.01 J; 0.0025 J]

57 Why is it necessary to provide a split-ring commutator on a d.c. motor?

58 With reference to a coil of wire arranged to rotate in a magnetic field system, explain briefly the principle of operation of a d.c. motor. State the factors affecting the speed at which the coil rotates.

Make sketches to show the position of the coil when the torque produced on the coil is (a) a maximum, (b) a minimum.

59 Figures 5.31(a) and (b) show a current-carrying coil situated in a magnetic field between two permanent magnets. Draw three sketches to show (a) the magnetic field produced by the permanent magnets only, (b) the

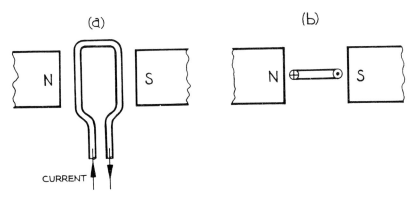

Fig. 5.31

magnetic field produced by the current-carrying coil only, (c) the combined magnetic field. Indicate on sketch (c) the direction in which the coil will try to move.

Give *two* practical applications of the force produced on a current-carrying coil situated in a magnetic field.

6   Alternating voltages and currents

6.1 A simple alternator

Electricity for supply to industrial and domestic consumers is generated in power stations using generators referred to as *alternators*.

A simple but inefficient alternator is shown in fig. 6.1, where a single-turn coil is rotated in a magnetic field. It was stated in chapter 5 that, when a conductor cuts through a magnetic field, an e.m.f. is induced in the conductor. In the circuit of fig. 6.1, two 'slip rings' are connected to the ends of the coil and the current is fed to the load resistor via 'brushes'. This is a convenient means of allowing the coil to rotate while still connecting its ends across the resistor. To find the *direction* of the current induced in the coil, Fleming's right-hand rule is used.

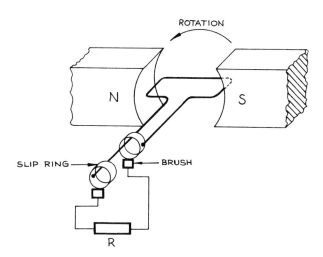

Fig. 6.1 A simple alternator

Figure 6.2 shows a coil rotating in an anticlockwise direction at a constant rotational speed in a magnetic field. The direction of the flux is from left to right (i.e. north to south). Considering fig. 6.2(a), the motion of coil side A is downwards and therefore, by Fleming's right-hand rule, the direction of the current is out of the paper as shown. For coil side B the current is into the paper. The coil and the load resistor form a closed circuit, so current flows into the resistor from coil side A to coil side B.

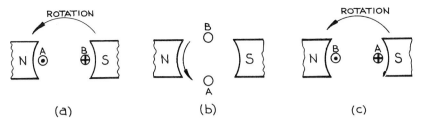

(a)   (b)   (c)

Fig. 6.2 Coil rotating in a magnetic field

Now consider fig. 6.2(b). At this point in the rotation, the coil sides are travelling parallel to the flux. Since they are not *cutting* any flux, there is no induced e.m.f. The current will therefore be zero.

Considering fig. 6.2(c), the coil has now travelled through half a revolution. The directions of the current in A and B are as shown. Notice that the current now flows from B to A, i.e. the direction of the current has been reversed.

As the coil travels through each complete revolution, the e.m.f. and current produced describe an *alternating* waveform, i.e. they act first in one direction and then in the opposite direction. One cycle of this waveform is shown in fig. 6.3. The current has its maximum or peak value (I_p) when the coil is cutting across the flux at the fastest rate, at the positions of figs 6.2(a) and (c). The peak e.m.f. is shown as E_p. The current is zero when the coil is not cutting any flux, as in fig. 6.2(b).

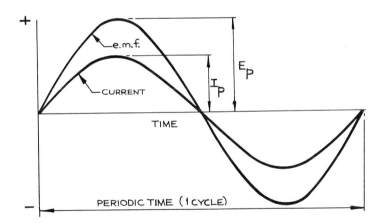

Fig. 6.3 One cycle of an alternating voltage and current

The e.m.f. and current waveforms may be described by the sinusoidal equations

$$e = E_p \sin \theta$$

and $$i = I_p \sin \theta$$

141

where e =   instantaneous e.m.f.

        i =   instantaneous current

        E_p =   peak e.m.f.

        I_p =   peak current

and θ =   angle of rotation of the coil from the vertical.

The terms 'instantaneous e.m.f.' and 'instantaneous current' mean the values of the e.m.f. and current at any instant in time.

This sinusoidal current is referred to as 'alternating current', normally abbreviated to a.c.

The *peak value* is the maximum value of the waveform. This is also referred to as the *amplitude* of the waveform.

The vertical distance between the positive and negative peaks is referred to as the *peak-to-peak value* (E_{p-p} and I_{p-p}). In a symmetrical waveform such as that shown in fig. 6.3, $E_{p-p} = 2E_p$.

Example 1   The current produced by an a.c. generator has a peak value of 20 A. Calculate the instantaneous value of the current when the coil is 30° past the vertical.

$$i = I_p \sin \theta$$

where $I_p = 20\,A$ and $\theta = 30°$

∴ $i = 20\,A \times \sin 30°$

     $= 20\,A \times 0.5 = 10\,A$

i.e. the instantaneous current when the coil is 30° past the vertical is 10 A.

Example 2   The instantaneous value of an alternating e.m.f. is given by

$$e = 100 \sin \theta \text{ volts}$$

Tabulate values for e at 30° intervals from $\theta = 0°$ to 360° and hence sketch a graph of e against θ.

Table 6.1 shows corresponding values of e and θ, and these are plotted in fig. 6.4.

Frequency and period

The *frequency* (f) of a waveform is the number of cycles performed in one second and is measured in hertz (Hz):

     1 Hz = 1 cycle per second

The *periodic time* or period (T) of a waveform is the time for one complete cycle and is measured in seconds (see fig. 6.3).

Table **6.1**

θ (degrees)	$\sin \theta$	$e = 100 \sin \theta$ (volts)
0	0	0
30	0.5	50
60	0.866	86.6
90	1	100
120	0.866	86.6
150	0.5	50
180	0	0
210	−0.5	−50
240	−0.866	−86.6
270	−1	−100
300	−0.866	−86.6
330	−0.5	−50
360	0	0

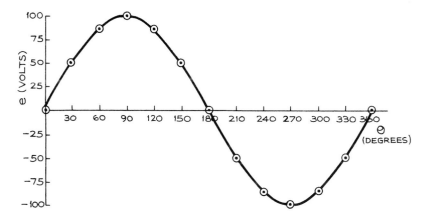

Fig. 6.4

Notice that $T = 1/f$,

i.e.   time, in seconds, for 1 cycle $= \dfrac{1}{\text{number of cycles/second}}$

Example 3   An alternating-current waveform has a period of 20 ms. Calculate the frequency.

$f = 1/T$

where $T = 20\,\text{ms} = 0.02\,\text{s}$

143

$$\therefore \quad f = \frac{1}{0.02\,\text{s}} = 50\,\text{Hz}$$

i.e. the frequency is 50 Hz.

The more usual form of the equation for an alternating current is in terms of the frequency:

$$i = I_p \sin 2\pi ft$$

This is derived from the original equation as follows.

Let the *angular velocity* of the coil be ω radians/second. The angle rotated through in time t is then given by

$$\theta = \omega t$$

i.e.   angular displacement = angular velocity × time

The equation for the current is given by

$$i = I_p \sin \theta = I_p \sin \omega t$$

Since one complete rotation is 2π radians, the angular velocity is given by

$$\omega = 2\pi f$$

i.e.   angular velocity = $\dfrac{\text{angular displacement}}{\text{per cycle}} \times \dfrac{\text{number of cycles}}{\text{per second}}$

Hence $i = I_p \sin 2\pi ft$

Example 4   An alternating current has a peak value of 5 A and a frequency of 50 Hz. Calculate the value of the instantaneous current after 4 ms.

$$i = I_p \sin 2\pi ft$$

where $I_p = 5\,\text{A}$ $f = 50\,\text{Hz}$ and $t = 4\,\text{ms} = 0.004\,\text{s}$

$$\therefore \quad i = 5\,\text{A} \times \sin(2\pi \times 50\,\text{Hz} \times 0.004\,\text{s})$$

$$= 5\,\text{A} \times \sin(0.4\pi)$$

$$= 4.76\,\text{A}$$

i.e. after 4 ms the instantaneous current is 4.76 A.

Example 5   An alternating e.m.f. is given by $e = 25 \sin 314t$ volts, where e is in volts and t in seconds. Calculate the e.m.f. after 2 ms.

$$e = 25 \sin 314t$$

where $t = 2\,\text{ms} = 0.002\,\text{s}$

$$\therefore \quad e = 25 \sin(314 \times 0.002) \text{ volts}$$

$$= 25 \sin 0.628 \text{ volts}$$

$$= 14.69 \text{ V}$$

i.e. after 2 ms the e.m.f. is 14.69 V.

Root-mean-square value of an alternating current

Since it is often the heating effect of a current that is important, another means of measuring alternating current is often used – this is called the root-mean-square value, or r.m.s. value, ($I_{r.m.s.}$) and is the value indicated by most ammeters. The r.m.s. value of an alternating current is defined as the equivalent d.c. value which would have the same heating effect.

Now the heating effect of an electric current is proportional to the power transferred, and

$$\text{instantaneous power} = i^2 R \text{ watts}$$

$$\therefore \quad \text{average power} = R \times \text{average value of } i^2$$

$$\therefore \quad \text{effective value of current} = \sqrt{\text{average value of } i^2}$$

This effective value is referred to as the 'root of the mean of the square' of the current or the 'root-mean-square' or 'r.m.s.' value.

The r.m.s. value of a *sinusoidal* alternating current may be calculated from

$$I_{r.m.s.} = \frac{I_p}{\sqrt{2}} = 0.707 I_p$$

Notice that the r.m.s. value is less than the peak value.

In the same way, the r.m.s. value of an alternating voltage is given by

$$E_{r.m.s.} = \frac{E_p}{\sqrt{2}} = 0.707 E_p$$

The terms 'alternating current' and 'alternating voltage' may be assumed to refer to *sinusoidally* alternating quantities unless otherwise stated. Also, it is worth noting that, when performing calculations on circuits which have an applied alternating voltage, the values given for voltage and current may be taken to be r.m.s. values unless otherwise stated.

Example 6   An alternating current has a peak value of 3 A and a frequency of 60 Hz. Calculate (a) its r.m.s. value, (b) its periodic time.

a) $I_{r.m.s.} = 0.707 I_p$

$$= 0.707 \times 3 \text{ A} = 2.12 \text{ A}$$

b) $T = \dfrac{1}{f} = \dfrac{1}{60 \text{ Hz}} = 0.0167 \text{ s} = 16.7 \text{ ms}$

i.e. the r.m.s. value is 2.12 A and the periodic time is 16.7 ms.

145

Example 7 Calculate the peak value of an a.c. mains supply which has an r.m.s. value of 240 V.

$$V_{r.m.s.} = 0.707 \, V_p$$

$$\therefore \quad V_p = 1.414 \times V_{r.m.s.}$$

$$= 1.414 \times 240 \, V$$

$$= 339.4 \, V$$

i.e. the peak value of the mains supply is 339 V.

Average value of an alternating current

In a symmetrical waveform such as the pure sine wave of fig. 6.3, the average value (taken over one complete cycle) is zero, since there is as much of the waveform above the zero line as there is below it. If we consider only one *half* cycle of the waveform, as shown in fig. 6.5, then the average value is given by

$$I_{av.} = \frac{\text{area under curve}}{\text{base width}}$$

$$\therefore \quad I_{av.} = \frac{\int_0^\pi I_p \sin \omega t \, d(\omega t)}{\pi}$$

$$= \frac{I_p}{\pi} \left[-\cos \omega t \right]_0^\pi$$

$$= \frac{2 I_p}{\pi}$$

$$= 0.637 I_p$$

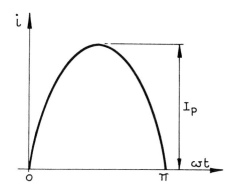

Fig. 6.5 Half cycle of an alternating waveform

146

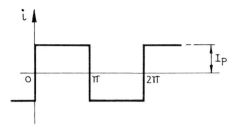

Fig. 6.6 A square wave

Example 8 Calculate the average value of a half cycle of the square wave shown in fig. 6.6.

$$I_{av.} = \frac{\text{area under curve}}{\text{base width}}$$

therefore, for a half cycle,

$$I_{av.} = \frac{I_p \times \pi}{\pi} = I_p$$

i.e. the average value of a half cycle of a square wave is equal to the peak value.

Form factor and peak factor
The form factor and peak factor of a waveform give an indication of the shape of the waveform:

$$\text{form factor} = \frac{\text{r.m.s. value}}{\text{average value}} = \frac{I_{r.m.s.}}{I_{av.}}$$

$$\text{peak factor} = \frac{\text{peak value}}{\text{r.m.s. value}} = \frac{I_p}{I_{r.m.s.}}$$

Example 9 Calculate the form factor and peak factor for a pure sine wave.

$$\text{Form factor} = \frac{I_{r.m.s.}}{I_{av.}}$$

where $I_{r.m.s.} = \dfrac{I_p}{\sqrt{2}}$ and $I_{av.} = \dfrac{2I_p}{\pi}$

$\therefore$ form factor $= \dfrac{I_p/\sqrt{2}}{2I_p/\pi} = \dfrac{\pi}{2\sqrt{2}} = 1.11$

peak factor $= \dfrac{I_p}{I_{r.m.s.}} = \dfrac{I_p}{I_p/\sqrt{2}} = \sqrt{2} = 1.414$

147

6.2 Non-sinusoidal waveforms

There are other repetitive waveforms which commonly occur in electrical and electronic engineering, and some of them are shown in fig. 6.7. Their features are given in Table 6.2. In the case of the pulse waveform of fig. 6.7(d), the period for which the waveform is high is referred to as the *mark*, and the distance between the pulses is referred to as the *space*.

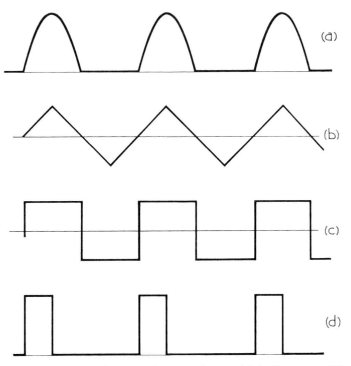

Fig. 6.7 Some commonly occurring waveforms: (a) half-wave rectified, (b) triangular, (c) square, (d) pulse.

Table 6.2 Features of sinusoidal and non-sinusoidal waveforms

	r.m.s. value	Average value Full-wave	Average value Half-wave	Form factor	Peak factor
Sinusoidal waveform	$0.707I_p$	0	$0.637I_p$	1.11	1.41
Half-wave rectified waveform	$0.5I_p$	$0.318I_p$	$0.637I_p$	0.78	2.0
Triangular waveform	$0.577I_p$	0	$0.5I_p$	1.15	1.73
Square waveform	I_p	0	I_p	1.0	1.0

A unidirectional waveform is one which is always positive or always negative (not both). The half-wave rectified sine wave and the pulse waveform are unidirectional, since we have taken the minimum level to be zero (i.e. 0 V).

6.3 Phase angle

The alternating voltage and current waveforms of fig. 6.3 are said to be *in phase* with one another, since their maximum and minimum values occur together. Two sinusoidal waveforms of the same frequency which do *not* have their maximum and minimum values occuring together are said to be *out of phase* with one another. This is the case with the waveforms shown in figs 6.8(a) and (b).

In fig. 6.8(a), v_2 reaches its maximum value 90° *after* v_1, and v_2 is therefore said to *lag* v_1 by 90°. In fig. 6.8(b), v_3 reaches its maximum value 90° *before* v_1, and v_3 is therefore said to *lead* v_1 by 90°. The angle by which the

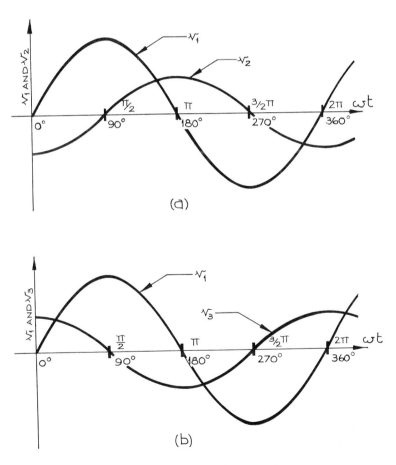

Fig. 6.8 Voltage and current waveforms 90° out of phase

149

waveforms lag or lead is referred to as the *phase angle* (i.e. in both of these cases the phase angle is 90°). Notice that in figs 6.8(a) and (b) v_1 is used as the *reference* waveform, since it passes through the origin.

Phase angles may be measured in either degrees or radians, where

π radians $= 180°$

∴   1 radian $\approx 57.3°$

6.4 Phasor representation of a sine wave

When performing a.c. calculations on circuits containing more than one component, it is often necessary to obtain the waveform for the addition of two or more alternating quantities. Due to the difficulty of adding sinusoidal waveforms by graphical methods, a *phasor* representation of sinusoidal waveforms is used. A phasor is a line with both *magnitude* (i.e. length) and *phase angle* (i.e. angle to the horizontal). The phasor relates to the sinusoidal waveform as follows:

a) the magnitude of the phasor represents the amplitude (or peak value) of the waveform (or the r.m.s. value may be used instead);
b) the angle of the phasor to the horizontal represents the phase angle.

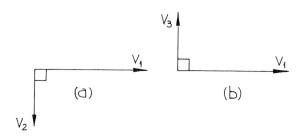

Fig. 6.9 Phasor representation of waveforms 90° out of phase

Figures 6.9(a) and (b) show the phasor representation of the waveforms of figs 6.8(a) and (b). The sinusoidal waveform v_1 in fig. 6.8 passes through the origin of the axes and is represented on the phasor diagram by a horizontal phasor from left to right. A horizontal phasor is referred to as a *reference phasor*. The length of phasor V_1 represents the amplitude (or peak value) of the waveform v_1. The amplitude of v_2 is half that of v_1, and it is therefore represented by a phasor with half the length of V_1, as shown in fig. 6.9(a).

v_2 lags v_1 by 90°, while v_3 leads v_1 by 90°, as shown. Notice that lagging phase angles are represented below the horizontal line while leading phase angles are represented above.

Example   Two a.c. voltages, v_1 and v_2, have peak values of 20 V and 30 V respectively. If v_2 lags v_1 by 30°, draw their phasor representation, using v_1 as the reference.

150

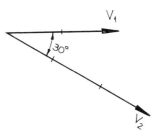

Fig. 6.10

Figure 6.10 shows the required phasors.

Notice that V_1 and V_2 are drawn in the ratio $2:3$.

6.5 Addition of sinusoidal waveforms

The advantage of using phasor representation of sinusoidal waveforms becomes apparent when *adding* two or more a.c. voltages. In the phasor diagram of fig. 6.11, the addition of the two a.c. voltages v_1 and v_2 may easily be carried out by taking the *resultant* of phasors V_1 and V_2. This is achieved by completing the parallelogram as shown in fig. 6.11(a), the resultant being the phasor V_3. Notice that the amplitude of v_3 and its phase angle ϕ_2 may be obtained directly from the phasor diagram.

The alternative graphical method of adding the two voltage waveforms is very cumbersome but is shown in fig. 6.11(b), where the dotted waveform represents the resultant waveform v_3.

One method of finding the magnitude and phase angle of the resultant from the phasor diagram is to use an accurate scale drawing and to measure the length of the resultant V_R and the phase angle ϕ.

Consider the addition of two phasors: one of 20 V leading the reference by $45°$ and the other of 25 V lagging the reference by $90°$. The phasor diagram of fig. 6.12 is drawn to the scale 10 mm $\equiv$ 5 V. This gives a resultant of approximately 18 V at $37°$ lagging.

A more accurate method is to use trigonometry. The horizontal component of V_R is the sum of the horizontal components of the 20 V and 25 V phasors:

$$V_{R,\,horizontal} = V_{20,\,horizontal} + V_{25,\,horizontal}$$
$$= 20\,V \times \cos 45° + 25\,V \times \cos 90°$$
$$= 20\,V \times 0.707 + 0$$
$$= 14.14\,V$$

Note that the 25 V phasor acts vertically and so has no horizontal component.

The vertical component of V_R is the combination of the 25 V vertically downwards and the vertical component of the 20 V phasor:

$$V_{R,\,vertical} = 25\,V - 20\,V \times \sin 45°$$
$$= 25\,V - 20\,V \times 0.707$$
$$= 25\,V - 14.14\,V = 10.86\,V$$

151

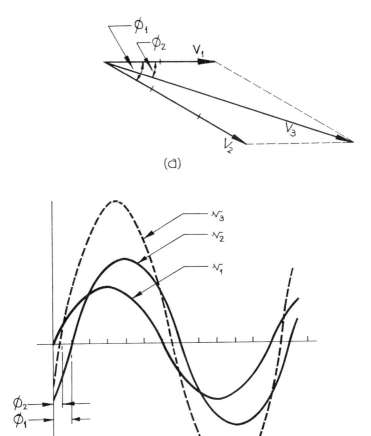

(a)

(b)

Fig. 6.11 Addition of two alternating waveforms using phasor addition and a graphical method

Now $V_R{}^2 = V_R{}^2{}_{,\,\text{horizontal}} + V_R{}^2{}_{,\,\text{vertical}}$

$\qquad = (14.14\,\text{V})^2 + (10.86\,\text{V})^2$

$\therefore \qquad V_R = \sqrt{317.88}\,\text{V}$

$\qquad = 17.83\,\text{V}$

The phase angle ϕ is found from

$$\tan \phi = \frac{V_{R,\,\text{vertical}}}{V_{R,\,\text{horizontal}}} = \frac{-10.86\,\text{V}}{14.14\,\text{V}} = -0.768$$

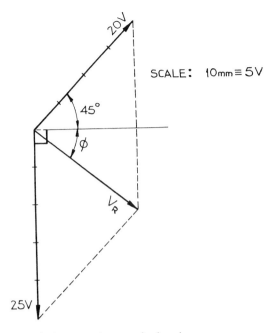

Fig. 6.12 Addition of phasors using a scale drawing

$$\therefore \qquad \phi = \arctan(-0.768) = -37.5° \quad \text{or} \quad -0.65 \text{ rad}$$

i.e. the resultant is 17.83 V at −0.65 rad lagging.

6.6 Mathematical representation of sinusoidal waveforms

A sinusoidal waveform can be represented by a mathematical equation which contains the same information as is provided by the graphical or the phasor representation.

We have already seen that the equation for a sinusoidal voltage is

$$e = E_p \sin \omega t$$

This is the equation of the voltage which passes through the origin (i.e. the reference voltage). For a sinusoidal voltage which is out of phase with this reference voltage, the equation becomes

$$e = E_p \sin(\omega t \pm \phi)$$

where the sign of ϕ depends on whether the voltage e leads or lags the reference voltage.

Example 1 Write the mathematical equation for the following sinusoidal voltages:

153

a) a reference voltage e_1 with amplitude 10 V,
b) a voltage e_2 lagging e_1 by $\pi/2$ (90°) and with amplitude 20 V,
c) a voltage e_3 leading e_1 by $\pi/4$ (45°) and with amplitude 30 V.

$$e_1 = 10 \sin \omega t$$

$$e_2 = 20 \sin (\omega t - \pi/2)$$

$$e_3 = 30 \sin (\omega t + \pi/4)$$

Example 2 Draw the phasor diagram and find the resultant of the following three voltages:

$$e_1 = 30 \sin \omega t$$

$$e_2 = 40 \sin (\omega t - \pi/6)$$

$$e_3 = 50 \sin (\omega t + \pi/3)$$

The phasor diagram of fig. 6.13 is drawn to a scale of $10 \text{ mm} \equiv 10 \text{ V}$.

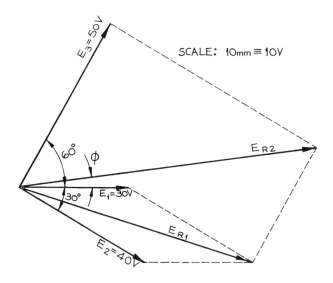

Fig. 6.13

Using the method of a scale drawing, the resultant of E_1 and E_2 is first obtained to give E_{R1}. Then the resultant of E_3 and E_{R1} is taken to give E_{R2}. The resultant E_{R2} and the phase angle ϕ are then measured from the diagram to give

$$E_{R2} = 93 \text{ V} \quad \text{and} \quad \phi = 15°$$

154

Using the trigonometrical method,

$$\frac{\text{horizontal component}}{\text{of resultant}} = \frac{\text{sum of horizontal components}}{\text{of } E_1, E_2, \text{ and } E_3}$$

$$= 30\,\text{V} + 40\,\text{V} \times \cos 30° + 50\,\text{V} \times \cos 60°$$

$$= 30\,\text{V} + 34.64\,\text{V} + 25\,\text{V}$$

$$= 89.64\,\text{V}$$

$$\frac{\text{vertical component}}{\text{of resultant}} = \frac{\text{sum of vertical components}}{\text{of } E_1, E_2, \text{ and } E_3}$$

$$= 30\,\text{V} \times \sin 0° + 50\,\text{V} \times \sin 60° - 40\,\text{V} \times \sin 30°$$

$$= 0 + 43.30\,\text{V} - 20\,\text{V}$$

$$= 23.30\,\text{V}$$

By the theorem of Pythagoras,

$$E_R{}^2 = (89.64\,\text{V})^2 + (23.20\,\text{V})^2$$

$$\therefore \quad E_R = 92.62\,\text{V}$$

$$\text{and} \quad \tan \phi = \frac{23.30\,\text{V}}{89.64\,\text{V}} = 0.26$$

$$\therefore \quad \phi = \arctan 0.26$$

$$= 14.57° \quad \text{or} \quad 0.25\,\text{rad}$$

$$\therefore \quad e_R = 92.62 \sin (\omega t + 0.25) \text{ volts}$$

i.e. the resultant is 92.62 V at a phase angle of 0.25 rad leading

Rectification of alternating waveforms is considered in chapter 9, after discussion of the operation of semiconductor diodes.

Exercises on chapter 6

1 A simple generator is represented by a coil rotating in a magnetic field as in fig. 6.14. Sketch the diagram and show the direction of the current in each side of the coil if the rotation is as shown. Assume the coil forms a closed path via a resistor.

2 Explain what is meant by the term 'alternating current' and explain, with the aid of a sketch, the following terms: (a) frequency, (b) period, (c) r.m.s. value, (d) instantaneous value of an alternating current.

An alternating voltage with a sinusoidal waveform has an r.m.s. value of 7.07 V. What is the peak value?   [10 V]

3 Write an expression showing the relationship between r.m.s. value and peak value for a sine wave. An alternating voltage has a maximum value of 141.4 V; calculate the r.m.s. value.   [100 V]

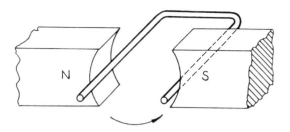

Fig. 6.14

4 An alternating e.m.f. is represented by $e = 100 \sin \theta$ volts. What will be the value of e when θ equals (a) $60°$? (b) $180°$? (c) 210?   [86.6 V; 0 V; -50 V]

5 An alternating current is given by $i = I_p \sin 628t$ amperes, where t is in seconds. What will be the value of i after 2 ms?   [$0.95 I_p$]

6 An alternating e.m.f. is represented by $e = 100 \sin 314t$ volts, where t is in seconds. What is (a) its r.m.s. value? (b) its frequency? (c) its period? [70.7 V; 50 Hz; 20 ms]

7 An alternating voltage has a frequency of 60 Hz and a maximum value of 1414 V. Calculate (a) the r.m.s. value, (b) the value after 0.0015 seconds. [1000 V; 757 V]

8 A sinusoidal alternating voltage has an r.m.s. value of 35.36 V and a frequency of 50 Hz. Plot the waveform with time horizontally and voltage vertically. What is the peak value?   [50 V]

9 The instantaneous value of a 50 Hz sinusoidal current is 2 A after 5 ms. Calculate the peak and r.m.s. values.   [2 A; 1.414 A]

10 The period of a sinusoidal alternating current is 20 ms. What is the frequency and what is the peak value if the value after 0.002 s is 15.08 A? [50 Hz; 25.67 A]

11 A voltage waveform has a peak value of 100 V and a frequency of 50 Hz. At what time after passing through zero will the voltage be equal to 70 V?   [2.47 ms]

12 A sinusoidal waveform performs 1 cycle in 16.67 ms. Calculate the frequency.   [60 Hz]

13 A sinusoidal voltage passes through its peak value five times in 100 ms. Calculate (a) its period, (b) its frequency.   [20 ms; 50 Hz]

14 Explain the term 'r.m.s. value' and why it is used.
    A sinusoidal alternating current has an r.m.s. value of 4.242 A and a frequency of 50 Hz. Give an equation which represents the instantaneous value of the current with time.   [$i = 6 \sin 314t$ A]

15 Explain the terms (a) r.m.s. value, (b) peak value, (c) frequency, (d) period of an alternating current.

16 A simple generator rotates at 3000 rev/min. If the maximum e.m.f. generated is 2 V, (a) what is the frequency of the alternating voltage? (b) give an equation which describes the instantaneous value of the e.m.f.   [50 Hz; $e = 2 \sin 314t$ V]

17 Sketch a simple alternating-current generator, showing how the two ends of the coil would be connected across a load resistor.

18 An alternating current is found to have the same heating effect as a direct current of 5 A. What are the r.m.s. value and the peak value of the alternating current? [5 A; 7.07 A]

19 The voltage across a resistor is given by $e = 100 \sin 628t$ volts, where t is in seconds. Calculate (a) the r.m.s. value, (b) the frequency of the supply. [70.72 V; 100 Hz]

20 Construct, using the same axes, one complete cycle of the following: (a) an alternating current of maximum value 1 A, 50 Hz; (b) an alternating current of maximum value 0.5 A, 50 Hz lagging the first by $\pi/4$ rad.

Calculate the r.m.s. value of each waveform. [0.707 A; 0.354 A]

21 Sketch, on graph paper, one complete cycle of a 20 V maximum, 50 Hz sinusoidal waveform. On the same axes, sketch the waveform of a 10 V maximum, 100 Hz sinusoidal voltage starting at the same instant.

22 Construct, to scale, one complete cycle of a sinusoidal voltage waveform having a peak value of 300 V. On the waveform clearly indicate (a) both peak values, (b) the negative half-cycle, (c) the positive half-cycle, (d) the r.m.s. value.

23 An alternating current has a symmetrical triangular waveform having a peak value of 10 A. Determine graphically (a) the average (half-cycle) value of the waveform, (b) the r.m.s. value. What are its peak factor and form factor? [5 A; 5.77 A; 1.73, 1.15]

24 Two alternating currents of sinusoidal waveform, I_1 and I_2, have maximum values of 10 A and 8 A respectively, I_2 lagging I_1 by $\pi/6$ rad. Using the same axes, construct graphs to scale to represent the variation of these currents over one complete cycle. On the same axes, construct a further graph to show the sum of the two waveforms and from this determine the maximum and r.m.s. values of the resultant current. [17.4 A; 12.3 A]

25 Explain what are meant by the frequency and periodic time of an alternating-current waveform. Explain what is meant by the phase difference between the voltage across a circuit and the current flowing through it.

Write an expression representing the instantaneous value of a sinusoidal voltage having an r.m.s. value of 7.07 V and a frequency of 100 Hz.

26 Sketch one cycle of a sinusoidal voltage having an amplitude of 10 V. On the same axes, sketch one cycle of a sinusoidal current wave having an amplitude of 1 A, lagging the voltage by 45°. On the current wave, mark clearly (a) one point where the rate of change of current is a minimum, (b) one point where the rate of change of current is a maximum. Sketch also the corresponding phasor diagram and calculate the r.m.s. and average values of the current. [0.707 A; 0 A]

27 The instantaneous value of an alternating voltage is given by $v = 400 \sin 3140\, t$ volts. Determine the frequency and periodic time of the waveform. [500 Hz; 2 ms]

28 a) State briefly the meaning of the term 'phasor' as applied to sinusoidal voltage and current waveforms.

b) The instantaneous values (in amperes) of the currents in the branches of a parallel circuit are given by

$$i_1 = 10 \sin (\omega t + \pi/6) \qquad i_2 = 5 \sin (\omega t + \pi/2)$$
$$i_3 = 5 \sin (\omega t - \pi/6)$$

The instantaneous value of the supply voltage is $200 \sin \omega t$.

Represent the above currents on a phasor diagram, to a scale of $1 \text{ cm} \equiv 1 \text{ A}$, and hence obtain the total current supplied to the circuit, expressed in the form $i = I_p \sin (\omega t \pm \phi)$.

c) Calculate the r.m.s. and average values of the current in (b) over half a cycle.   [$i = 16.24 \sin (\omega t + 0.64)$ A; 11.48 A; 10.34 A]

29   The instantaneous values (in volts) of three alternating voltages are given by

$$v_1 = 100 \sin (\omega t - \pi/3) \qquad v_2 = 5 \sin (\omega t + \pi/6)$$
$$v_3 = 20 \sin (\omega t + \pi/2)$$

Represent the above voltages on a phasor diagram and hence find the values of (a) $v_1 + v_2 + v_3$, (b) $v_1 - v_2 - v_3$. In each case, express the resultant in the form $v = V_p \sin (\omega t \pm \phi)$.   [$v = 84.03 \sin (\omega t - 0.87)$ V; $v = 118.27 \sin (\omega t - 1.17)$ V]

30   The instantaneous values (in volts) of three e.m.f.'s are given respectively by

$$v_1 = 100 \sin (628t - \pi/2) \qquad v_2 = 50 \sin (628t + \pi/3)$$
$$v_3 = 80 \sin (628t + \pi/6)$$

Represent the above e.m.f.'s on a phasor diagram and hence find (a) $v_1 + v_2 + v_3$, (b) $v_1 + v_2 - v_3$. Express the resultant in each case in the form $v = V_p \sin (628t \pm \phi)$. State the frequency of the above waveform. [$v = 95.75 \sin (628t - 0.18)$ V; $v = 106.36 \sin (628t - 2.0)$ V; 100 Hz]

31   Using graph paper, draw to scale, using a common base of time, the complete cycle of the following voltages:

$$v_1 = 20 \sin 314t \text{ volts} \quad \text{and} \quad v_2 = 15 \sin (314t - \pi/6) \text{ volts}$$

Three parallel branches of an electrical network carry the following currents:

$$i_1 = 20 \sin \omega t \qquad i_2 = 16 \sin (\omega t - 60°) \qquad i_3 = 12 \cos \omega t$$

Draw a phasor diagram of these currents to a scale of $1 \text{ cm} \equiv 2 \text{ A}$ and from it determine (a) the expression for the total instantaneous current flowing into the network, (b) the r.m.s. value of this total current. [$i = 28.06 \sin (\omega t - 4°)$; 19.84 A]

32   Explain the meaning of the terms 'root-mean-square value' and 'average value' as applied to an alternating waveform.

One cycle of an alternating waveform is shown in fig. 6.15. Draw one half of this waveform to a suitable scale and from the graph determine (a) the average value of the voltage, (b) the r.m.s. value of the voltage. [5.1 V; 4.46 V]

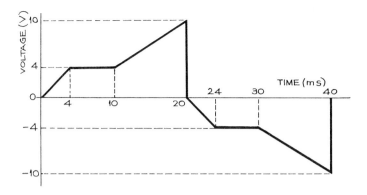

Fig. 6.15

33 For the waveform of fig. 6.16, calculate (a) the average value for one half cycle, (b) the r.m.s. value, (c) the peak factor, (d) the form factor. [5.4 V; 5.84 V; 1.54; 1.08]

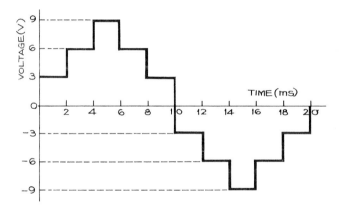

Fig. 6.16

7 Single-phase a.c. circuits

In this chapter we shall consider the relationship between the voltage and current in electrical circuits containing resistance, capacitance, and inductance where the applied voltage is sinusoidal (i.e. an a.c. voltage).

7.1 Purely resistive circuit

When an a.c. voltage is applied across a pure resistance, as shown in fig. 7.1(a), the current which flows is sinusoidal and is in phase with the applied voltage. The graphical and phasor representations are as shown in figs 7.1(b) and (c).

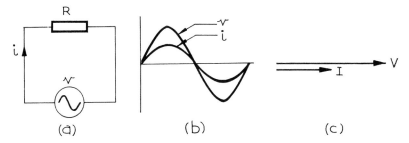

Fig. 7.1 Alternating voltage and current in a pure resistance

The instantaneous values of voltage and current are related by Ohm's law:

$$R = \frac{v}{i}$$

where R is the resistance of the circuit. The unit of resistance is the ohm (Ω).

In the phasor representation we generally use the peak (or maximum) values, and these are therefore related by

$$R = \frac{V_p}{I_p}$$

When an a.c. voltage is applied across a circuit which is not purely resistive, then the current which flows is out of phase with the applied voltage, as we shall see below.

7.2 A purely inductive circuit

In a purely inductive circuit, as shown in fig. 7.2(a), the current i lags the voltage v by 90° or $\pi/2$ radians. The graphical and phasor representations are as shown in figs 7.2(b) and (c), with the current as the reference.

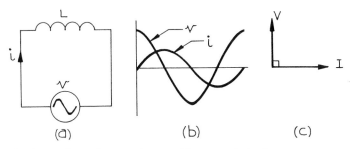

Fig. 7.2 Alternating voltage and current in a pure inductance

The reason for this phase difference is that, when a current flows in an inductor, an e.m.f. is induced which is proportional to the rate at which the current changes (remember $e = -L \, di/dt$, where L is the inductance of the coil). When the current waveform is passing through zero (i.e. changing at its greatest rate, see fig. 7.2(b)) then the induced e.m.f. will be maximum. Similarly, when the current is at its greatest positive or greatest negative value (i.e. has stopped changing, see fig. 7.2(b)) then the induced e.m.f. will be zero. In a pure inductor, the applied voltage v would be exactly equal and opposite to the induced e.m.f. Thus the waveforms of the applied voltage v and the current i in a pure inductor are as shown in fig. 7.2(b).

7.3 A purely capacitive circuit

In a purely capacitive circuit, as shown in fig. 7.3(a), the current i leads the voltage v by 90° or $\pi/2$ radians. The graphical and phasor representations are as shown in figs 7.3(b) and (c), with the current as the reference.

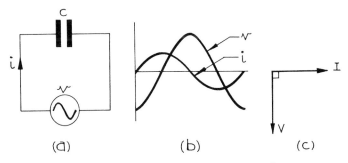

Fig. 7.3 Alternating voltage and current in a pure capacitance

The reason for this phase difference is as follows.
We define current as rate of flow of charge,

$$\therefore \quad i = \frac{dq}{dt}$$

Also $\quad q = Cv$

$$\therefore \quad i = C\frac{dv}{dt}$$

Thus the current flow is proportional to the rate of change of the applied voltage. When the applied voltage is passing through zero (i.e. changing at its fastest rate) the current is maximum. When the voltage is at its greatest positive or greatest negative value (i.e. has stopped changing) then the current is zero, as shown in fig. 7.3(b).

7.4 Inductive and capacitive reactance

When an a.c. voltage is applied across a purely inductive or purely capacitive circuit, then the current which flows is determined by the *reactance* of the circuit. Reactance is the ratio of the applied voltage to the current, and is used for the case where the voltage and current are 90° out of phase with one another, such as in a pure inductance or capacitance. The term resistance is used for the ratio of voltage to current only for the case where they are in phase.

Reactance is given the symbol X.

In terms of the peak values of voltage and current, the reactance may be defined by

$$X = \frac{V_p}{I_p}$$

If r.m.s. values are used for the applied voltage and current, then

$$X = \frac{0.707\, V_p}{0.707\, I_p} = \frac{V_{r.m.s.}}{I_{r.m.s.}}$$

Since reactance is the ratio of voltage to current, it is measured in ohms.

Inductive reactance

The symbol for inductive reactance is X_L.

The inductive reactance of a circuit is found from

$$X_L = \omega L = 2\pi f L$$

where $\quad f$ = frequency $\quad \omega = 2\pi f$ = angular velocity

and $\quad L$ = inductance in henrys

Notice that inductive reactance increases linearly with frequency; i.e. X_L is proportional to frequency.

Capacitive reactance

The symbol for capacitive reactance is X_C.

The capacitive reactance of a circuit is given by

$$X_C = \frac{1}{\omega C} = \frac{1}{2\pi f C}$$

where C = capacitance in farads

Notice that capacitive reactance decreases with increasing frequency; i.e. X_C is inversely proportional to frequency.

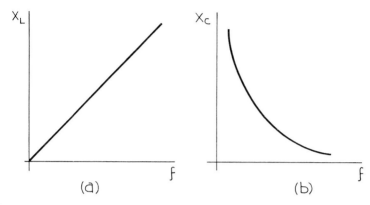

(a)   (b)

Fig. 7.4 Graphs of variation of inductive and capacitive reactance with frequency

The graphs in fig 7.4 show the variation of X_L and X_C with frequency. Notice that at low frequencies inductive reactance is small while capacitive reactance is very large. As the frequency increases, inductive reactance increases proportionally while capacitive reactance varies in inverse proportion to the frequency.

Example 1   Calculate the reactance of a 20 mH inductor at (a) 500 Hz, (b) 50 kHz.

$$X_L = 2\pi f L$$

where L = 20 mH = 20×10^{-3} H

a) f = 500 Hz

$\therefore$ $X_L = 2\pi \times 500\,\text{Hz} \times 20 \times 10^{-3}$ H

      = 62.8 Ω

b) f = 50 kHz = 50×10^3 Hz

$\therefore$ $X_L = 2\pi \times 50 \times 10^3\,\text{Hz} \times 20 \times 10^{-3}$ H = 6280 Ω = 6.28 kΩ

i.e. at 500 Hz the inductive reactance is 62.8 Ω while at 50 kHz it is 6.28 kΩ.

Example 2   Calculate the reactance of a $1\,\mu F$ capacitor at (a) $100\,Hz$, (b) $10\,kHz$.

$$X_C = 1/2\pi f C$$

where $C = 1\,\mu F = 1 \times 10^{-6}\,F$

a) $f = 100\,Hz$

$$\therefore \quad X_C = \frac{1}{2\pi \times 100\,Hz \times 1 \times 10^{-6}\,F}$$

$$= 1.59 \times 10^3\,\Omega = 1.59\,k\Omega$$

b) $f = 10\,kHz = 10 \times 10^3\,Hz$

$$\therefore \quad X_C = \frac{1}{2\pi \times 10 \times 10^3\,Hz \times 1 \times 10^{-6}\,F}$$

$$= 15.9\,\Omega$$

i.e. at $100\,Hz$ the capacitive reactance is $1.59\,k\Omega$, while at $10\,kHz$ it is $15.9\,\Omega$.

7.5 Circuits possessing resistance and inductance in series

For circuits which have a combination of both resistance and reactance, it is best to use a phasor diagram to find the relationship between the applied voltage and the current.

In the circuit of fig. 7.5(a), an a.c. voltage v is applied across a resistance R and an inductance L which are connected in series. The current i which flows is determined by both the resistance and the reactance. In drawing the phasor diagram, the a.c. current is used as the reference phasor since the *same* current flows in both components. The voltages across the resistance and inductance are shown as v_R and v_L. Using the peak values to draw the phasor diagram, V_R is in phase with I, while V_L leads I by $90°$ as shown in

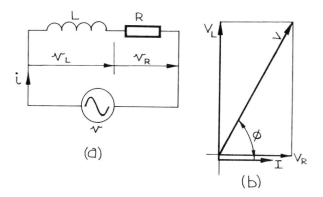

(a)

(b)

Fig. 7.5 A series R–L circuit and phasor diagram

164

fig. 7.5(b). The resultant applied voltage V is found by completing the parallelogram.

By the theorem of Pythagoras,

$$V^2 = V_R{}^2 + V_L{}^2$$
$$\therefore \quad V = \sqrt{V_R{}^2 + V_L{}^2}$$

The phase angle between the applied voltage V and the current I is ϕ, where

$$\tan \phi = \frac{V_L}{V_R}$$

7.6 Impedance

In a.c. circuits, the term *impedance* is used for the ratio of the applied voltage to the current where the phase angle between voltage and current is neither exactly $0°$ nor exactly $90°$; i.e. it is the term used where resistance and reactance are combined together. Impedance is given the symbol Z and its unit is the ohm (Ω).

The phasor diagram for the series R-L circuit of fig. 7.5 is redrawn in fig. 7.6(a) with the voltages V_R and V_L given as IR and IX_L respectively. The resultant voltage V is given by IZ.

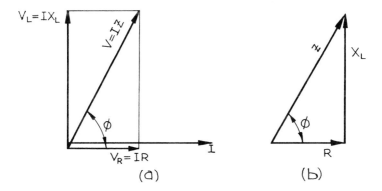

Fig. 7.6 Phasor diagram and impedance triangle for a series R-L circuit

From fig. 7.6(a), by the theorem of Pythagoras,

$$(IZ)^2 = (IR)^2 + (IX_L)^2$$
$$\therefore \quad I^2 Z^2 = I^2 R^2 + I^2 X_L{}^2$$

Dividing throughout by I^2 gives

$$Z^2 = R^2 + X_L{}^2$$

or $\quad Z = \sqrt{R^2 + X_L{}^2}$

Since $X_L = \omega L$, then
$$Z = \sqrt{R^2 + \omega^2 L^2}$$

This is the equation for the impedance of the series R–L circuit of fig. 7.5(a).

Also $\quad \tan \phi = \dfrac{I X_L}{IR} = \dfrac{X_L}{R} = \dfrac{\omega L}{R}$

The phasor diagram may be simplified to the *impedance triangle* of fig. 7.6(b)

Example 1   A coil is represented by a 0.15 H inductance in series with a 100 Ω resistance. The coil is connected across a supply voltage of 240 V at a frequency of 50 Hz. Calculate (a) the reactance of the coil, (b) the impedance of the coil, (c) the current in the coil, (d) the phase angle between the voltage and the current.

a) $X_L = 2\pi f L$

where $f = 50\,\text{Hz}$ and $L = 0.15\,\text{H}$

∴ $X_L = 2\pi \times 50\,\text{Hz} \times 0.15\,\text{H}$

$\quad\quad = 47.1\,\Omega$

b) $Z = \sqrt{R^2 + X_L^2}$

where $R = 100\,\Omega$ and $X_L = 47.1\,\Omega$

∴ $Z = \sqrt{(100\,\Omega)^2 + (47.1\,\Omega)^2}$

$\quad\quad = 110.5\,\Omega$

c) $I = V/Z$

where $V = 240\,\text{V}$ and $Z = 110.5\,\Omega$

∴ $I = \dfrac{240\,\text{V}}{110.5\,\Omega} = 2.17\,\text{A}$

d) $\tan \phi = \dfrac{X_L}{R}$

where $X_L = 47.1\,\Omega$ and $R = 100\,\Omega$

∴ $\tan \phi = \dfrac{47.1\,\Omega}{100\,\Omega} = 0.471$

∴ $\phi = \arctan 0.471$

$\quad\quad = 25.2°$

i.e. the coil reactance is 47.1 Ω, its impedance is 110.5 Ω, the current is 2.17 A, and the phase angle is 25.2°.

Example 2 A coil is connected to a d.c. supply of 10 V and passes a current of 100 mA. The coil is now connected to a 10 V 50 Hz a.c. supply and the new current is 50 mA. Calculate the resistance and inductance of the coil.

When the coil is connected to a d.c. supply, the inductance of the coil does not affect the d.c. current,

$$\therefore \quad R = V/I$$

where $V = 10 \text{ V}$ and $I = 100 \text{ mA} = 0.1 \text{ A}$

$$\therefore \quad R = \frac{10 \text{ V}}{0.1 \text{ A}} = 100 \text{ }\Omega$$

With an a.c. supply, both the resistance and the reactance affect the current.

$$Z = V/I$$

where $V = 10 \text{ V}$ and $I = 50 \text{ mA} = 0.05 \text{ A}$

$$\therefore \quad Z = \frac{10 \text{ V}}{0.05 \text{ A}} = 200 \text{ }\Omega$$

Now $Z^2 = R^2 + X_L^2$

$$\therefore \quad X_L^2 = Z^2 - R^2$$

$$\therefore \quad X_L = \sqrt{Z^2 - R^2}$$

where $Z = 200 \text{ }\Omega$ and $R = 100 \text{ }\Omega$

$$\therefore \quad X_L = \sqrt{(200 \text{ }\Omega)^2 - (100 \text{ }\Omega)^2}$$

$$= 173.2 \text{ }\Omega$$

Since $X_L = \omega L = 2\pi f L$

then $L = \dfrac{X_L}{2\pi f}$

where $X_L = 173.2 \text{ }\Omega$ and $f = 50 \text{ Hz}$

$$\therefore \quad L = \frac{173.2 \text{ }\Omega}{2\pi \times 50 \text{ Hz}} = 0.55 \text{ H}$$

i.e. the resistance of the coil is 100 Ω and the inductance is 0.55 H.

Example 3 A coil of resistance 50 Ω and inductance 0.15 H is connected in series with another coil of resistance 25 Ω and inductance 0.2 H across a 240 V 50 Hz a.c. supply. Calculate the current and the p.d. across each coil.

Total series resistance = 50 Ω + 25 Ω = 75 Ω

Total series inductance = 0.15 H + 0.2 H = 0.35 H

167

Now $I = V/Z$

where $V = 240$ V

and $Z = \sqrt{R^2 + \omega^2 L^2} = \sqrt{R^2 + (2\pi fL)^2}$

$\qquad = \sqrt{(75\,\Omega)^2 + (2\pi \times 50\,\text{Hz} \times 0.35\,\text{H})^2}$

$\qquad = 133\,\Omega$

$\therefore \quad I = \dfrac{240\,\text{V}}{133\,\Omega} = 1.8\,\text{A}$

Now consider the first coil:

$\qquad Z_1 = \sqrt{R_1{}^2 + (2\pi fL_1)^2}$

where $R_1 = 50\,\Omega$ and $L_1 = 0.15$ H

$\therefore \quad Z_1 = \sqrt{(50\,\Omega)^2 + (2\pi \times 50\,\text{Hz} \times 0.15\,\text{H})^2}$

$\qquad = 68.7\,\Omega$

$\therefore \quad V_1 = IZ_1 = 1.8\,\text{A} \times 68.7\,\Omega$

$\qquad\qquad = 123.7$ V

Now consider the second coil:

$\qquad Z_2 = \sqrt{R_2{}^2 + (2\pi fL_2)^2}$

where $R_2 = 25\,\Omega$ and $L_2 = 0.2$ H

$\therefore \quad Z_2 = \sqrt{(25\,\Omega)^2 + (2\pi \times 50\,\text{Hz} \times 0.2\,\text{H})^2}$

$\qquad = 67.6\,\Omega$

$\therefore \quad V_2 = IZ_2 = 1.8\,\text{A} \times 67.6\,\Omega$

$\qquad\qquad = 121.7$ V

i.e. the current is 1.8 A and the voltages across the coils are 123.7 V and 121.7 V.

Notice that these two voltages do not add algebraically to give 240 V. This is because the two voltages are not in phase and can only be added by phasor addition.

7.7 Circuits possessing resistance and capacitance in series

In the circuit of fig. 7.7(a), an a.c. voltage v is applied across a resistance and capacitance connected in series. The voltage across the resistance is v_R and that across the capacitance v_C. The phasor diagram is shown in fig. 7.7(b), where the current is the reference phasor. Signifying the quantities by their peak values, V_R is in phase with I while V_C lags I by $90°$. Completing the parallelogram gives the resultant, V, where

$$V^2 = V_R{}^2 + V_C{}^2$$

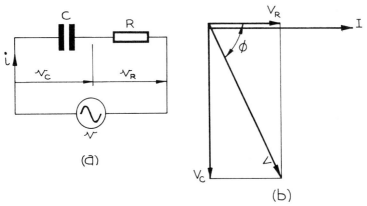

Fig. 7.7 A series R-C circuit and phasor diagram

$$\therefore \quad V = \sqrt{V_R{}^2 + V_C{}^2}$$

and $\quad \tan\phi = \dfrac{V_C}{V_R}$

Redrawing the phasor diagram as shown in fig. 7.8(a),

$$(IZ)^2 = (IR)^2 + (IX_C)^2$$

$$\therefore \quad Z^2 = R^2 + X_C{}^2$$

or $\quad Z = \sqrt{R^2 + X_C{}^2}$

Since $\quad X_C = 1/\omega C$

then $\quad Z = \sqrt{R^2 + 1/\omega^2 C^2}$

This is the equation for the impedance of the series R-C circuit.

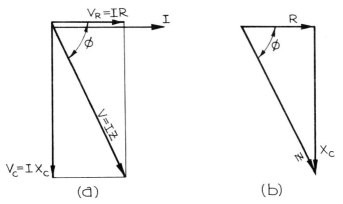

Fig. 7.8 Phasor diagram and impedance triangle for a series R-C circuit

169

Also $\quad \tan \phi = \dfrac{IX_C}{IR} = \dfrac{X_C}{R} = \dfrac{1}{\omega CR}$

The corresponding impedance triangle is shown in fig. 7.8(b).

Example A $0.015\,\mu F$ capacitor and a $10\,k\Omega$ resistor are connected in series across a 10 V 1 kHz supply. Calculate (a) the capacitive reactance, (b) the impedance, (c) the current, (d) the phase angle.

a) $X_C = 1/2\pi f C$

where $f = 1\,kHz = 1000\,Hz$ and $C = 0.015\,\mu F = 0.015 \times 10^{-6}\,F$

$\therefore \quad X_C = \dfrac{1}{2\pi \times 1000\,Hz \times 0.015 \times 10^{-6}\,F} = 10.6\,k\Omega$

b) $Z = \sqrt{R^2 + X_C^2}$

where $R = 10\,k\Omega = 10 \times 10^3\,\Omega$ and $X_C = 10.6\,k\Omega = 10.6 \times 10^3\,\Omega$

$\therefore \quad Z = \sqrt{(10 \times 10^3\,\Omega)^2 + (10.6 \times 10^3\,\Omega)^2}$

$\qquad = 14\,600\,\Omega = 14.6\,k\Omega$

c) $I = V/Z$

where $V = 10\,V$ and $Z = 14.6\,k\Omega = 14.6 \times 10^3\,\Omega$

$\therefore \quad I = \dfrac{10\,V}{14.6 \times 10^3\,\Omega} = 0.68 \times 10^{-3}\,A = 0.68\,mA$

d) $\tan \phi = \dfrac{X_C}{R} = \dfrac{10.6 \times 10^3\,\Omega}{10 \times 10^3\,\Omega} = 1.06$

$\therefore \qquad \phi = \arctan 1.06 = 46.7°$

i.e. the capacitive reactance is $10.6\,k\Omega$, the impedance is $14.6\,k\Omega$, the current is 0.68 mA, and the phase angle is $46.7°$.

7.8 Power in a.c. circuits

We have already seen that applying an a.c. voltage across a resistance causes a current to flow which is in phase with the voltage. The graphs of v and i against time are shown in fig. 7.9, together with the waveform for the power in the resistance (this is found by multiplying together the values of v and i at each instant).

The average value of the power is shown by the dotted line and may be seen to be half the peak value of the power waveform,

$\therefore \quad$ average power $= \dfrac{V_p I_p}{2} = \dfrac{V_p}{\sqrt 2} \times \dfrac{I_p}{\sqrt 2} = V_{r.m.s.}\,I_{r.m.s.}$

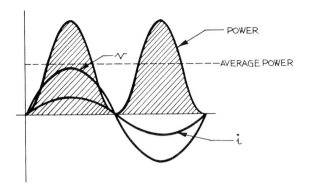

Fig. 7.9 Waveform for the a.c. power in a resistive circuit

Alternatively, since $\quad V_{\text{r.m.s.}} = I_{\text{r.m.s.}} R$

then $\quad$ average power $= I^2_{\text{r.m.s.}} R$

The waveforms for the power dissipated in purely inductive and purely capacitive circuits are shown in figs 7.10(a) and (b) respectively. The power waveforms are again found by multiplying together the values of v and i at each instant. Notice that when v and i are both positive or both negative, then power is taken from the supply. When, however, one of the quantities is negative while the other is positive, then the power is negative; i.e. power is fed back into the supply. In the case of pure reactance (inductive or capacitive), there is as much power fed back into the supply as there is taken from it, and therefore the average power consumed is zero. This is an important result and should be remembered. It occurs because inductors and capacitors store energy on one part of the voltage cycle and feed it back into the supply on the subsequent part. In the inductor, the energy is stored

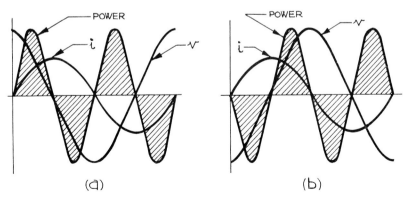

Fig. 7.10 Waveform for the a.c. power in purely inductive and purely capacitive circuits

171

in the form of a magnetic field. In the capacitor, the energy is stored as an electric field.

The waveform for the power dissipated in a series R-C network is shown in fig. 7.11. In this case there is more power taken from the supply than is fed back into it, since some power is dissipated in the resistor. The average power consumed is therefore positive.

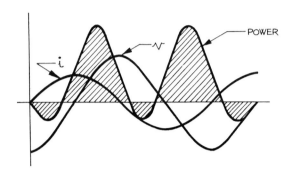

Fig. 7.11 Waveform for the a.c. power in an R-C circuit

It may be seen that the power consumed by a network is determined not only by the magnitude of the voltage and current but also by the phase angle between the two. The equation for the average power dissipated in a circuit is given by

$$\text{power} = \text{current} \times \frac{\text{component of the voltage}}{\text{in phase with the current}}$$

This may be seen from the phasor diagram of fig. 7.12(a), where the component of the voltage in phase with the current is $V \cos \phi$. Denoting the average power by the symbol P we have, therefore,

$$P = VI \cos \phi$$

where V and I are r.m.s. values. This is the general equation for the average power in an a.c. circuit and should be remembered.

Notice that, for a pure resistance, V and I are in phase and $\phi = 0$ (and $\cos 0 = 1$),

$\therefore$ average power $= VI$

For a pure reactance, $\phi = 90°$ (and $\cos 90° = 0$),

$\therefore$ average power $= 0$

as already stated.

From the impedance triangle of fig 7.12(b),

$$\cos \phi = \frac{R}{Z}$$

172

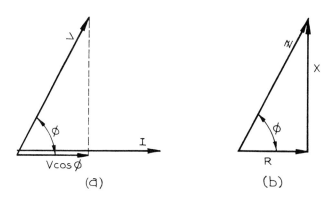

Fig. 7.12

Also $V = IZ$

$$\therefore \quad P = VI \cos \phi = (IZ)I\frac{R}{Z} = I^2R$$

Example A coil has a reactance of 15 Ω and a resistance of 10 Ω when connected across a 200 V 50 Hz a.c. supply. Calculate (a) the current, (b) the average power consumed, (c) the phase angle between the voltage and the current.

a) $I = V/Z$

where $V = 200\,\text{V}$

and $Z = \sqrt{R^2 + X_L^2} = \sqrt{(10\,\Omega)^2 + (15\,\Omega)^2} = 18\,\Omega$

$\therefore \quad I = \dfrac{200\,\text{V}}{18\,\Omega} = 11.1\,\text{A}$

b) $P = I^2R$

where $I = 11.1\,\text{A}$ and $R = 10\,\Omega$

$\therefore \quad P = (11.1\,\text{A})^2 \times 10\,\Omega$

$\quad\quad\quad = 1230\,\text{W} = 1.23\,\text{kW}$

c) $\tan \phi = \dfrac{X_L}{R} = \dfrac{15\,\Omega}{10\,\Omega} = 1.5$

$\therefore \quad\quad \phi = \arctan 1.5 = 56.3°$

i.e. the current is 11.1 A, the average power consumed is 1.23 kW, and the phase angle is 56.3°.

7.9 Power factor

The power factor of a circuit is defined by

$$\text{power factor} = \frac{\text{true power}}{\text{apparent power}}$$

where the 'true power' is the average power consumed and the 'apparent power' is equal to VI, where V and I are r.m.s. values.

We have seen that the true power consumed by a resistive–reactive network is given by

$$P = VI \cos \phi$$

$$\therefore \quad \text{power factor} = \frac{VI \cos \phi}{VI} = \cos \phi$$

Example   A coil takes a current of 0.5 A from a 240 V a.c. supply. A wattmeter connected in the circuit indicates a power dissipation of 90 W. Calculate (a) the true power, (b) the apparent power, (c) the power factor, (d) the phase angle between the voltage and the current.

a)   Wattmeters indicate true power,

$$\therefore \quad P = 90\,\text{W}$$

b)   Apparent power $= VI$
$$= 240\,\text{V} \times 0.5\,\text{A} = 120\,\text{W}$$

c)   Power factor $= \dfrac{\text{true power}}{\text{apparent power}}$

$$= \frac{90\,\text{W}}{120\,\text{W}} = 0.75$$

d) $\cos \phi = $ power factor $= 0.75$

$$\therefore \quad \phi = \arccos 0.75 = 41.4°$$

i.e. the true power is 90 W, the apparent power is 120 W, the power factor is 0.75, and the phase angle is 41.4°.

7.10 Power, volt amperes, and reactive volt amperes

Figure 7.13(a) shows the phasor diagram for a resistive–reactive circuit, and fig. 7.13(b) shows the corresponding power phasor diagram. In fig. 7.13(b), S represents the apparent power, where

$$S = VI$$

and is referred to as the volt amperes (VA).

P represents the true power, where

$$P = VI \cos \phi$$

174

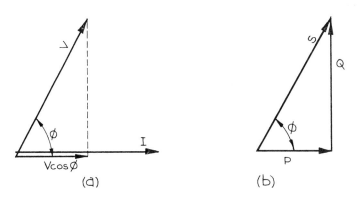

Fig. 7.13

and Q represents the reactive volt amperes (VAr), where

$$Q = VI \sin \phi$$

When true power is given in kilowatts (kW), the corresponding terms for S and Q are kilovolt amperes (kVA) and reactive kilovolt amperes (kVAr).

Example 1 A single-phase induction motor takes a current of 20 A at a power factor of 0.8 lagging from a 240 V a.c. supply. Calculate the kVA, the power, and the kVAr.

a) $S = VI$

   $= 240\,V \times 20\,A$

   $= 4800\,VA = 4.8\,kVA$

b) $P = S \times \text{p.f.}$

   $= 4.8\,kVA \times 0.8$

   $= 3.84\,kW$

c) $Q = S \sin \phi$

where $\cos \phi = 0.8$

$\therefore$ $\phi = \arccos 0.8 = 36.87°$ and $\sin \phi = 0.6$

$\therefore$ $Q = 4.8\,kVA \times 0.6$

   $= 2.88\,kVAr$

i.e. the kVA is 4.8 kVA, the power is 3.84 kW, and the kVAr is 2.88 kVAr.

Example 2 Two induction motors are connected in parallel and take the following loads from an a.c. supply: 2 kW at a power factor of 0.8 lagging, 5 kW at a power factor of 0.6 lagging. Calculate the total power, kVA, kVAr, and power factor.

175

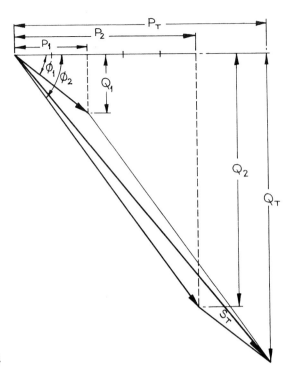

Fig. 7.14

The power phasor diagram is shown in fig. 7.14, where $\cos \phi_1 = 0.8$ therefore $\phi_1 = -36.9°$ and $\cos \phi_2 = 0.6$ therefore $\phi_2 = -53.1°$. (The minus signs are included as the power factors are lagging.)

a) The total power is found by adding the power components:

$$P_T = P_1 + P_2$$
$$= 2\,kW + 5\,kW = 7\,kW$$

b) The kVAr is found by taking the vertical components of the phasors:

$$Q_1 = P_1 \tan \phi_1 = 2\,kW \times \tan(-36.9°)$$
$$= 2\,kW \times (-0.75) = -1.5\,kVAr$$
$$Q_2 = P_2 \tan \phi_2 = 5\,kW \times \tan(-53.1°)$$
$$= 5\,kW \times (-1.33) = -6.66\,kVAr$$

The total kVAr is therefore

$$Q_T = Q_1 + Q_2$$
$$= -1.5\,kVAr + (-6.66\,kVAr) = -8.16\,kVAr$$

c) To find the total kVA, complete the parallelogram as shown in fig. 7.14. The total kVA is shown by S_T.

Horizontal component of $S_T = P_T = 7\,\text{kW}$

Vertical component of $S_T = Q_T = -8.16\,\text{kVAr}$

$$\therefore \quad S_T{}^2 = P_T{}^2 + Q_T{}^2$$

$$\therefore \quad S_T = \sqrt{(7\,\text{kW})^2 + (-8.16\,\text{kVAr})^2}$$

$$= 10.75\,\text{kVA}$$

d) Power factor $= \dfrac{P_T}{S_T} = \dfrac{7\,\text{kW}}{10.75\,\text{kVA}}$

$$= 0.65$$

i.e. the total power is 7 kW, the total kVAr is 8.16 kVAr, the total kVA is 10.75 kVA, and the overall power factor is 0.65 lagging.

Example 3 A substation supplies the following single-phase loads: (i) 500 kW at unity power factor, (ii) 200 kW at p.f. 0.9 leading, (iii) 750 kW at p.f. 0.8 lagging, (iv) 400 kVA at p.f. 0.6 lagging. Calculate the total kVA load supplied and its power factor.

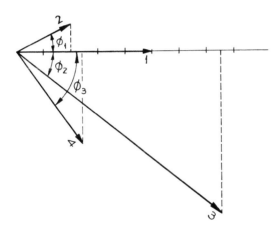

Fig. 7.15

The power phasor diagram is shown in fig 7.15, with the loads marked 1–4. Notice that where the load is given in kW, this represents the horizontal component of the phasor; where it is given in kVA, this represents the length of the phasor.

The phase angles of the loads are

$$\phi_1 = \arccos 0.9 = 25.8°$$

$$\phi_2 = \arccos 0.8 = -36.8°$$

$$\phi_3 = \arccos 0.6 = -53.1°$$

The total kVA load (S) has components as follows:

horizontal component (P) = 500 kW + 200 kW + 750 kW
$$+ 400 \text{ kVA} \times 0.6$$

$$\therefore \quad P = 1450 \text{ kW} + 240 \text{ kW}$$
$$= 1690 \text{ kW}$$

vertical component (Q) = 200 kW $\times \tan \phi_1$ + 750 kW $\times \tan \phi_2$
$$+ 400 \text{ kVA} \times \sin \phi_3$$

$$\therefore \quad Q = 200 \text{ kW} \times \tan 25.8° + 750 \text{ kW} \times \tan(-36.8°)$$
$$+ 400 \text{ kVA} \times \sin(-53.1°)$$
$$= (96.7 - 561 - 319.9) \text{ kVAr}$$
$$= -784.2 \text{ kVAr}$$

$$\therefore \quad \text{total kVA } (S) = \sqrt{P^2 + Q^2}$$
$$= \sqrt{(1690 \text{ kW})^2 + (-784.2 \text{ kVAr})^2}$$
$$= 1863 \text{ kVA}$$
$$= 1.86 \text{ MVA}$$

$$\text{Overall power factor} = \frac{P}{S} = \frac{1690 \text{ kW}}{1863 \text{ kVA}} = 0.91$$

i.e. the total load is 1.86 MVA at a power factor of 0.91.

7.11 Series combinations of inductance, capacitance, and resistance

Consider the series L-C-R circuit of fig. 7.16(a). The corresponding phasor diagram is shown in fig. 7.16(b), with the current used as the reference phasor since it flows through all three components. The voltages across the components are represented by V_R, V_L, and V_C, which have the directions shown in the phasor diagram. Since V_L leads I by 90° and V_C lags by 90°, then the phasors V_L and V_C are in opposition and their combined result is $V_L - V_C$ as shown.

The resultant voltage V of the three voltages may be found by completing the parallelogram as shown in fig. 7.16(b).

Applying the theorem of Pythagoras,

$$V^2 = V_R{}^2 + (V_L - V_C)^2$$

and
$$\tan \phi = \frac{V_L - V_C}{V_R}$$

An alternative phasor diagram is shown in fig. 7.17(a), where

$$(IZ)^2 = (IR)^2 + I^2(X_L - X_C)^2$$

178

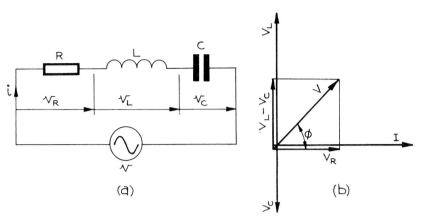

Fig. 7.16 A series $L-C-R$ circuit and phasor diagram

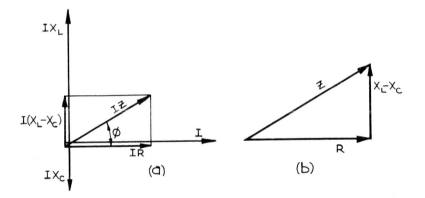

Fig. 7.17 Phasor diagram and impedance triangle for a series $L-C-R$ circuit

$$\therefore \quad Z^2 = R^2 + (X_L - X_C)^2$$

$$\therefore \quad Z = \sqrt{R_2 + (X_L - X_C)^2}$$

or $\quad Z = \sqrt{R^2 + (\omega L - 1/\omega C)^2}$

Also $\quad \tan \phi = \dfrac{X_L - X_C}{R} = \dfrac{\omega L - 1/\omega C}{R}$

The corresponding impedance triangle is shown in fig. 7.17(b).

It should be noted that three possible conditions exist for this circuit:

a) $\quad X_L < X_C$

b) $\quad X_L = X_C$

179

c) $X_L > X_C$

These three conditions are shown in the phasor diagrams of fig. 7.18. The three conditions may all be obtained from the same L-C-R circuit, but at different frequencies.

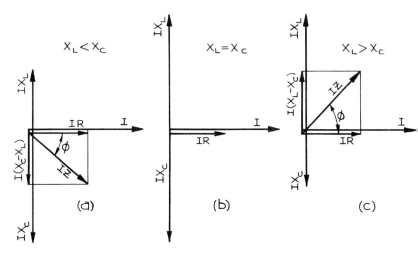

Fig. 7.18 Phasor representation of a series L-C-R circuit at various frequencies

At low frequencies the circuit is mainly capacitive and has the phasor diagram of fig. 7.18(a). At high frequencies the inductive effect predominates, giving the phasor diagram of fig. 7.18(c). At some intermediate frequency the condition of fig. 7.18(b) exists, such that the inductive and capacitive effects exactly cancel. We may find the frequency at which this occurs as follows.

At this frequency,

$$IX_L = IX_C$$

$\therefore \qquad X_L = X_C$

$\therefore \qquad \omega L = \dfrac{1}{\omega C}$

$\therefore \qquad \omega^2 = \dfrac{1}{LC}$

$\therefore \qquad \omega = \dfrac{1}{\sqrt{(LC)}}$

hence $\quad f = \dfrac{\omega}{2\pi} = \dfrac{1}{2\pi \sqrt{(LC)}}$

180

At this condition the circuit is *purely resistive* and therefore the phase angle is zero. This condition is called *resonance* and is the condition where the supply voltage and the current are exactly *in phase*.

Notice that the voltage across the inductor (V_L) and that across the capacitor (V_C) may be many times the supply voltage V. At this particular frequency, energy is passed back and forth between the inductor and the capacitor at the natural oscillation frequency of the circuit, and only a small supply voltage is needed to sustain the oscillations. This may be likened to the motion of a swing where, at just the right oscillation frequency, large oscillations may be achieved with only a small forcing motion (i.e. the condition of resonance).

Example 1   A capacitor of 10 nF is connected in series with a coil of resistance 500 Ω and inductance 10 mH. The circuit is connected across a 15 V 12 kHz supply. Calculate (a) the impedance of the circuit, (b) the current, (c) the phase angle.

$$X_L = 2\pi f L$$

where $f = 12\,\text{kHz} = 12 \times 10^3\,\text{Hz}$ and $L = 10\,\text{mH} = 0.01\,\text{H}$

$$\therefore \quad X_L = 2\pi \times 12 \times 10^3\,\text{Hz} \times 0.01\,\text{H}$$

$$= 753.6\,\Omega$$

$$X_C = \frac{1}{2\pi f C}$$

where $C = 10\,\text{nF} = 10 \times 10^{-9}\,\text{F}$

$$\therefore \quad X_C = \frac{1}{2\pi \times 12 \times 10^3\,\text{Hz} \times 10 \times 10^{-9}\,\text{F}} = 1327\,\Omega$$

a) $Z = \sqrt{R^2 + (X_L - X_C)^2}$

where $R = 500\,\Omega$ $X_L = 753.6\,\Omega$ and $X_C = 1327\,\Omega$

$$\therefore \quad Z = \sqrt{(500\,\Omega)^2 + (753.6\,\Omega - 1327\,\Omega)^2}$$

$$= 761\,\Omega$$

b) $I = V/Z$

where $V = 15\,\text{V}$ and $Z = 761\,\Omega$

$$\therefore \quad I = \frac{15\,\text{V}}{761\,\Omega} = 0.020\,\text{A} = 20\,\text{mA}$$

c) $\tan\phi = \dfrac{X_L - X_C}{R}$

where $X_L = 753.6\,\Omega$ $X_C = 1327\,\Omega$ and $R = 500\,\Omega$

$$\therefore \quad \tan \phi = \frac{753.6\,\Omega - 1327\,\Omega}{500\,\Omega} = \frac{-573.4}{500} = -1.15$$

$$\therefore \quad \phi = \arctan(-1.15) = -48.9°$$

The minus sign indicates that the voltage is lagging the current; i.e. the impedance is 761 Ω, the current is 20 mA, and the phase angle is 48.9° lagging.

Notice that X_C being greater than X_L presents no problems with the equations.

Example 2   A coil of inductance 1 mH and resistance 10 Ω is connected in series with a capacitor of 500 pF to a 5 V variable-frequency supply. Calculate (a) the resonant frequency of the circuit, (b) the current at resonance.

a) $f = 1/2\pi \sqrt{(LC)}$

where $L = 1\,\text{mH} = 0.001\,\text{H}$ and $C = 500\,\text{pF} = 500 \times 10^{-12}\,\text{F}$

$$\therefore \quad f = \frac{1}{2\pi \sqrt{(0.001\,\text{H} \times 500 \times 10^{-12}\,\text{F})}}$$

$$= 225 \times 10^3\,\text{Hz} = 225\,\text{kHz}$$

b) At resonance, the circuit is purely resistive

$$\therefore \quad I = V/R$$

where $V = 5\,\text{V}$ and $R = 10\,\Omega$

$$\therefore \quad I = \frac{5\,\text{V}}{10\,\Omega} = 0.5\,\text{A}$$

i.e. the resonant frequency is 225 kHz and the current at this frequency is 0.5 A.

Exercises on chapter 7
1   A coil has an inductance of 0.08 H. Determine its reactance at (a) 50 Hz, (b) 5 kHz.   [25 Ω; 2512 Ω]
2   Sketch graphs to show the variation of reactance with frequency for (a) an inductor, (b) a capacitor. Label the axes of the graphs.
    Calculate the reactance of a capacitor of 500 pF capacitance at a frequency of 10 MHz.   [31.8 Ω]
3   Explain the term 'reactance'. State how the reactance of a capacitor and an inductor vary with frequency.
    A coil having negligible resistance has a reactance of 62.84 Ω when connected to a 240 V 50 Hz sinusoidal supply. Determine the current and the inductance of the coil. The coil is then removed and replaced by a variable capacitor. Find the value of the capacitance required for the magnitude of

the current to remain unchanged. Sketch, on the same axes, waveforms of current and voltage for each circuit.   [3.82 A; 0.2 H; 50.6 μF]

4   The frequency of a supply to a 2 μF capacitor is varied between 500 Hz and 5 kHz. Calculate the reactance of the capacitor at these two values of frequency. Sketch, approximately to scale, the graph of the reactance against frequency within this range.   [159 Ω; 15.9 Ω]

5   A pure inductor of 8 H inductance is connected to a 240 V 50 Hz supply of sinusoidal waveform. Calculate the current flowing through the inductor and sketch the phasor and wave diagrams to represent the current and voltage. [95.5 mA]

6   A capacitor has a reactance of 50 Ω and is connected to a 50 Hz sinusoidal supply. Given that the current in the circuit is 5 A, find the voltage of the supply and the value of the capacitance.

A 10 mH inductor is connected to a 10 V 1 kHz sinusoidal supply. Find the current in the circuit.

For each circuit above, draw waveforms of current and voltage to a common base of time.   [250 V; 63.7 μF; 159 mA]

7   With the aid of a suitably labelled diagram, describe how to determine the relationship between the reactance of a capacitor and the frequency of the supply. Sketch a typical graph of reactance against frequency. When connected to a 24 V a.c. supply, a 10 μF capacitor has a reactance of 15.92 Ω. Calculate (a) the current taken by the capacitor, (b) the frequency of the supply.   [1.5 A; 1kHz]

8   Distinguish between 'resistance' and 'reactance' as applied to an a.c. circuit.

A 50 mH inductor is connected to the output of a 200 V variable-frequency a.c. supply, and the frequency is adjusted to 1000 Hz. Find the current in the circuit.

The inductor is now removed and replaced by a 0.25 μF capacitor, and the frequency is adjusted until the original current flows in the circuit. Calculate this value of frequency.   [637 mA; 2.03 kHz]

9   a) The instantaneous value of an alternating voltage is given by $v = 400 \sin 3140t$ volts. Determine the frequency and periodic time of the waveform.

b) This voltage is applied to a 100 mH inductor. Obtain the expression for the instantaneous current, and calculate the r.m.s. value of this current. [500 Hz; 2 ms; $i = 1.27 \sin (3140t - \pi/2)$ A; 0.90 A]

10   A current $i = 10 \sin 6280t$ mA flows through a 2 μF capacitor and then in a 100 mH inductor. Determine (a) the frequency, (b) the periodic time, (c) the expression giving the instantaneous voltage across the capacitor, (d) an expression giving the instantaneous voltage across the inductor, (e) the r.m.s. voltage corresponding to (d).

For the circuit containing the capacitor, sketch waveforms of current and voltage to a common base of time, indicating the maximum values and the phase displacement.   [1 kHz; 1 ms; $v = 0.8 \sin (6280t - \pi/2)$ V; $v = 6.28 \sin (6280t + \pi/2)$ V; 4.44 V]

11   The p.d. across a load is given by $v = 200 \sin 314t$ volts and the current through the load by $i = 40 \sin (314t - \pi/6)$ amperes. Calculate (a) the frequency, (b) the r.m.s. values of voltage and current, (c) the power consumed by the load, (d) the power factor of the load, (e) the resistance and reactance of the series circuit which comprises the load.   [50 Hz; 141.4 V; 28.3 A; 3.46 kW; 0.866; 4.32 Ω; 2.5 Ω]

12   A potential difference $v = 240 \sin (314t + \pi/9)$ volts is applied to a circuit which takes a current of $i = 4.8 \sin (314t + \pi/3)$ amperes. Calculate (a) the frequency; (b) the power factor, stating whether it is leading or lagging; (c) the power taken by the circuit; (d) the values of the components of the simplest series circuit which will take the above current from the given supply.   [50 Hz; 0.77 leading; 441 W; 38.3 Ω; 99 μF]

13   A coil is connected to a d.c. supply of 12 V and passes a current of 50 mA. The coil is now connected to a 12 V 50 Hz supply and the new current is 20 mA. Calculate the resistance and inductance of the coil. [240 Ω; 1.75 H]

14   A coil has a resistance of 20 Ω and an inductance of 0.08 H. Determine its impedance at (a) 50 Hz, (b) 5 kHz.   [32.1 Ω; 2512 Ω]

15   When a 240 V d.c. supply is connected to a certain coil, the coil takes a current of 5 A. When the supply is changed to 240 V 50 Hz a.c. the current falls to 4.12 A. Explain the reason for this reduction in current, and calculate the inductance and resistance of the coil.   [48 Ω; 0.1 H]

16   A coil having an inductance of 1 mH and resistance 100 Ω is connected to a 100 V 10 kHz supply. Calculate (a) the impedance, (b) the current, (c) the voltage across the resistance, (d) the voltage across the inductance.

Sketch the phasor diagram showing all voltages, current, and phase angle. [118 Ω; 847 mA; 84.7 V; 53.2 V]

17   Two coils, having resistances of 50 Ω and 25 Ω and inductances of 0.159 H and 0.239 H respectively, are connected in series to a 240 V 50 Hz a.c. supply. Calculate the current flowing and the p.d. across each coil. [1.65 A; 116.6 V; 130.5 V]

18   A resistor of 40 Ω is connected in series with a capacitor of 40 μF across a 60 Hz supply. The voltage across the resistor is 100 V. Calculate (a) the circuit current, (b) the voltage across the capacitor.

Construct a phasor diagram and hence determine the supply voltage and the phase angle of the circuit.   [2.5 A; 165.9 V; 193.7 V; 59°]

19   A capacitor of 0.1 μF is connected in series with a 2 kΩ resistor to a 200 V 1 kHz supply. Calculate (a) the impedance, (b) the current, (c) the voltage across the capacitor, (d) the voltage across the resistor.

Sketch the phasor diagram, showing all voltages, current, and phase angle.   [2.56 kΩ; 78.1 mA; 124.4 V; 156.2 V]

20   A capacitor of 100 μF is connected across a 240 V 50 Hz supply. Calculate the required kVA rating of the capacitor.   [1.81 kVA]

21   A resistor of 120 Ω is connected in series with a variable inductor having negligible resistance across a 400 V 50 Hz supply.

a) If the inductor is adjusted to 0.51 H, calculate (i) the current taken from the supply, (ii) the p.d.'s across the resistor and across the inductor, (iii) the phase angle between the supply voltage and the supply current.

b) The inductor is now adjusted until the supply current lags the supply voltage by 30°. Calculate (i) the new value of the inductor, (ii) the current taken from the supply.   [2 A, 240 V, 320.3 V, 53.2°; 0.022 H, 2.96 A]

22   A reactor of 0.5 mH inductance and negligible resistance is connected in series with a coil of resistance 100 Ω and inductance 1.5 mH, to a supply of 5 kHz frequency. Calculate the impedance of this circuit.   [118 Ω]

23   A voltage represented by $v = 200 \sin 314t$ volts is applied to a series circuit made up of a 10 Ω resistor and a coil of inductance 0.08 H and negligible resistance.

a) Obtain an expression for the instantaneous value of the current in the form $i = I_p \sin (\omega t \pm \phi)$.

b) Express similarly (i) the voltage across the coil, (ii) the voltage across the resistor.   [$i = 7.4 \sin (314t - 68.3°)$ A; $v_L = 186 \sin (314t + 21.7°)$ V; $v_R = 74 \sin (314t - 68.3°)$ V]

24   A choking coil is connected in series with a loss-free capacitor of reactance 10 Ω across a 100 V single-phase supply. If the circuit takes 5 A and 300 W at a lagging power factor, calculate (a) the resistance of the choking coil, (b) the power factor of the whole circuit, (c) the power factor of the choking coil.

Sketch the voltage phasor diagram for this circuit.   [12 Ω; 0.6; 0.42]

25   An a.c. circuit supplied from a 50 V source consists of two parallel branches, A and B. Branch A is an *L–R* circuit taking 8 A at p.f. 0.6 lagging. Branch B is a capacitor taking 3 A. Draw the circuit diagram and insert the current values. Draw the phasor diagram, to scale, and hence determine the total current supplied and its power factor. Clearly mark each phasor and indicate the reference phasor.   [5.9 A; 0.82 lagging]

26   Explain the terms 'active power', 'reactive power', and 'apparent power' as applied to a circuit with sinusoidal voltage and current.

27   Instruments connected to measure the input to a single-phase motor indicate the following values: 240 V, 16 A, and 3 kW. Calculate the motor power factor.   [0.78]

28   A 420 W 240 V single-phase load takes a current of 2.5 A. Find the input (a) kVA, (b) power factor, (c) kVAr.   [0.6 kVA; 0.7; 0.43 kVAr]

29   The following values were recorded in a load test of a single-phase motor. Calculate the power factor of the motor.

Voltmeter reading	240 V
Ammeter reading	8 A
Wattmeter reading	1600 W

Draw a diagram showing how these instruments are connected in the motor circuit.   [0.83]

30   Two single-phase loads are connected in parallel. One takes a current of 20 A at 0.6 power factor lagging and the other takes 15 A at 0.707 power factor lagging. Determine the total load current and the overall power factor when the loads are connected to a 250 V 50 Hz supply.   [34.9 A; 0.65 lagging]

31   A 240 V single-phase supply feeds the following loads: incandescent lamps taking a load of 3.84 kW, fluorescent lamps taking a load of 2.40 kVA at 0.8 power factor leading, a motor load of 3.92 kW at 0.707 power factor lagging. Graphically or otherwise, determine (a) the total current, (b) the active power, (c) the reactive power taken from the supply, (d) the overall power factor. [8.63 A; 2.05 kW; 0.32 kVAr; 0.99 lagging]

32 The following single-phase loads are supplied by a power station: 400 kW at unity power factor, 800 kW at 0.8 power factor lagging, 500 kVA at 0.6 power factor lagging, 300 kW at 0.9 power factor leading. By calculation or phasor diagram to scale, determine the total kVA load supplied and its power factor. [1.99 kVA; 0.90 lagging]

33 The circuit shown in fig. 7.19 has the following details: $R = 20\,\Omega$, $L = 10\,\text{mH}$, $C_1 = 25\,\text{nF}$, $C_2 = 25\,\text{nF}$. Calculate its impedance at 20 kHz. [1097 Ω]

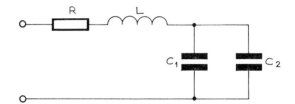

Fig. 7.19

34 The formula $f = 1/2\pi \sqrt{(LC)}$ is used in conjunction with resonant-circuit calculations. Explain what each term stands for and give the unit in which it is measured.

35 A series circuit consists of an inductance, resistance, and capacitance connected to a variable-frequency supply. On a common axis, sketch curves of inductive and capacitive reactance and impedance to a base of frequency. On the graph, indicate the impedance of the circuit at the resonant frequency.

36 A capacitor of 10 nF is connected in series with a coil of inductance 10 mH and resistance 500 Ω to a supply of 20 V at 12 kHz. Calculate (a) the current, (b) the phase angle. Sketch the phasor diagram, showing all voltages and current. [26.3 mA; 48.9°]

37 A coil of resistance R and inductance L is connected in series with a capacitance C and applied to a variable-frequency supply of V volts. Sketch a typical phasor diagram for the following conditions of frequency: (a) below resonance, (b) at resonance, (c) above resonance. Label all voltages, current, and phase angle.

38 A circuit consists of a 20 Ω resistor, a 0.2 H inductor, and an 80 μF capacitor connected in series to a 240 V 50 Hz supply. Determine (a) the current in the circuit; (b) the power consumed by the circuit; (c) the overall power factor, stating whether leading or lagging; (d) the p.d. across each of the three components. [8 A; 1.28 kW; 0.67 lagging; 160 V, 502 V, 320 V]

39 A coil having a resistance of 50 Ω and an inductance of 2 H is connected in series with a capacitor of 8 μF across a 10 V variable-frequency supply. On the same axes, sketch graphs to show the effect of the resistance, inductive reactance, and capacitive reactance when the frequency is varied over a very wide range, and mark on the graph the resonant frequency.

Calculate the current flowing and the p.d. across the capacitor at resonance.　[39.8 Hz; 200 mA; 100 V]

40　A series circuit consists of a 16 Ω resistor, an inductor of reactance 22 Ω, and a capacitor of reactance 10 Ω. If a current of 5 A flows through the combination, (a) calculate the p.d. across each of the components in the circuit; (b) construct the phasor diagram, showing the current and all the voltages; (c) use the diagram to find the total supply voltage.　[80 V, 110 V, 50 V; 100 V]

41　When a 100 V 50 Hz supply is applied to a series L–C–R circuit, the voltage across the inductor is 120 V, that across the resistor is 80 V, and that across the capacitor is 60 V. If 100 V 25 Hz is now applied, (a) what will be the new separate voltage drops? (b) state, giving reasons, whether the power factor of the circuit is now lagging or leading.　[60 V; 80 V; 120 V]

42　A coil of resistance 5 Ω and inductance 0.05 H is connected in series with a capacitor of capacitance 800 μF across a 200 V 50 Hz sinusoidal supply. Calculate (a) the current, (b) the power factor, (c) the voltage across the coil, (d) the voltage across the capacitor.

Draw to scale a phasor diagram showing the supply, capacitor, and control voltages and the current.　[36 A; 0.9; 188.7 V; 143.3 V]

43　a) A series circuit consists of an inductor of resistance 10 Ω and inductance 159 μH and a variable capacitor connected to a 50 mV 1 MHz sinusoidal supply. The capacitance is varied to produce resonance in the circuit. Calculate (i) the value of the capacitor, (ii) the value of the current.

b) For what value of capacitance will the current at this frequency be reduced to 10% of its value at resonance?　[159 pF, 5 mA; 159 pF or 160 pF]

44　Using the same axes, with steps of 10 Hz over a range of frequencies from 0 to 60 Hz, plot curves showing how reactance varies with frequency for (a) an inductor of 0.1 H, (b) a capacitor of 150 μF. Use the curves to find the frequency at which maximum current will flow in a circuit consisting of a coil in series with a capacitor, having the values given above.　[41.1 Hz]

8   Measuring instruments and measurements

8.1 Introduction

In any branch of science or engineering it is important to be able to measure the quantities being used.

In electric circuits, some of the commonly occuring quantities are current, voltage, power, and resistance. The instruments which measure these are called the ammeter, voltmeter, wattmeter, and ohmmeter respectively.

8.2 Ammeters and voltmeters

An ammeter measures current. Current flows through a circuit and therefore the ammeter must be connected in series with the circuit, as shown in fig. 8.1. The current flowing through the circuit will thus flow through the ammeter. Notice that an ammeter has a low resistance and should never be connected directly across a supply voltage, since there would be nothing to limit the current flow and the instrument would be damaged.

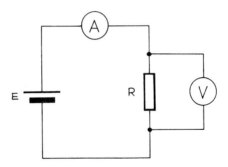

Fig. 8.1 Circuit including an ammeter and a voltmeter

A voltmeter measures electromotive force and potential difference. The potential difference across a resistance may be measured by connecting the voltmeter across the resistance. The voltmeter is therefore connected in parallel with the resistance, as shown in fig. 8.1. Notice that voltage does not flow like electric current. Voltage may be compared to pressure, as in the water analogy discussed in chapter 2 – it causes electric current to flow but does not flow itself.

There are a number of possible ways in which an electric current can cause the deflection of a pointer on a scale. In the instruments to be considered here it is the magnetic effect of an electric current which is utilised to produce the deflecting force.

It is important to realise that both the voltmeter and the ammeter use an electric current to produce a deflection, but in the case of the voltmeter only a very small current is allowed to flow (say $50\,\mu A$ or $100\,\mu A$). It is the design of the instrument which is different in each case rather than the basic construction; i.e. an ammeter has a low resistance while a voltmeter has a high resistance.

8.3 The moving-coil instrument

The permanent-magnet moving-coil instrument depends for its operation on the reaction between the current in a moveable coil and the field of a fixed permanent magnet.

It consists of a coil suspended in a magnetic field as shown in fig. 8.2. The current to be measured passes through the coil and reacts with the magnetic field to produce a torque. In any current-measuring instrument, a restoring torque is required so that the instrument may be calibrated (i.e. so that the pointer does not swing right over to the end stop whatever the current). This restoring torque is provided by a control spring. The moving coil has many turns, to provide a large torque, and is wound around a soft-iron core to provide a path of low magnetic reluctance in which the flux can readily exist. The coil is balanced on pivots at each end, and a pointer connected to the coil moves across a scale as shown. The current is fed to the coil via the control springs. The reading is given on the dial when the resisting torque, set up by the control springs, is equal to the deflecting torque of the coil.

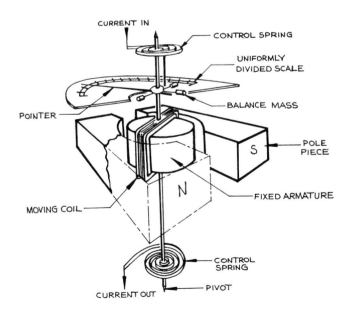

Fig. 8.2 A moving-coil instrument

An important feature of the moving-coil instrument is that the scale is linear: this is made possible by shaping the pole pieces as shown, to provide a uniform magnetic flux density over the entire movement.

Damping of the movement must be provided in any moving-pointer instrument, to damp oscillations and prevent overshoot of the pointer. In the case of the moving-coil instrument, this damping is provided by winding the coil on an aluminium former. When the coil moves through the magnetic field, small circulating currents (eddy currents) flow in the aluminium former. These currents react with the magnetic field to produce a restraining torque while the coil is in motion and thus damp out oscillations. Instrument damping is generally arranged to allow just one small overshoot, to show that the pointer is not sticking.

One disadvantage of the moving-coil instrument is that it will not measure alternating current, since this would attempt to move the pointer back and forth at the frequency of the alternating current and would result in no motion at all.

Features:
a) measures d.c. only,
b) linear scale,
c) high sensitivity,
d) may be used as a d.c. ammeter with a shunt,
e) may be used as a d.c. voltmeter with a multiplier resistor.
(Shunts and multipliers are discussed in sections 8.6 and 8.7.)

8.4 The moving-iron instrument
The moving-iron instrument may be used to measure both a.c. and d.c. voltage and current.

One type (the repulsion moving-iron instrument) has a fixed and a moving piece of iron inside a coil, as shown in fig. 8.3. When current passes through the coil, a magnetic flux is produced which magnetises both irons in the same

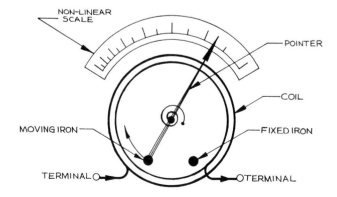

Fig. 8.3 A moving-iron instrument

190

direction. Since like magnetic poles repel each other, the moving iron pushes away from the fixed iron. A coiled spring provides the restoring torque so that the meter may be calibrated. The scale is non-linear, due to the non-uniform force between the irons, and gives poor accuracy at low readings.

In the practical instrument the moving iron is rectangular in shape, as shown in fig. 8.4, while the fixed iron is in the shape of a tapered 'scroll' to improve the scale linearity.

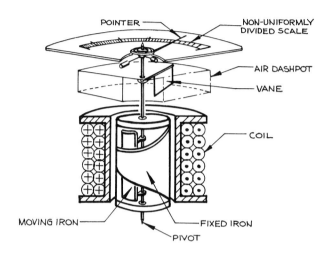

Fig. 8.4 A moving-iron instrument

One advantage of the moving-iron instrument is that it measures both alternating and direct current. It is a fairly robust instrument and is suitable for laboratory measurements at mains frequency (50 Hz). Damping is provided by means of the vane and air dashpot shown in fig. 8.4. The main disadvantage of the instrument is that it is not accurate for frequencies above about 100 Hz.

Features:
a) measures direct and alternating current;
b) non-linear scale;
c) may be used as an ammeter, but shunts should not be used, due to non-linearity;
d) may be used as a voltmeter, directly or with multiplier resistors;
e) is accurate only for frequencies below about 100 Hz.

8.5 Rectifier instruments
A rectifier is a device which allows current to pass one way only, rather like a non-return valve in a fluid system (see chapter 9). When connected in series with a moving-coil instrument, as shown in fig. 8.5, a rectifier allows the instrument to be used for the measurement of a.c. voltage and current. The

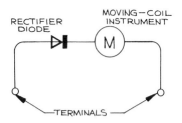

Fig. 8.5 A rectifier instrument

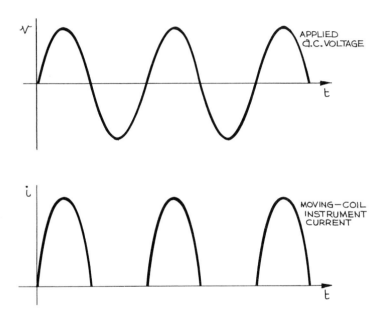

Fig. 8.6 Voltage and current waveforms for a rectifier instrument

rectifier allows the current to flow only during one half of the voltage wave-form, as shown in fig. 8.6.

The instrument indicates the average value of the current flowing through it, and thus gives a reading proportional to the average value of a half-wave rectified waveform. Although the instrument is average-responding, the scale is normally calibrated in r.m.s. values. This means that the reading is correct only when measuring waveforms for which it has been calibrated – i.e. pure sine waves – it cannot be used for accurate measurement of d.c. voltage or non-sinusoidal waveforms such as sine waves with harmonics, triangular waves, square waves, etc. It gives accurate readings for a.c. voltages up to about 20 kHz, but at low frequency the pointer fluctuates and readings are not accurate below about 20 Hz.

Features:
a) measures a.c. only,
b) linear scale,
c) high sensitivity,
d) may be used as an a.c. ammeter with a shunt resistor,
e) may be used as an a.c. voltmeter with a multiplier resistor,
f) waveform error (i.e. readings are accurate only for purely sinusoidal waveforms),
g) accurate for frequencies between about 20 Hz and 20 kHz.

8.6 Range of an instrument

Ammeters and voltmeters are used to measure current and voltage over a wide range of values. An instrument should be chosen which has a full-scale deflection (f.s.d.), or range, that suits the range of current or voltage being measured. For example, it would be no use trying to measure a current of a few microamperes on a meter which had a f.s.d. of 1 A or even 1 mA – the deflection would be too small. A meter would be required with an f.s.d. of $10\,\mu A$ or $100\,\mu A$.

Many instruments have the facility of varying the range by changing a switch position. Instruments with this facility which measure current, voltage, and resistance are called *multimeters*. A typical multimeter is shown in fig. 8.7.

Fig. 8.7 A multimeter

In a multimeter, to enable the same meter to be used for various ranges of current and voltage, *shunt resistors* and *multiplier resistors* are used as described in sections 8.6 and 8.7.

Example The multimeter shown in fig. 8.8 is set to read d.c. current. What is the instrument reading?

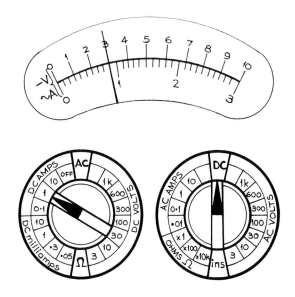

Fig. 8.8

Answer 0.3 A d.c. Notice that the scale used is the one which corresponds with the f.s.d. indicated on the range switch.

8.7 Ammeter shunts

Meters are normally constructed to have a high sensitivity and therefore give full-scale deflection with only a small current (typically $100\,\mu\text{A}$). A meter may be used to measure a larger current by the addition of a *shunt*. This is a resistor connected across the instrument so that some of the current bypasses the meter.

A meter (M) with an f.s.d. of $100\,\mu\text{A}$ and a resistance of $5\,\Omega$ is shown in fig. 8.9(a). The maximum current which the instrument can measure is $100\,\mu\text{A}$. If, however, a $5\,\Omega$ resistor is connected in parallel with the meter as in fig. 8.9(b) then the combined parallel resistance is $2.5\,\Omega$. When $100\,\mu\text{A}$ now flows through the meter, a current of $100\,\mu\text{A}$ also flows through the resistor. The total current is $200\,\mu\text{A}$ and the meter may be recalibrated for an f.s.d. of $200\,\mu\text{A}$. This, of course, does not mean that $200\,\mu\text{A}$ flows through the meter at f.s.d., but $200\,\mu\text{A}$ flows through the combination of meter and resistor. A resistor used in this way is called a *shunt*.

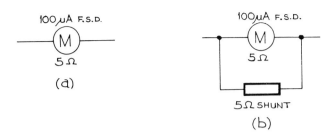

Fig. 8.9 Meter with shunt

Example 1   A meter has an f.s.d. of 1 mA and a resistance of 100 Ω. If a 0.01 Ω shunt resistor is connected across the meter as shown in fig 8.10, calculate the new f.s.d. of the combination.

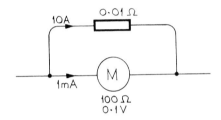

Fig. 8.10

At f.s.d.,   meter current $= 1\,\text{mA} = 0.001\,\text{A}$

　　　　meter resistance $= 100\,\Omega$

∴　voltage across meter at f.s.d. $= 0.001\,\text{A} \times 100\,\Omega$

　　　　　　　　　$= 0.1\,\text{V}$

This voltage also appears across the 0.01 Ω resistor,

∴　shunt-resistor current at f.s.d. $= \dfrac{0.1\,\text{V}}{0.01\,\Omega} = 10\,\text{A}$

　　Total current $= 10\,\text{A} + 0.001\,\text{A}$

　　　　　$\approx 10\,\text{A}$

i.e. the new f.s.d. of the combination is approximately 10 A.
　　Notice that the value of the shunt resistor needs to be known accurately.

Example 2   A meter has an f.s.d. of 1 mA and a resistance of 2 Ω. Calculate the value of the shunt resistance to be added in parallel so that the instrument can be recalibrated for an f.s.d. of 1 A.

195

At f.s.d.,   total current = 1 A

meter current = 1 mA = 0.001 A

∴   shunt-resistor current = 1 A − 0.001 A

= 0.999 A

Voltage across meter = 0.001 A × 2 Ω

= 0.002 V

This same voltage appears across the shunt resistor,

$$\therefore \quad \text{shunt resistor} = \frac{0.002\ V}{0.999\ A} = 2.002\ m\Omega$$

i.e. a shunt resistor of 2.002 mΩ is required.

Notice that in many cases the shunt resistor is very small.

8.8 Voltmeter multipliers

A meter may be used to measure voltage by the addition of a *multiplier*. This is a resistor connected in series with the instrument so that some of the voltage is dropped across it.

Fig. 8.11 Meter with multiplier

A meter (M) with an f.s.d. of 100 μA and a resistance of 5 Ω is shown in fig. 8.11 (a). The voltage required across the meter to give f.s.d. is, by Ohm's law, 100 μA × 5 Ω = 500 μV. This is a very small voltage and normally it is required to measure voltages in the range, say, 0.1 V to 100 V. Suppose that a 100 kΩ multiplier is connected to this meter as shown in fig. 8.11 (b). By Ohm's law, the required voltage to give an f.s.d. of 100 μA is then 100 μA × 100 kΩ = 10 V. (Notice that the 5 Ω due to the meter may be neglected.) The meter may now be calibrated with an f.s.d. of 10 V and be used as a voltmeter.

It is important to notice that both the ammeter and voltmeter may use a 100 μA meter, which depends for its movement on current passing through it. As previously stated, the ammeter has a low resistance, due to the use of a shunt, while the voltmeter has a high resistance, due to the use of a multiplier.

Example   A meter has an f.s.d. of 1 mA and a resistance of 100 Ω. Calculate the value of the multiplier resistor required so that the instrument may be recalibrated for 10 V f.s.d.

Current at f.s.d. $= 1\,\text{mA} = 0.001\,\text{A}$

The total resistance of multiplier and meter to give f.s.d. with 10 V applied is

$$\frac{10\,\text{V}}{0.001\,\text{A}} = 10\,\text{k}\Omega$$

Now, meter resistance $= 100\,\Omega$

∴ multiplier resistance $= 10\,\text{k}\Omega - 100\,\Omega = 9.9\,\text{k}\Omega$

i.e. a $9.9\,\text{k}\Omega$ multiplier is required.

8.9 Ohmmeter

An ohmmeter is a means of measuring resistance, and is incorporated into most multimeters. It uses the same meter movement as the ammeter and voltmeter, but the zero is at the opposite end of the scale (see the resistance scale on the meter shown in fig. 8.7).

The circuit of an ohmmeter is shown in fig. 8.12; it incorporates a cell (C) and a variable resistance (R). A resistor connected across the terminals XY allows current to flow, causing the meter pointer to deflect. The amount by which the pointer deflects varies inversely with the value of the resistance; for this reason, the resistance scale has zero at the right-hand side and the pointer deflects more towards the left with increasing values of resistance.

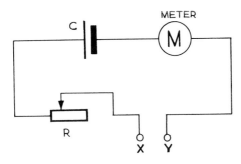

Fig. 8.12 Ohmmeter circuit

The method of use is as follows. The terminals XY are first shorted together and the variable resistor R is adjusted until the resistance reading on the meter is zero. The 'short' is then removed and the unknown resistance is connected across the terminals XY. The resistance value may now be read directly from the meter scale. The meter shown in fig. 8.7 has three range settings:

'Ω', on which range the scale reading should be read directly;
'$\Omega \div 100$', on which range the scale reading is to be divided by 100;
'$\Omega \times 100$', on which range the scale reading is to be multiplied by 100.

These enable a wide range of resistances to be measured.

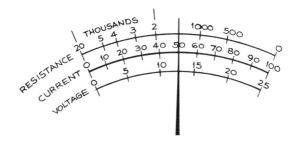

Fig. 8.13 Multimeter scale

Example   A multimeter is set to read resistance on the $\Omega \times 100$ range, having been initially zeroed. If the reading is as shown in fig. 8.13, what is the resistor value?

Answer   150 kΩ (i.e. 1500 $\Omega \times 100$, since the switch is on the '$\times$ 100' range).

8.10 Digital measuring instruments

An instrument which indicates the reading by the movement of a pointer over a scale is referred to as an 'analogue' instrument (see fig. 8.7). An alternative form of display, which is becoming more common, presents the reading as a sequence of digits, and instruments with this form of display are referred to as 'digital' instruments. Digital measuring instruments have the advantage that the measured quantity is displayed in numerical form – in comparison to the moving-pointer type of instrument they are quicker and easier to read. A digital multimeter is shown in fig. 8.14.

Fig. 8.14 A digital multimeter

Digital multimeters have the same facilities as ordinary multimeters in that they measure a range of values of direct and alternating voltage and current as well as resistance.

When used to measure voltages, digital instruments are usually referred to as d.v.m.'s (digital voltmeters).

8.11 Measurement of power

The power in a load resistor may be found by measuring the voltage V across the resistor and the current I through the resistor. The power is then given by the equation

$$P = VI$$

This method may be used to give accurate measurement of power in a *resistive* load for both d.c. and a.c. voltages.

When measuring a.c. power in a circuit which is not purely resistive – i.e. where the load is inductive or capacitive – the above method gives incorrect results, due to the voltage and current being out of phase. In this case a watt-meter must be used.

Dynamometer wattmeter

A wattmeter may be used to give accurate readings of power in any type of load in both a.c. and d.c. circuits. The instrument is sensitive to the phase difference between the voltage and the current and thus indicates true power. The instrument consists of two low-resistance current coils, which are fixed a small distance apart, and a high-resistance voltage coil which is free to move as shown in fig. 8.15. The current flowing through the current coils produces a uniform magnetic field between them. The voltage is connected across the voltage coil, and a torque is thus produced in the coil, just as in the moving-coil voltmeter.

The pointer is attached to the pivot shaft and turns with the coil. The turning effort is resisted by the control springs. The force on the voltage coil is proportional to the current flowing in the voltage coil multiplied by the strength of the magnetic field produced by the current coils. The deflection is thus proportional to the voltage multiplied by the current.

If the voltage and current are alternating, the instrument will still read correctly since the directions of the current in both the voltage coil and the field coils change together, thus maintaining the force on the coil in the same direction all the time. The instrument therefore indicates power in both a.c. and d.c. circuits.

Damping is provided in the form of a vane and an oil or air dashpot, as shown in fig. 8.15.

There are two possible ways of connecting the wattmeter to measure the power dissipated in a load. Both connections give a reading which is slightly in error, and a correction factor is required.

In the connection of fig. 8.16(a) the voltage coil measures the voltage across both the load resistor and the current coils. It is therefore necessary

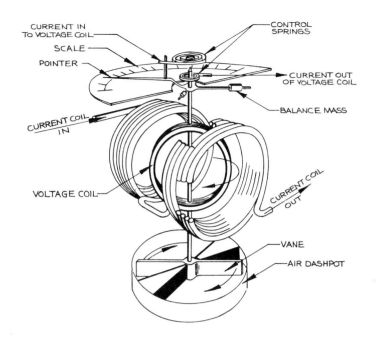

Fig. 8.15 Dynamometer wattmeter

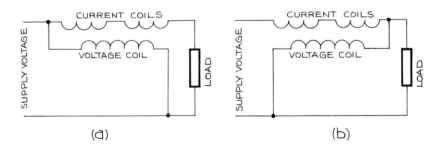

Fig. 8.16 Two methods of wattmeter connection

to correct the reading by subtracting the power dissipated in the current coils (I^2R_c):

$$P_{\text{actual}} = P_{\text{reading}} - I^2R_c$$

where I = current in current coils

and R_c = current-coil resistance

This connection is most suitable for measuring power in high-resistance loads, where R_c is small compared to the load resistance.

200

Connecting the coils as shown in fig. 8.16(b) means that the current coils measure the current in both the load resistor and the voltage coil. In this case the correction is to subtract from the reading the power dissipated in the voltage coil (V^2/R_v):

$$P_{actual} = P_{reading} - V^2/R_v$$

where $\quad V$ = voltage across voltage coil

and $\quad R_v$ = voltage-coil resistance

This connection is most suitable for measuring power in low-resistance loads, where R_v is large compared to the load resistance.

Example The current coil of a wattmeter has a resistance of 1 Ω and the voltage coil has a resistance of 10 kΩ. The meter is used in a d.c. circuit to measure the power taken by a load from a 250 V supply. If the wattmeter indicates 420 watts when connected as shown in fig. 8.16(a), calculate the true power taken by the load.

With the connection of fig 8.16(a), the actual power is given by

$$P_{actual} = P_{reading} - I^2 R_c$$

where $\quad P_{reading} = 420\,W$

$$I = \frac{P}{V} = \frac{420\,W}{250\,V} = 1.68\,A \quad \text{and} \quad R_c = 1\,\Omega$$

$$\therefore \quad P_{actual} = 420\,W - (1.68\,A)^2 \times 1\,\Omega$$

$$= 420\,W - 2.8\,W$$

$$= 417.2\,W$$

i.e. the power taken by the load is 417.2 W.

8.12 The cathode-ray oscilloscope

The cathode-ray oscilloscope (CRO) is an instrument used for measuring voltage waveforms. Its main advantage is that the shape of the waveform is displayed on a screen.

The main component of the cathode-ray oscilloscope is the tube. It consists of an *electron gun* which produces a source of electrons that are converged into a narrow beam by the *focusing equipment*. The beam is directed on to a *screen* which is coated with a fluorescent material so that a spot of light is produced where the beam strikes it.

The *deflection system* consists of two sets of plates and enables movement of the position of the spot on the screen. A voltage applied to the *Y*-plates causes the spot to move in a vertical direction, while applying a voltage to the *X*-plates causes movement in a horizontal direction.

The whole system is contained in a glass tube which is evacuated to allow the electrons to pass along the tube without colliding with atoms of air.

How a waveform is produced

Consider the application of a d.c. voltage to the Y-plates. When the upper plate is positive, the negatively charged electron beam will be deflected towards it. The deflection will be upwards as shown in fig. 8.17(a). When the lower plate is positive, the beam will be deflected downwards as shown in fig 8.17(b).

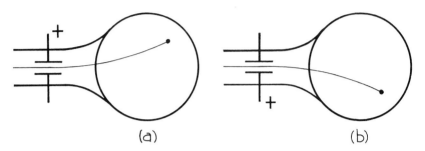

Fig. 8.17 Y-plate deflection

Now consider the application to the Y-plates of an alternating voltage which is in the form of a sine wave. The spot will move up and down the screen. Due to the slight persistence of the trace on the screen, a vertical line will be displayed as shown in fig. 8.18. If the instrument is calibrated with a graduated scale in front of the screen, as shown in fig. 8.19, then the voltage height can be measured.

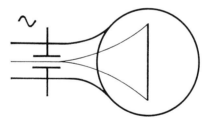

Fig. 8.18 Deflection with an a.c. voltage

This vertical line, however, provides no information about the *shape* of the waveform. In order to display the waveform shape, the trace must move across the screen. The circuit which makes this possible is called the *time-base generator*. It produces a voltage waveform called a 'saw-tooth', which is shown in fig. 8.20.

This saw-tooth waveform is applied across the X-plates. It causes the spot to move at a steady speed across the screen from left to right and then suddenly fly back to the start.

When a sinusoidal voltage is applied to the Y-plates, the waveform displayed will be as shown in fig. 8.21.

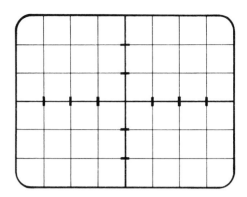

Fig. 8.19 Graduated scale or graticule in front of screen

Fig. 8.20 Sawtooth waveform

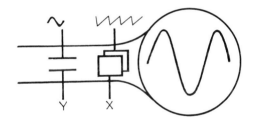

Fig. 8.21 Waveform display

The time for the spot to move across the screen is set by the time-base generator. It is therefore possible to measure the period of the waveform (i.e. the time for one complete cycle). From this measurement the frequency may be calculated.

Uses of the cathode-ray oscilloscope

The CRO has a wide range of applications in all branches of science and engineering. It can be used to measure voltage directly, or to measure current by causing the current to pass through a known resistance of a small value and using the CRO to measure the voltage across the resistance.

It can also be used to display the voltage waveforms from the following:

a) an electrical-tachometer output, for the measurement of angular velocity;
b) a strain-gauge output, used for measuring mechanical strain;
c) a thermocouple, used for the measurement of temperature;
d) an electronic-amplifier output;
e) an electrical-transducer output, for the measurement of force, pressure, acceleration, vibration, etc.

The advantages of the cathode-ray oscilloscope are

i) it displays the shape of the waveform being measured;
ii) the size, frequency, and phase of the waveforms can be measured;
iii) alternating signals up to a frequency of 10 MHz or higher can be measured accurately;
iv) it has a very high input resistance (about 1 MΩ) and therefore does not load the circuit which is being measured. This means, for example, that the voltage produced by a record-player pick-up may be displayed and measured accurately using a cathode-ray oscilloscope. An instrument which does not have a high resistance is unsuitable, since it would take too much current from the pick-up.

8.13 How to use the cathode-ray oscilloscope
The following description should be reinforced by practical investigation. A typical cathode-ray oscilloscope is shown in fig. 8.22. A block diagram is shown in fig. 8.23, and the function of each control is described below.

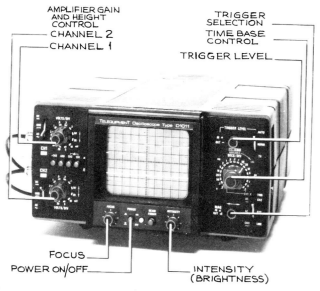

Fig. 8.22 Cathode-ray oscilloscope

204

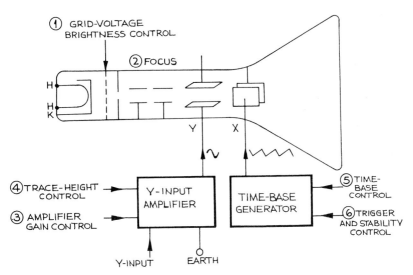

Fig. 8.23 Oscilloscope block diagram

1 Intensity (or brightness control)
This determines the brightness of the spot on the screen. It should not be set too high since it can damage the screen.

2 Focus
This adjustment allows the operator to produce a small clear spot or a thin line when measuring a waveform.

3 Amplifier-gain control (volts/div)
This control amplifies (makes larger) or attenuates (makes smaller) the size of the waveform applied to the Y-plates. Amplifier gain should be set to give a waveform of suitable size to almost fill the screen. The amplifier has a range of fixed gain settings, each switch position being calibrated in volts/centimetre (volts/div). This enables the waveform height to be accurately measured.

The oscilloscope shown can display two waveforms simultaneously (channel 1 and 2). It therefore also has two independent amplifier-gain controls.

4 Trace-height control
This control is normally called the 'Y-shift' and is connected to the amplifier. It allows the waveform to be moved up or down the screen. There is one Y-shift for each channel.

5 Time-base control (time/div)
This controls the rate at which the spot travels across the screen. A range of fixed switch positions is available, each position being calibrated in milliseconds per centimetre (ms/cm) or microseconds per centimetre (μs/cm).

The time-base control enables the time for one complete cycle (i.e the periodic time) to be accurately measured. From the periodic time, the frequency (or number of cycles per second) of the waveform can be determined.

6 Trigger-level control
This control is used to ensure a steady trace. If the trigger level is incorrectly set, a waveform as shown in fig. 8.24 will be obtained, making measurement almost impossible.

Fig. 8.24 Incorrect setting of trigger level

The function of the trigger circuit is to delay the time-base sweep until the input signal is just beginning a new cycle. This ensures that the trace starts at the same point on each sweep, thus producing a single waveform.

7 Trigger selection
Most oscilloscopes have two input channels and therefore two traces. The trigger-selection switch enables the time base to be triggered either externally or from the output of channel 1 or 2.

8 A.C./D.C./GND switch
This switch will normally be used in the a.c. position. In this position a coupling capacitor removes the d.c. component of the input signal to the Y-amplifier. The d.c. switch position may be used if it is desired to include the d.c. component of the input waveform, or if the waveform is distorted on a.c. due to the input coupling capacitor. The GND (ground) position enables the setting of the zero-volts level on the screen.

Use of the CRO to measure frequency and phase angle
The CRO may be used to measure the frequency of a waveform by measuring the time for one cycle using a suitably calibrated time-base. The frequency is then found from

$$f = \frac{1}{\text{period}} = \frac{1}{T}$$

The phase difference between two waveforms of the same frequency may be found by lining up the axes of the two waveforms as shown in fig. 8.25(a) and then measuring t and T. The phase angle is then found from

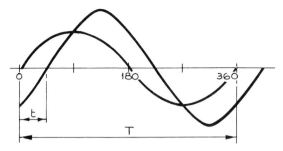

Fig. 8.25 Two waveforms out of phase

$$\frac{\phi}{360°} = \frac{t}{T}$$

Example 1 State the control which requires adjustment in the oscilloscope traces shown in fig. 8.26. The input signal is a sine wave.

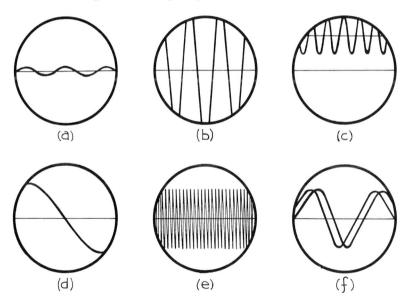

Fig. 8.26 Oscilloscope waveforms with controls incorrectly adjusted

a) Y-amplifier gain set too low.
b) Y-amplifier gain set too high.
c) Trace height (Y-shift) too high.
d) Time-base set too fast.
e) Time-base set too slow.
f) Trigger and stability not adjusted.

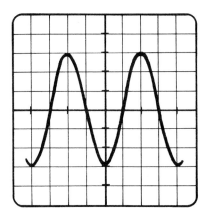

Fig. 8.27

Example 2   A signal applied to an oscilloscope gives a trace as shown in fig. 8.27. The amplifier gain setting is 10 V/cm and the time-base setting is 100 ms/cm. Calculate (a) the waveform voltage from peak to peak, (b) the time for one complete cycle (i.e. the period), (c) the number of cycles in a second (i.e. the frequency).

a)   Peak-to-peak height = 6 cm at 10 V/cm

∴   peak-to-peak voltage = 6 cm × 10 V/cm

$$= 60 \text{ V}$$

i.e. the waveform voltage from peak to peak is 60 V.

b) One complete cycle measures 4 cm at 100 ms/cm

∴   time for one complete cycle = 4 cm × 100 ms/cm

$$= 400 \text{ ms} = 0.4 \text{ s}$$

i.e. the time for one complete cycle is 400 ms, or 0.4 s.

c) The waveform performs 1 cycle in 0.4 s

∴   number of cycles per second $= \dfrac{1 \text{ cycle}}{0.4 \text{ s}}$

$$= 2.5 \text{ cycles per second}$$

$$= 2.5 \text{ Hz}$$

i.e. the waveform performs 2.5 cycles per second, or its frequency is 2.5 Hz.

8.14 The electronic voltmeter
The electronic voltmeter is basically a moving-coil instrument driven from an electronic amplifier. The signal voltage to be measured is connected to the input of the amplifier. Its advantages are that it has a high input resistance (of

the order of $10\,\text{M}\Omega$), so that it takes only a very small current from the circuit under test, and that it has a good frequency response (of the order to $10\,\text{MHz}$).

These features are important when performing tests on, say, a piece of electronic equipment, where a standard multimeter would take too much current and therefore alter the voltage which it is trying to measure. Also the multimeter is accurate only up to frequencies of the order of $10\,\text{kHz}$.

Some types of electronic voltmeter provide the facility for measuring both a.c. and d.c. voltages, while others are used for a.c. only.

There are electronic voltmeters to meet all types of measuring applications. As well as the general-purpose type, there are radio-frequency electronic voltmeters for performing tests at high frequency, and microvoltmeters for measuring very small signal levels. Before making a measurement with an electronic voltmeter, the user should be quite clear as to its area of application.

Probes are often provided with oscilloscopes and electronic voltmeters and are generally used to minimise the loading effect of the measuring instrument. The term 'probe' has come to have a variety of interpretations and a probe may simply consist of a coaxial lead terminated with prods, in this case being used to prevent pick-up distorting the signal being measured.

Electronic voltmeters are also referred to as 'valve' voltmeters.

8.15 Bridge methods

Bridge methods are used mainly for accurate measurement of component values such as resistance, capacitance, and inductance.

The most straightforward bridge circuit is the Wheatstone bridge, which is used for accurate measurement of resistance. (It is more accurate than the ohmmeter, although less convenient.)

The basic arrangement consists of a four-arm resistance bridge ABCD, as shown in fig. 8.28, where R_x is the resistance to be measured, R_s is a fixed standard resistance, and R_1 and R_2 are variable standard resistances. A d.c. supply is provided across AC, with a facility for varying the current flow. A

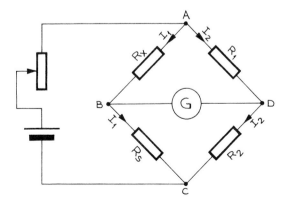

Fig. 8.28 Wheatstone bridge

galvanometer is connected across BD. (A galvanometer is a very sensitive d.c. current-measuring instrument using the same principle as the moving-coil instrument.)

To obtain a *balance*, the values of R_1 and R_2 are adjusted until the galvanometer reading is zero (or a minimum). At this condition, zero (or negligible) current flows in the galvanometer and therefore the current in R_x must equal that in R_s. Also, the current in R_1 must equal that in R_2. This is the condition shown in fig. 8.28.

The voltages across the arms are therefore

$$V_{AB} = I_1 R_x$$
$$V_{BC} = I_1 R_s$$
$$V_{AD} = I_2 R_1$$
$$V_{DC} = I_2 R_2$$

Also, since no current flows in the galvanometer, the voltage at B must equal that at D;

$\therefore \qquad V_{AB} = V_{AD}$

and $\qquad V_{BC} = V_{DC}$

or $\qquad I_1 R_x = I_2 R_1$ (i)

and $\qquad I_1 R_s = I_2 R_2$ (ii)

Dividing equation (i) by equation (ii) gives

$$\frac{I_1 R_x}{I_1 R_s} = \frac{I_2 R_1}{I_2 R_2}$$

or $\qquad \dfrac{R_x}{R_s} = \dfrac{R_1}{R_2}$

This gives a means of calculating R_x if the values of R_s, R_1, and R_2 are known.

Notice that the value of R_x is independent of the current flowing through it and of the voltage applied across the bridge. The supply voltage does not need to be known, and slight variations in this voltage throughout the test will have no effect on the measurement.

It should be noted that the method uses the *comparison* of an unknown resistance with known standard resistances. The accuracy therefore depends on the accuracy of the standards and upon the sensitivity of the galvano-meter.

Bridge methods are often referred to as *null methods* since they depend on varying standard components to obtain a 'null' reading on the galvanometer.

In the commercial Wheatstone bridge, the resistors R_s, R_1, and R_2 are contained in a box and are adjusted by dial switches. R_1 and R_2 usually consist of four resistors each, these being $10\,\Omega$, $100\,\Omega$, $1000\,\Omega$, and $10\,000\,\Omega$. Together, they thus provide a *ratio* by which R_s is multiplied to obtain the value of the unknown. In this case, the multiplying ratio is between 10/10 000 (i.e. 0.01) and 10 000/10 (i.e. 100).

Example A Wheatstone bridge is used to measure an unknown resistance and is at balance with $R_1 = 10\,\Omega$, $R_2 = 1000\,\Omega$, and $R_s = 3628\,\Omega$. Calculate the value of the unknown resistance.

$$R_x/R_s = R_1/R_2$$

where $R_s = 3628\,\Omega$ $R_1 = 10\,\Omega$ and $R_2 = 1000\,\Omega$

$$\therefore \quad R_x = 3628\,\Omega \times \frac{10\,\Omega}{1000\,\Omega}$$

$$= 36.28\,\Omega$$

i.e. the unknown resistance is 36.28 Ω.

8.16 The d.c. potentiometer

The d.c. potentiometer is an accurate method of measuring d.c. voltage. It is a null method and compares the voltage to be measured with an accurate known voltage.

A simple slide-wire potentiometer is shown in fig. 8.29. A metre length of high-resistance wire with uniform cross-sectional area is connected between A and B, and a 2 V accumulator is connected across it. A Weston cadmium cell (which has a very accurate and stable voltage of 1.0186 V) is connected as the reference standard in the position V_s. Notice that the polarities of both cells must be in the same sense – say both negative terminals on the left-hand side. One method of calibrating the slide wire is as follows.

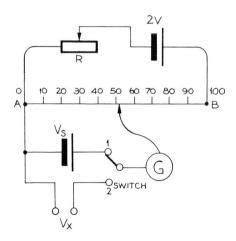

Fig. 8.29 Simple d.c. potentiometer

With the switch in position 1, the slider is positioned on the wire at precisely 50.9 cm. The variable resistor is then adjusted until the galvano-meter reads zero deflection. At this condition, the voltage of the standard cell is exactly balanced by the voltage tapped off along the wire (the wire acts as a potential-divider),

i.e. $50.9 \text{ cm} \equiv 1.0186 \text{ V}$

or $1 \text{ cm} \equiv 0.02 \text{ V}$

The voltage to be measured (V_x) is now connected in place of the standard cell by changing the switch to position 2. The slider is then adjusted until there is zero deflection on the galvanometer.

The reading on the slide wire is then taken (say l cm), and multiplying this length by the potentiometer constant of 0.02 V/cm gives the value of the unknown voltage V_x:

$$V_x = l \times 0.02 \text{ volts}$$

One disadvantage of the d.c. potentiometer is that any variation in the supply voltage will affect the result. Readings should therefore be taken quickly after standardising the potentiometer, and a well charged cell should be used as the d.c. source. It is however, a very accurate means of measuring d.c. voltages, with accuracies of the order of 0.1% or better.

Accurate commercial potentiometers are available and are often used for calibrating d.c. voltmeters and ammeters.

Example   A slide-wire potentiometer uses a 0.5 m wire and is standardised by setting the slider to 20.4 cm and obtaining a balance using a standard Weston cell. When an unknown voltage is measured using the potentiometer, the null reading is obtained at 30 cm. Calculate the potentiometer constant and the value of the unknown voltage.

When standardising the potentiometer,

$20.4 \text{ cm} \equiv 1.0186 \text{ V}$

∴ $1 \text{ cm} \equiv 1.0186 \text{ V}/20.4 = 0.05 \text{ V}$

i.e. the potentiometer constant is 0.05 V/cm.

Unknown voltage = potentiometer constant × l

where $l = 30 \text{ cm}$

∴   unknown voltage = 0.05 V/cm × 30 cm

= 1.5 V

i.e. the value of the unknown voltage is 1.5 V.

8.17 Errors in measurement

Any measuring instrument should have the minimum effect on the quantity being measured. For example, an ammeter must have a very low resistance, otherwise it will itself alter the current flowing through the circuit: a voltmeter, however, should have a very high resistance, so that it takes only a small current from the circuit under test.

In practice, both instruments have some small effect on the circuit under test, and therefore the reading is always slightly in error. It is important to make the correct choice of instrument for each particular measurement, to ensure that this error is small.

When choosing a voltmeter, we are generally concerned with its input resistance and its frequency response. Multimeters of either the analogue or digital type generally have an input resistance of the order of $20\,\text{k}\Omega$ on the 1 volt scale. The input resistances of oscilloscopes and electronic voltmeters are much higher, of the order of $10\,\text{M}\Omega$.

Example 1   A transducer produces a signal voltage of $100\,\text{mV}$ from a source resistance of $1\,\text{k}\Omega$. A voltmeter is connected to measure this voltage as shown in fig. 8.30. Calculate the actual reading on the voltmeter and the percentage error (a) if a multimeter is used on the $100\,\text{mV}$ range (where it has a resistance of $2\,\text{k}\Omega$), (b) if a valve voltmeter is used which has an input resistance of $50\,\text{k}\Omega$.

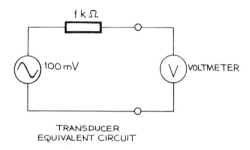

Fig. 8.30 Measurement of transducer signal

This is simply a potential-divider problem.
a) Using the multimeter,

$$\text{voltmeter reading} = \frac{2\,\text{k}\Omega}{2\,\text{k}\Omega + 1\,\text{k}\Omega} \times 100\,\text{mV}$$

$$= \tfrac{2}{3} \times 100\,\text{mV}$$

$$= 66.6\,\text{mV}$$

$$\text{percentage error} = \frac{100\,\text{mV} - 66.6\,\text{mV}}{100\,\text{mV}} \times 100\%$$

$$= \frac{33.3\,\text{mV}}{100\,\text{mV}} \times 100\% = 33.3\%$$

213

b) Using the valve voltmeter,

$$\text{voltmeter reading} = \frac{50\,\text{k}\Omega}{50\,\text{k}\Omega + 1\,\text{k}\Omega} \times 100\,\text{mV}$$

$$= \frac{50\,\text{k}\Omega}{51\,\text{k}\Omega} \times 100\,\text{mV} = 98\,\text{mV}$$

$$\text{percentage error} = \frac{100\,\text{mV} - 98\,\text{mV}}{100\,\text{mV}} \times 100\%$$

$$= \frac{2\,\text{mV}}{100\,\text{mV}} \times 100\% = 2\%$$

i.e. using the multimeter, the reading is 66.6 mV with an error of 33.3%; using the valve voltmeter, the reading is 98 mV with an error of only 2%.

The input resistance of a multimeter is specified on the instrument case. The value of input resistance depends on the range setting used, since each voltage-range setting uses a different multiplier resistor in series with the meter. This means that the input resistance is higher on, say, the 10 V range than it is on the 1 V range. For this reason the manufacturer specifies the instrument input resistance in ohms/volt (Ω/V). To find the actual value of input resistance, the user must multiply the Ω/V by the voltage at full-scale deflection (f.s.d.) for the particular range chosen.

Example 2   A multimeter is stated as having an input resistance of 20 kΩ/V. What is the actual input resistance on each of the following ranges: (a) 1 V f.s.d., (b) 10 V f.s.d., (c) 100 V f.s.d.?

Input resistance (R_{in}) = 20 kΩ/V × f.s.d.

a) R_{in} = 20 kΩ/V × 1 V = 20 kΩ

b) R_{in} = 20 kΩ/V × 10 V = 200 kΩ

c) R_{in} = 20 kΩ/V × 100 V = 2 MΩ

Notice that the input resistance varies considerably with the range setting and, although satisfactory on one setting, may be unsuitable for the particular measurement on another setting.

Multimeters are unsuitable for measurement of frequencies above about 10 kHz, and so above this frequency an oscilloscope or valve voltmeter would be used. The multimeter is, however, cheaper and usually self-contained (i.e. it requires no mains supply).

8.18 Scales

Various types of scale are used in analogue measuring instruments, and with some types the accuracy of the instrument may vary over the scale length. The non-linear scale of the moving-iron instrument shown in fig. 8.31(a) makes it unsuitable for measuring values at the low end of the scale.

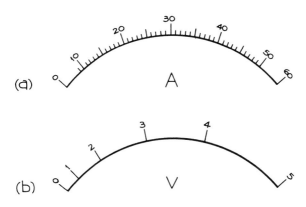

Fig. 8.31 Meter scales

Some instruments have a scale which indicates the *effective range*. The scale of fig. 8.31(a) indicates that any accuracy specification is applicable only within the range 8 A to 50 A.

BS 89:1977 is the British Standard for 'Direct-acting indicating electrical instruments and their accessories'. It considers accuracy as an indication of how closely the measured value agrees with the true value of the quantity being measured, and instruments are classified according to an accuracy class which may be one of the following:

0.05   0.1   0.2   0.5   1   1.5   2.5   5

The accuracy class is in fact the maximum permissible percentage error of the instrument; for example, an instrument in accuracy class 0.5 may have an error not exceeding 0.5%, etc. The accuracy class states the accuracy to which the instrument has been calibrated and is generally marked on the instrument dial.

Exercises on chapter 8

1   An ammeter of resistance $0.01 \, \Omega$ is connected in series with a resistor to a 2 V supply. Calculate the ammeter reading if the value of the resistor is (a) $0.1 \, \Omega$, (b) $1 \, \Omega$.   [18.18 A; 1.98 A]

2   A $20 \, \Omega$ resistor is connected in series with an ammeter across a 1 V supply. Calculate the reading on the ammeter if its internal resistance is (a) $10 \, \Omega$, (b) $1 \, \Omega$, (c) $0.01 \, \Omega$.   [0.033 A; 0.048 A; 0.05 A]

3 Two 3.3 kΩ resistors are connected in series across a 15 V supply. Calculate the reading on a voltmeter connected across one of the resistors if the voltmeter resistance is (a) 5 kΩ, (b) 20 kΩ, (c) 1 MΩ.   [5.64 V; 6.93 V; 7.5 V]

4 Describe with the aid of diagrams how the same moving-coil meter can be used (a) as a voltmeter, (b) as an ammeter. Show, by means of a simple circuit, how a voltmeter and ammeter are used.

5 Show how a shunt is connected to extend the range of an ammeter and calculate the value of shunt resistor to be connected across a 1 A ammeter of resistance 0.2 Ω to enable the instrument to read up to 5 A.   [0.05 Ω]

6 The coil of a moving-coil meter has a resistance of 5 Ω and a full-scale deflection is produced with a current of 15 mA. Explain how the range of the meter may be extended to give full-scale deflection at 60 mA, and calculate the value of the shunt resistance required.   [1.67 Ω]

7 A moving-coil meter of resistance 50 Ω and f.s.d. 500 µA is to be used as a voltmeter of range 0–10 V. Calculate the value of the multiplier resistor and show how it would be connected to the instrument.   [20 kΩ]

8 A moving-coil meter has a resistance of 5 Ω and gives full-scale deflection when 0.075 V is applied across it. Calculate the value of multiplier resistor required to give full-scale deflection at 240 V.   [16 kΩ]

9 A milliammeter has a resistance of 15 Ω and gives f.s.d. with 5 mA. Calculate the voltage required across the meter to give f.s.d. What resistance would need to be added in series with the meter to enable it to read f.s.d. with 100 V applied?   [0.075 V; 20 kΩ]

10 A meter has a resistance of 100 Ω and takes 1 mA for f.s.d. What value of shunt resistor is required for the instrument to be recalibrated for an f.s.d. of 1 A?   [0.1001 Ω]

11 A meter has a resistance of 100 Ω and takes 1 mA for f.s.d. What value of multiplier resistor is required for the instrument to be recalibrated for a f.s.d. of 10 V?   [9900 Ω]

12 A milliammeter gives f.s.d. with a current of 1 mA and has a resistance of 5 Ω. Calculate the resistance to be added (a) in parallel to enable the instrument to read up to 10 A, (b) in series to enable the instrument to read up to 100 V.   [0.0005 Ω, 100 kΩ]

13 An ohmmeter as shown in fig. 8.12 is zeroed with a short across the terminals XY. If the meter has an f.s.d. of 1 mA and a resistance of 10 Ω, calculate the value of the series resistor when the instrument is zeroed. The battery voltage is 1.5 V.   [1490 Ω]

14 An ohmmeter reads 1.7 kΩ. What is the resistance being measured if the range switch is set on (a) Ω? (b) Ω ÷ 100? (c) Ω × 100?   [1.7 kΩ; 17 Ω; 170 kΩ]

15 An unknown resistance is measured by using an ammeter and voltmeter. The ammeter has a resistance of 0.8 Ω and the voltmeter has a resistance of 150 Ω. If the voltmeter is in parallel with the resistor and the instruments read 4.6 A and 8 V, calculate (a) the approximate resistance, (b) the accurate resistance.   [1.74 Ω; 1.758 Ω]

16 An ammeter and voltmeter of resistance 2 Ω and 350 Ω respectively are used to measure a resistance of (a) 5 Ω, (b) 500 Ω. Show which would be the most suitable connection for each case and calculate the readings if the supply voltage used is 10 V.   [1.44 A, 7.11 V; 19.92 mA, 10 V]

17   A multimeter has its scale calibrated from 0 to 100. The pointer is on division 63. What is the correct reading if the range is set to (a) 25 V d.c.? (b) 100 mA? (c) 50 V? (d) 1 A?   [15.75 V, 63 mA; 31.5 V, 0.63 A]

18   State the advantage of digital-reading instruments compared with those using a pointer on a scale. Which of these two methods of display would be more accurate?

19   Two resistors, of 20 kΩ and 30 kΩ, are connected in series across a 100 V supply. Calculate the current taken from the supply. Determine the new value of current if a voltmeter of resistance 60 kΩ is connected across the 30 kΩ resistor. What will be the reading on the voltmeter?   [2 mA; 2.5 mA; 50 V]

20   Two 10 kΩ resistors are connected in series across a 10 V d.c. supply. What will be the reading of a voltmeter having a full-scale deflection of 10 V and resistance (a) 1000 Ω/V and (b) 20 000 Ω/V when used to measure the voltage across one of the resistors?

Compare the values measured with those calculated across the same resistor without a voltmeter connected. Which of the above instruments would be better for voltage measurement in high-resistance circuits? [3.33 V; 4.88 V]

21   A 10 kΩ resistor is connected in series with an unknown resistor R. The combination is fed from a 10 V d.c. supply, and a 0–10 V voltmeter having a sensitivity of 1000 Ω/V is connected across the 10 kΩ resistor and reads 5 V. Calculate (a) the value of R, (b) the potential difference across each resistor with no voltmeter connected.   [5 kΩ; 6.67 V; 3.33 V]

22   With the aid of a circuit diagram, explain how a low resistance should be measured using the ammeter–voltmeter method. State the reason for using the circuit shown.

23   State why a high-impedance voltmeter should be used in preference to a low-impedance one. Give reasons for your answer.

24   State briefly two reasons for the use of an a.c. electronic voltmeter in an electronic circuit.

25   Give one reason why a suitable probe can improve the performance of an a.c. electronic voltmeter.

26   State how the response of an a.c. electronic voltmeter will be affected by (a) the input impedance of the instrument, (b) the waveform of the applied signal, (c) the frequency of the applied signal.

27   Neatly sketch a moving-coil meter and name all the parts. Explain how the movement is deflected, controlled, and damped.

28   Explain how a coiled spring is used in indicating instruments to provide the restoring torque. What is the reason for using this spring and what would be the effect of removing the spring?

29   Which would be the most suitable meter to measure (a) an a.c. voltage of 20 V at 50 Hz? (b) a d.c. current of 200 μA?

30   a) Describe with the aid of a labelled sketch the construction and principle of operation of a moving-iron meter.

b) State the advantages and disadvantages of such a meter.

31   Compare the advantages and disadvantages of the moving-coil meter and the moving-iron meter. Which instrument would be chosen to measure a current of 6 A at 60 Hz?

32   Two electrical measuring instruments have the following specification: (a) d.c. only, linear scale, high sensitivity, suitable for use as voltmeter or ammeter; (b) a.c. and d.c., non-linear scale, frequency limit 100 Hz, suitable for use as voltmeter and ammeter. Name an instrument which meets the specification in each case.

33   Explain why a moving-iron ammeter of f.s.d. 10 A would be unsuitable for measuring a current of 1–2 A.

34   Describe with the aid of a diagram the construction of the moving-iron meter and show how the range can be extended to read higher voltage levels.

35   Explain how deflection, damping, and control are achieved in a moving-iron meter.

36   Under what circuit conditions should (a) a moving-coil instrument and (b) a moving-iron instrument be used?

A resistance, variable from 20 Ω to 200 Ω, is connected to a 200 V d.c. supply. With the aid of a suitably labelled circuit diagram, describe how the current and voltage may be measured at different values of resistance. How can the corresponding values of power be obtained from the instrument readings? State, with reason, the type of instrument preferred (moving-iron or moving-coil), and suggest a required full-scale deflection for each.

37   a) Compare the advantages and disadvantages of moving-iron and rectifier moving-coil instruments for the purpose of measuring alternating currents.

b) A moving-coil ammeter, a moving-iron ammeter, and a 120 Ω resistor are connected in series across a 240 V sinusoidal a.c. supply. If the resistance of the ammeters is negligible, calculate the reading on each of the ammeters.

c) What would be the readings if a rectifier were connected in series with the circuit of (b), assuming that the rectifier has zero forward resistance and infinite reverse resistance?   [0, 1.414 A; 0.636 A, 1 A]

38   Giving brief reasons, state the type of voltmeter which would be selected for each of the following specifications: (a) a.c., 25 Hz–20 kHz, average-responding; (b) d.c. only; (c) d.c./a.c., 25–100 Hz, r.m.s.-responding; (d) a.c., 25 Hz–1 MHz, high-impedance. In each case, state how the scale is divided.

39   a) An alternating-voltage signal of constant magnitude and variable frequency is applied to a moving-iron voltmeter. It is found that, as the frequency increases, the voltmeter reading decreases. Explain the reason for this.

b) If an alternating current of constant magnitude and variable frequency is to be measured with a moving-iron ammeter, state, giving reasons, whether or not the same frequency errors would be observed.

c) 'The range of a moving-iron ammeter should not be extended using a shunt.' Comment on the truth or otherwise of this statement when such a meter is used on an a.c. supply.

40 Draw the circuit diagram of a simple diode voltmeter and describe its operation. Compare the characteristics of a simple diode voltmeter with those of a moving-iron voltmeter.

When a simple diode voltmeter was used on a low-frequency supply, the pointer was seen to oscillate. Explain the reason for this.

41 a) A moving-coil instrument is to be used to measure a.c. sinusoidal voltages by connecting it in series with a resistor and a rectifier. Sketch a circuit diagram and explain the operation of the instrument if the rectifier is (i) half-wave, (ii) full-wave, stating in each case the value of the voltage indicated in terms of the peak value.

b) A moving-coil instrument has a resistance of 10 kΩ. Determine the instrument reading if a diode is connected in series and an alternating voltage of 50 V r.m.s. is applied.   [2.25 mA]

42 What are the three main features which must be provided in an electrical indicating instrument so that, in normal use, the needle reaches a point on the scale in an acceptable time, without oscillating. How are these features achieved in the dynamometer wattmeter?

43 Draw a suitable diagram to indicate the main features of a single-phase dynamometer wattmeter. Show that its indication depends upon the average power when it is used in an a.c. circuit.

Give a circuit diagram to show a method of connection to measure the power supplied to a single-phase load.

44 Draw circuit diagrams to show the two methods of connecting a wattmeter to measure the power in a single-phase a.c. circuit and, for each method, state the correction which must be applied to the wattmeter reading.

45 A wattmeter, voltmeter, and load resistor R are connected as shown in fig. 8.32. The wattmeter reads 524 W and the voltmeter 200 V. Calculate (a) the power loss due to the voltage coil of the wattmeter, (b) the power loss due to the voltmeter, (c) the power absorbed by the load resistor, (d) the current in the load resistor, (e) the value of the load resistor. The resistance of the voltmeter is 5 kΩ and the resistance of the voltage circuit of the wattmeter is 2.5 kΩ.   [16 W; 8 W; 500 W; 2.5 A; 80 Ω]

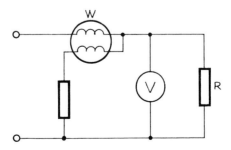

Fig. 8.32

46 a) With the aid of sketches of the magnetic fields, describe how a deflecting torque is produced in a dynamometer instrument.

b) Draw circuit diagrams to show how the meter is connected to measure the power taken by (i) a low-impedance load, (ii) a high-impedance load.

47 Why is a time-base control necessary on a cathode-ray oscilloscope, and what is meant by the term 'triggering'?

Sketch the front panel of an oscilloscope that you will be using in experiments. Label the essential controls and briefly describe the function of each.

48 The oscilloscope trace shown in fig. 8.33 shows the 'ripple' on the output voltage of a d.c. generator. If the Y-amplifier scale setting is 0.5 V/cm what is the maximum ripple voltage from peak to peak?   [2 V]

49 A piezo-electric record-player pick-up produces a voltage of 0.5 V and has a resistance of 1 MΩ. An oscilloscope with an input resistance of 10 MΩ is used to measure the voltage. Calculate the reading on the oscilloscope. If this voltage is instead connected to an a.c. voltmeter with an input resistance of 1 kΩ, calculate the reading on the voltmeter. (Hint: this is merely a potential-divider question.) What conclusions can be drawn from these readings?   [0.455 V; 0.5 mV]

50 A cathode-ray oscilloscope is used in conjunction with a radar transmitter to estimate the distance of an aircraft. When the transmitter emits a radar pulse, a direct 'blip' is indicated on the screen. The reflected signal is received a small time later and is also displayed on the screen. The trace is shown in fig. 8.34, with the oscilloscope time-base set to 200 μs/cm. Calculate the time between direct and reflected signals.   [1 ms]

51 The oscilloscope trace in fig. 8.35 is shown with the Y-amplifier gain set to 1 V/cm and the time-base set to 10 ms/cm. Calculate (a) the size of the waveform from peak to peak, (b) the period, (c) the frequency.   [6 V; 40 ms; 25 Hz]

52 A triangular-shaped alternating waveform of 50 V peak to peak and 400 Hz is displayed on an oscilloscope. The graticule is calibrated as follows:

Vertically   1 cm ≡ 20 V
Horizontally   1 cm ≡ 1 ms

Draw the graticule and sketch the waveform to cover two full cycles.

53 An ultrasonic transmitter and receiver are used to detect a crack in a metal block. When the ultrasonic signal is transmitted, a pulse appears on the oscilloscope. Also displayed are the pulses reflected from the crack and from the end of the block. The trace is shown in fig. 8.36 for a block 10 cm wide. Calculate the distance to the crack.   [4.17 cm]

54 A dual-beam oscilloscope is used to measure the charge and discharge times of a capacitor. The waveform is displayed on one channel and a 50 Hz waveform is displayed on the other (see fig. 8.37). Calculate (a) the charge time (voltage rising), (b) the discharge time (voltage falling).   [80 ms; 60 ms]

55 An oscilloscope is used, together with a microphone connected at its

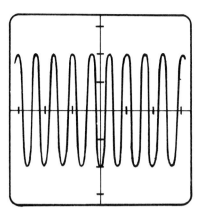

Fig. 8.33

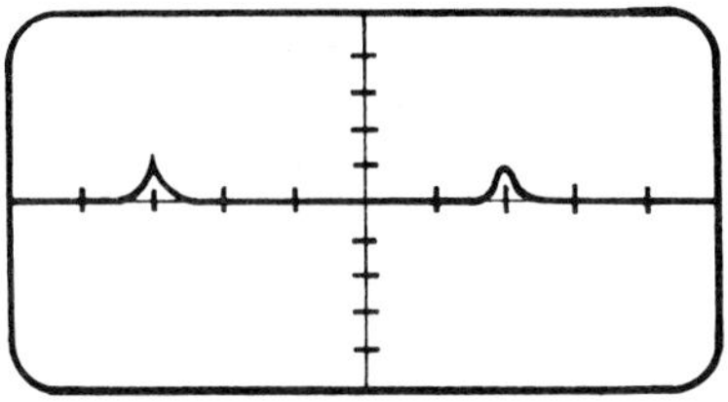

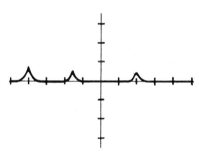

Fig. 8.34

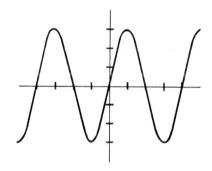

Fig. 8.35

Fig. 8.36

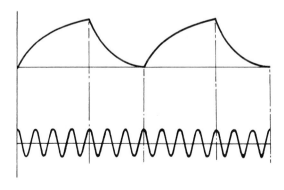

Fig. 8.37

221

input, to detect and measure the vibration of a tuning fork. If 25.6 cycles are measured in a 10 cm trace width, calculate the frequency of the tuning fork. The time-base is set at 10 ms/cm.   [256 Hz]

56   State an application where an oscilloscope is more useful than a digital voltmeter, and an application where the digital voltmeter is the more useful.

57   A conveyor belt is driven at 0.4 m/s. A photosensitive device detects parcels moving along the conveyor and displays a pulse on the upper trace of an oscilloscope as shown in fig. 8.38. The lower trace is derived from a 1 Hz pulse generator. Calculate the distance between the parcels.   [1 m]

58   A strain gauge is connected to a beam and, in conjunction with an electrical bridge circuit, is wired to display the beam oscillations. The display is as shown in fig. 8.39. Calculate the beam oscillation frequency and period if the oscilloscope time-base is set at 100 ms/cm.   [5 Hz; 200 ms]

59   A waveform displayed on an oscilloscope is shown in fig. 8.40. If the waveform has a 50 Hz ripple content, calculate the frequency of the main waveform.   [4.17 Hz]

60   Make a sketch of a cathode-ray tube and label the cathode, X- and Y-plates, final anode, grid, focusing system, and fluorescent screen. What are the additional requirements to enable the instrument to display a waveform?

61   A microphone is connected across the Y-input of an oscilloscope and is used to display the oscillation of a 1 kHz tuning fork. Sketch 10 centimetres of the expected oscilloscope trace when the time-base is set at 20 ms/cm.

62   A strain-gauge bridge is used to measure the strain on a suspension bridge. The output is monitored on an oscilloscope. The strain-gauge bridge gives an output change of 25 mV for a change in strain of 1 mm/m. If the bridge experiences a sinusoidal strain of frequency 2 Hz and amplitude 0.3 mm/m, draw the waveform seen on the oscilloscope and calculate its amplitude in cm. Vertical gain set to 1 mV/cm; horizontal gain set to 1 s/cm.   [7.5 cm]

63   The oil-pressure changes in a motor-car engine are monitored by using a pressure sensor connected to the same point as the pressure gauge. The sensor has an output of 12 mV for an input pressure change of 3 bar. The output is connected to an oscilloscope with vertical gain set to 5 mV/cm. If the oscilloscope is zeroed with the pressure at zero, calculate the deflection on the oscilloscope if the pressure suddenly increases to 4.5 bar.   [3.6 cm]

64   A pressure transducer and oscilloscope are used to display the combustion cycle of a petrol engine. The pressure gauge has a constant of 2 mV/bar. Draw the expected waveform on the oscilloscope. If the maximum pressure is 60 bar and the minimum pressure is 1 bar calculate the change in deflection on the oscilloscope if the vertical gain is set to 10 mV/cm.   [11.8 cm]

65   The vibrations of an aircraft wing tip are monitored using a strain-gauge bridge and an oscilloscope. During a flight test, the peak-to-peak deflection on the oscilloscope is 5.5 cm and the period of the waveform 2.2 cm. The strain-gauge bridge gives an output of 15 mV for 1 cm of wing-tip deflection. Calculate the amplitude and frequency of the wing-tip oscillation. The oscilloscope settings are vertical gain 10 mV/cm, horizontal gain 100 ms/cm. [3.67 cm; 4.55 Hz]

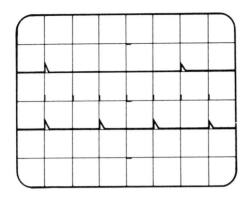

Fig. 8.38

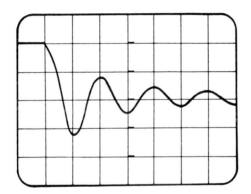

Fig. 8.39

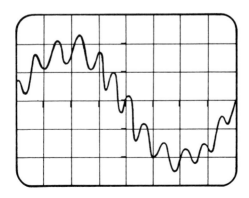

Fig. 8.40

66 The time-base of an oscilloscope rises linearly in 2.4 ms and the flyback time is 0.1 ms. How many complete cycles of a 2 kHz sine wave will be displayed on the screen? What will be the effect of changing the frequency to (a) 1 kHz? (b) 200 kHz?   [4.8; 2.4; 480]

67 Two photocells placed 1 m apart are used to detect the passage of a bullet. As the bullet passes, a pulse is generated from each photocell and is monitored on an oscilloscope. The two pulses on the screen are 6.3 cm apart and the horizontal gain is set to 10 ms/cm. Calculate the speed of the bullet. [15.87 m/s]

68 An oscilloscope is used to monitor a heartbeat. There are 12 pulses displayed on a 10 cm screen width. Calculate the heart rate if the horizontal gain is set to 1 s/cm.   [72 pulses/min]

69 A Wheatstone-bridge arrangement gives balance such that PQ = 100 Ω, QR = 10 Ω, and PS = 85 Ω. A resistor of unknown value is connected across the points RS, a p.d. of 1.5 V is maintained across PR, and a galvano-meter is connected across QS. Sketch the circuit diagram and calculate the value of the unknown resistance.   [8.5 Ω]

70 Figure 8.41 shows a Wheatstone-bridge circuit for measuring the value of an unknown resistance R_x, where R_1 and R_2 are the ratio arms and R_s is a decade box. Derive an equation for the unknown resistance, in terms of the other component values, when the bridge is balanced.

If R_1 = 1000 Ω, R_2 = 10 Ω, and R_s = 3424 Ω, calculate the value of the unknown resistance.   [34.24 Ω]

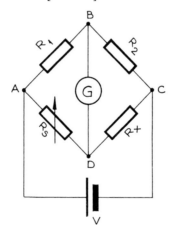

Fig. 8.41

71 With the aid of a circuit diagram, describe how a Wheatstone bridge is used to measure an unknown resistance. Deduce the balance conditions from first principles, and hence express the unknown resistance in terms of known quantities.

In a balanced Wheatstone bridge, the resistance of the arm opposite the unknown resistance is 2000 Ω, while the resistances of the other arms are 745.6 Ω and 1000 Ω. Calculate the value of the unknown resistance. [1491.2 Ω]

224

72 With the aid of a circuit diagram, describe a slide-wire form of Wheatstone bridge. Derive an expression for the unknown resistance in terms of the known quantities.

The calculated resistance as obtained from readings of the above bridge is 650 Ω. Given that the known standard resistor is 500 Ω and the total length of the slide wire is 1 m, determine the position of the slider when balance is obtained. Show this position clearly on a diagram.   [56.52 cm]

73   a) With the aid of a circuit diagram, describe how the d.c. slide-wire potentiometer is used to measure an unknown current.

b) In a test to determine the internal resistance of a cell, the terminal voltage of the cell on open circuit was found to be 1.968 V and when connected to a 10 Ω standard resistor it was 1.927 V. Calculate the internal resistance of the cell.   [0.213 Ω]

74   a) With the aid of a circuit diagram, describe how the slide-wire metre potentiometer is used to measure the unknown value of a resistor.

b) A resistor measured by this method has 1 A flowing through it when 6.42 V is measured across it. Calculate the value of the unknown resistor.   [6.42 Ω]

75   With the aid of a suitably labelled diagram, explain how the slide-wire potentiometer is used to measure (a) the open-circuit terminal voltage of a cell, (b) the value of an unknown current. For each case, show clearly how the unknown is obtained from the measurements taken.

76   Sketch the auxiliary circuit necessary to measure a p.d. outside the range of the normal d.c. potentiometer. Explain the method of measurement.

77   a) State the main advantages of measuring the e.m.f. of a cell by means of a potentiometer.

b) A standard cell having an e.m.f. of 1.0186 V is connected to a simple potentiometer, and balance conditions are obtained with a length of 500 mm. Draw the complete circuit diagram, including all necessary equipment.

When the standard cell is replaced by a second cell, balance is given with a length of 600 mm. Calculate the e.m.f. of the second cell. Calculate the internal resistance of the cell if its terminal voltage is 1.1 V when it is delivering a current of 100 mA.   [1.22 V; 1.2 Ω]

78   Using a simple d.c. potentiometer circuit to determine the e.m.f. of a cell, balance is obtained with a length of 509 mm when a standard cell having an e.m.f. of 1.0186 V is in circuit. When the standard cell is replaced by the cell under test, balance is obtained with a length of 775 mm. Calculate the e.m.f. of the cell under test.   [1.55 V]

79   Draw a circuit diagram of a simple d.c. potentiometer which may be used to determine the e.m.f. of a cell. Using such a circuit, the e.m.f. of a Leclanché cell was measured. The results obtained were

> Leclanché cell – balance obtained at 925 mm
> Standard cell – balance obtained at 609 mm
> E.m.f. of standard cell = 1.018 V

Determine the e.m.f. of the Leclanché cell.   [1.55 V]

9 Semiconductor diodes and rectification

9.1 Introduction

Semiconductor devices find application both in the electronics industry and in the electrical power industry. There is a wide variety of semiconductor devices available, some of which are designed to handle currents of the order of milliamperes while others are able to handle currents of hundreds of amperes.

This chapter is concerned with the physics of the operation of semiconductor diodes and with their application in rectifier circuits.

9.2 Conductors, insulators, and semiconductors

A simple but somewhat superficial definition of a semiconductor is 'a material whose resistivity is midway between that of a perfect insulator and that of a perfect conductor'. The resisitivity of conductors (say copper) is of the order of 10^{-6} ohm cm, that of semiconductors 1 ohm cm, while that of insulators (say glass) is 10^{13} ohm cm.

To understand why some materials act as conductors while others act as insulators, it is necessary to consider what happens when an electric current flows in a solid conductor.

Matter is made up of atoms which consist of a central nucleus surrounded by electrons. Each electron has a negative charge, and the total negative charge on all the electrons is balanced by an equal and opposite positive charge on the nucleus. The electrons are tightly bound to their parent atom, and can break free only if some additional energy is imparted to them by an external source (say heat, light, or an electric field). The electrons are then called *free electrons*. Electric current is the flow of these free electrons.

At a given temperature, conductors have many more free electrons than have insulators, and conductors thus have a much lower electrical resistance.

There is no such thing as a perfect insulator, and any insulator will carry a small electric current. The difference between an insulator and a semiconductor is the ease with which electrons can be made to break free from their parent atom to act as current carriers. There are more free electrons in semiconductors than there are in insulators.

When an electron has gained sufficient energy and has broken free from the parent atom, then the atom is said to be *ionised*, since it is short of one electron. The atom was initially electrically neutral, and therefore the loss of one electron has left the ionised atom (ion) with a net positive charge.

The space left where the electron has broken free is referred to as a *hole*, which is another way of saying an electron vacancy. We thus talk of *electron-hole pairs* being produced when atoms are ionised.

Raising the temperature gives more energy for ionisation and therefore results in the generation of more electron–hole pairs. Raising the temperature of a semiconductor therefore increases its conductivity.

We have seen that the resistivity of insulators and semiconductors *decreases* with temperature, due to the thermally generated electron–hole pairs. It is therefore sensible to ask why the resistivity of conductors such as copper *increases* with temperature. The reason is that raising the temperature of solids also increases the random vibration of the atoms, thus interfering with the flow of electrons. In conductors it is this effect which predominates, since there are already plenty of electrons available to act as current carriers. With semiconductors and insulators, the effect of increasing the number of free electrons predominates. Graphs of resistivity against temperature for the three types of material are shown in fig. 9.1.

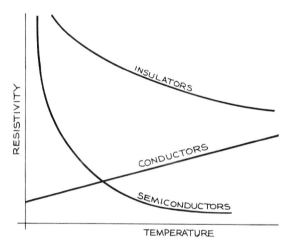

Fig. 9.1 Variation of resistivity with temperature for insulators, semiconductors, and conductors

9.3 Crystal structure

We have said that atoms consist of a central positive nucleus surrounded by electrons. The electrons exist in various shells (or energy levels).

The most commonly used semiconductor materials are silicon and germanium. These are both group-IV elements, which means that the outer shell of the atom has four electrons. These are call the *valence electrons*, and they largely determine the properties of the element.

The silicon and germanium atom may be represented as shown in fig. 9.2. The four valence electrons are represented by four dots, while the nucleus and the remaining electrons are represented by the central circle. The total charge on the electrons is equal to the positive charge on the nucleus, so that the atom is electrically neutral.

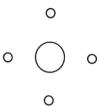

Fig. 9.2 Symbolic representation of a silicon or germanium atom

When two atoms come close enough together, they tend to share electrons. The electron orbits encircle both nuclei and this electron sharing results in a bond between the atoms. This is called *covalent bonding*, and silicon (or germanium) atoms link together in this way by sharing the valence electrons of neighbouring atoms.

A diagrammatic representation of the crystal structure of silicon and germanium is shown in fig. 9.3. Each atom shares its four valence electrons with its four neighbouring atoms. This pure silicon or germanium is referred to as *intrinsic* semiconductor material, i.e. it contains no impurities but is a semiconductor in its own right. In practice there are some free electrons with associated holes as a result of the semiconductor being at room temperature.

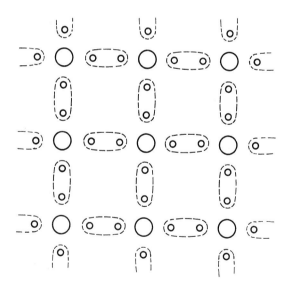

Fig. 9.3 Crystal structure of silicon and germanium

The semiconductor theory that follows applies to both silicon and germanium.

9.4 p-type and n-type semiconductors

To produce the p-type and n-type semiconductors used in diodes and transistors, small amounts of impurity are added to the intrinsic semiconductor. This is called *doping*.

To produce an n-type semiconductor, the impurity atoms added have five valence electrons (pentavalent), examples of such materials being phosphorus, arsenic, and antimony. As shown in fig. 9.4, four of the valence electrons form covalent bonds but the fifth electron is surplus and becomes free to act as a current carrier; n-type material thus has an excess of free electrons, which (electrons being negatively charged) explains the reason for calling it n-type. These impurity atoms are called *donor* atoms, since each donates a free electron.

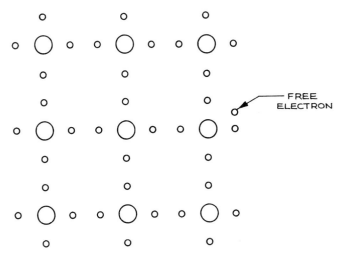

Fig. 9.4 Addition of a donor impurity

To produce a p-type semiconductor, an impurity with three valence electrons (trivalent) is used. Examples are boron, aluminium, and indium. As shown in fig. 9.5, when the covalent bonds form with the surrounding silicon atoms, one bond is left unformed due to the deficiency of one electron. This deficiency is called a *hole*. It is convenient to think of this hole as having a positive charge since it attracts any surrounding electrons. The hole may effectively move by an electron jumping into it from a neighbouring atom and leaving a hole there. These positive holes may in this way act as current carriers and, since they have an effective positive charge, this explains the reason for calling the material p-type. The impurity atoms in p-type material are called *acceptor* atoms.

9.5 The pn junction

The pn junction is called a *diode*. As we shall see, it allows current to flow in one direction but not in the other, rather like a non-return valve in a fluid

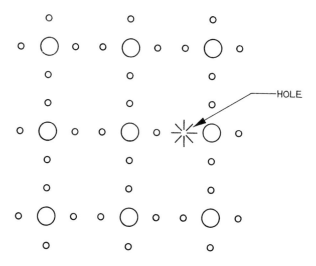

Fig. 9.5 Addition of an acceptor impurity

system. It consists of a p-type region and an n-type region, both formed in the same piece of silicon.

The construction and circuit symbol of a diode are shown in fig. 9.6. The p-side electrode is called the anode, while the n-side electrode is called the cathode. The direction of the 'arrow' of the diode in fig. 9.6 shows the direction of *conventional* current flow, i.e. from positive to negative of the supply voltage. This current flow is, of course, the flow of electrons from negative to positive of the supply voltage.

The pn junction of fig. 9.7 shows the mobile current carriers which in the p-type material are holes (symbolised by an open circle) and in the n-type material are electrons (symbolised by a solid circle).

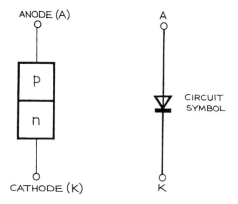

Fig. 9.6 Semiconductor diode

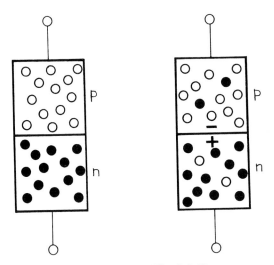

Fig. 9.7 pn junction   Fig. 9.8 Charge across a pn junction

Due to normal diffusion, some holes drift through into the n-type material and some electrons drift through into the p-type. This diffusion leaves the parent atoms close to the junction in the n-type material each short of one electron, and the parent atoms close to the junction in the p-type material are each short of one hole. This results in a small charge existing across the junction, as shown in fig. 9.8. This charge repels further diffusion of current carriers. The charged region at the junction is free of carriers and is referred to as the *depletion region* or the *barrier region*.

9.6 Forward and reverse bias
Now let us see how the device allows current to pass one way only.

In the circuit of fig. 9.9, an electric cell is connected across the pn junction with the positive side of the cell connected to the p–type material. This arrangement is referred to as *forward bias* and has the effect of reducing the depletion region, i.e. reducing the charge existing across the junction. If the forward bias is increased sufficiently, current starts to flow. Above this

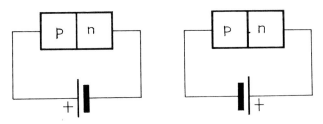

Fig. 9.9 Forward bias   Fig. 9.10 Reverse bias

231

voltage, the current increases with increased voltage. The diode thus conducts when forward-biased.

If the cell is now reversed, as shown in fig. 9.10, then the pn junction is said to be *reverse-biased*. This increases the depletion region and prevents the flow of current. The diode thus prevents conduction when reverse-biased.

9.7 Leakage current

In the discussion of the conditions in pure (intrinsic) silicon, it was stated that electron–hole pairs are generated due to the semiconductor material being at room temperature. These *thermally generated electron–hole pairs* are also present in the material of the pn junction. This results in there being a small number of free electrons in the p-type material, as well as the larger number of holes. Similarly, in the n-type material there are mostly free electrons, but also a few holes.

The current carriers which there are most of in the particular material are referred to as *majority carriers*. The small number of other carriers are called *minority carriers*.

In the pn junction with reverse bias, there is a very small current due to these minority carriers. This current is referred to as *leakage* current and may be likened to leakage through a valve in a fluid pipeline. In many applications of semiconductors this leakage current is a disadvantage, and it should therefore be kept as small as possible.

Leakage current is temperature-dependent, increasing with increasing temperature, due to thermally generated electron–hole pairs. In germanium the sensitivity to temperature is significant, but the temperature sensitivity of silicon is much less. Silicon is therefore used almost exclusively in present-day semiconductor devices.

9.8 The diode characteristic

Figure 9.11 shows a graph of voltage and current for a silicon diode under forward- and reverse-bias conditions. Such a graph is called a *diode characteristic*. As the forward voltage is increased, the forward current starts to flow as soon as the depletion region has been overcome (at about 0.6 V). Once this voltage has been reached, the current increases rapidly for only a small increase in voltage. If the current is allowed to become excessively large, then the device will be destroyed. For this reason, a series resistor is normally included in the diode circuit.

In the reverse direction, only a small leakage current flows. At some value of reverse-bias voltage, the device breaks down and current will flow. If the current is not limited by a series resistor, the diode will be damaged irreparably. The value of this breakdown voltage is stated in the manufacturer's data and should not be exceeded.

The characteristic of a germanium diode is similar to that of the silicon diode, except that forward conduction takes place at a low voltage (about 0.4 V) and that the reverse leakage current is much higher.

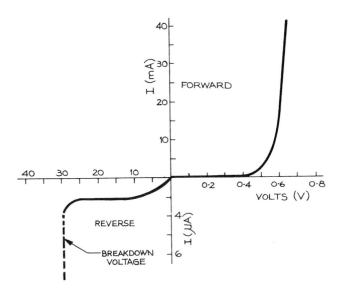

Fig. 9.11 Silicon-diode characteristic

9.9 Half-wave rectification

The consumer electricity supply is in the form of a sinusoidal voltage, and, when a low-voltage d.c. supply is required, the a.c. voltage must first be transformed down to a lower a.c. voltage and then be *rectified*. This is the type of supply that is required by most electronic circuits, such as amplifiers, oscillators, and electronic switching circuits.

Rectification is the conversion of an alternating voltage to a unidirectional voltage, as shown in fig. 9.12. The waveform of fig. 9.12(b) shows a *half-wave* rectified voltage. This is so called because only the positive-going part of the waveform appears after rectification.

In the circuit of fig. 9.13, when A is positive with respect to B then current can flow through the diode and the resistor. When the voltage polarity is reversed, current cannot flow. Notice that conventional current flows in the direction of the 'arrow' of the diode symbol. If the supply voltage is an a.c. waveform, as shown in fig. 9.12(a), then the current flowing in the resistor (and therefore the voltage across the resistor) will be as shown in fig. 9.12(b). Although this is not a smooth direct voltage, it varies only in a positive direction.

This unidirectional voltage may be *smoothed*, such that it is almost a direct voltage, by the use of a large capacitor as shown in fig. 9.14(a). The capacitor stores charge during the positive-going period of the waveform and supplies charge to the load during the other period. Used in this way, the capacitor acts rather like a reservoir in a water-storage system and is referred to as a *reservoir capacitor*. The waveform across the resistor will now

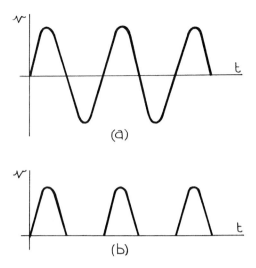

Fig. 9.12 (a) Alternating-current waveform, (b) half-wave-rectified waveform

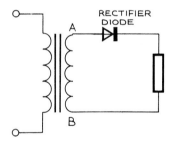

Fig. 9.13 Rectifier circuit using a diode

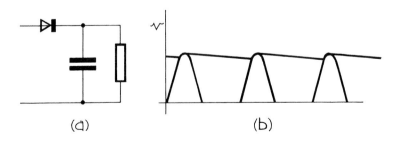

Fig. 9.14 Rectification and smoothing

234

be as shown in fig. 9.14(b) and is sufficiently close to being a direct voltage
to satisfy many requirements.

9.10 Full-wave rectification
An improvement on half-wave rectification is full-wave rectification, with a
waveform as shown in fig. 9.15. This may be accomplished by using

a) a bridge rectifier, as shown in fig. 9.16; or
b) a centre-tapped transformer together with two diodes, as shown in
   fig. 9.18.

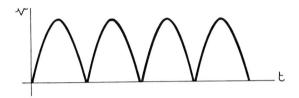

Fig. 9.15 Full-wave-rectified waveform

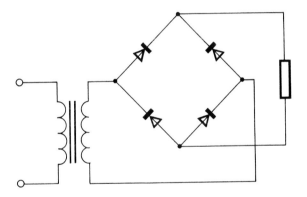

Fig. 9.16 Bridge rectifier

The bridge rectifier
The direction of current in the bridge rectifier during each half of the voltage
waveform is as shown in fig. 9.17.

During the positive half cycle of the a.c. input, when A is positive with
respect to B, then the current flow is through the diodes in the direction
shown in fig. 9.17(a).

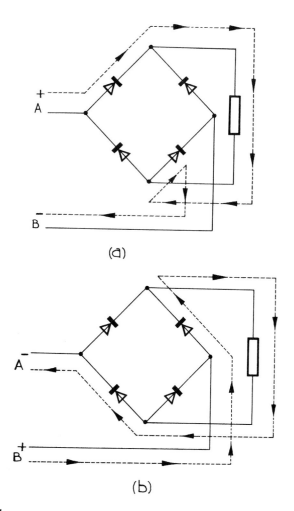

(ⅾ)

(b)

Fig. 9.17

During the negative half cycle, when A is negative with respect to B, then the current flow is through the diodes as shown in fig. 9.17(b).

Notice that the current flow in the load resistor is always in the same direction. The waveform of the voltage across the load resistor is shown in fig. 9.15.

The centre-tapped-transformer rectifier
In the centre-tapped-transformer rectifier, fig. 9.18, the current paths are as shown in fig. 9.19.

During the period when A is positive with respect to B, then only diode D_1 conducts. When B is positive with respect to A, then only diode D_2 conducts.

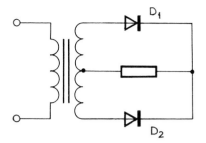

Fig. 9.18 Centre-tapped-transformer rectifier

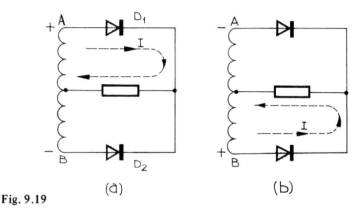

Fig. 9.19

Again the direction of the current in the load resistor is always in the same direction, and the voltage waveform is the same as that of fig. 9.15.

Connecting a reservoir capacitor across the load resistor gives the waveform shown in fig. 9.20.

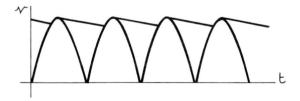

Fig. 9.20 Full-wave rectification with smoothing

Exercises on chapter 9

1   Explain briefly how p- and n-type semiconductor materials are utilised in a junction diode. Briefly explain the action of the diode when provided with (a) forward bias, (b) reverse bias.

2 Explain what are meant by the terms 'p-type' and 'n-type' semiconductors.
Explain briefly the principle of operation of a junction diode. With the aid
of a circuit diagram, describe how the forward and reverse current/voltage
characteristics of a junction diode are obtained.

3 Explain briefly the principal differences between p-type and n-type
semiconductors.
Show how these semiconductors are utilised to produce a junction diode,
and sketch a typical characteristic.

4 Name the majority carriers in (a) a p-type semiconductor, (b) an n-type
semiconductor.

5 Explain briefly the following terms as applied to semiconductors: 'donor
atom', 'acceptor atom', 'hole'.

6 With the aid of diagrams, explain the terms 'valence electron', 'donor
atom', 'minority carrier'.

7 Explain what is meant by 'doping' in connection with semiconductors.
Sketch a typical current/voltage static characteristic curve for a semiconductor diode, and explain how this differs from an ideal characteristic.

8 Sketch, on the same axes, the forward and reverse characteristics of a
pn-junction diode constructed from (a) silicon, (b) germanium. On your
graph, indicate typical forward operating voltages.
Give a typical application for each type of diode.

9 Sketch a typical forward and reverse characteristic for a pn junction
diode and identify the reverse breakdown voltage.

10 What is meant by the term 'peak inverse voltage' when associated with
a rectifier diode?

11 Draw a circuit diagram to show how the forward and reverse characteristics of a pn-junction diode may be obtained. Explain why a high-impedance
d.c. voltmeter is used to measure the voltage when obtaining the reverse
characteristic.

12 Draw a circuit diagram to show how two diodes and a centre-tapped
transformer may be used to give full-wave rectification of a sinusoidal a.c.
supply. On the diagram, show the position of the load, and sketch the input
and output waveforms.

13 Draw the circuit of a full-wave rectifier complete with smoothing
circuit and resistive load. Briefly explain the action of the circuit, and sketch
the current waveform. With the aid of a sketch, explain what would happen
to the p.d. across the load resistor if one of the diodes became open-circuit.

14 A smoothing circuit is made up of a choke and two electrolytic
capacitors. Draw the circuit arrangement and explain the action of each
component. Draw typical input and output waveforms, and give typical
values for each component for connection to a 50 Hz supply.

15 Draw the circuit arrangements for full-wave rectifiers of the bridge
and centre-tapped-transformer types. Compare their advantages and
disadvantages as regards number of diodes required and peak inverse voltage
required for the diodes in each case.

10   Transistors

10.1 Introduction
The transistor has virtually replaced the thermionic valve in most amplifying
and switching applications. Also, modern semiconductor technology has
enabled the development of integrated-circuit 'chips', which are very small and
cheap devices capable of performing complex logical and amplifying functions.

Historically, the first mass-produced transistor was made using alloy-
junction technology, but this has now been replaced by the *planar* process in
which doping impurities are selectively diffused into the surface of the silicon
slice using a *masking* technique.

Various types of transistor are available, including bipolar transistors,
field-effect transistors, and unijunction transistors, and each of these devices
has its own particular characteristics which make it more suitable for one
application or another. The most widely used device is the bipolar transistor,
and this is the type which will be considered here.

A low-frequency power-transistor chip

10.2 Transistor operation

The pnp bipolar transistor may be thought of as a sandwich of n-type material between two p-type layers, as shown in fig. 10.1(a). An alternative arrangement is the npn, which is a p-type layer sandwiched between two n-type layers as shown in fig. 10.1(b). The three layers must all be diffused into the same piece of silicon.

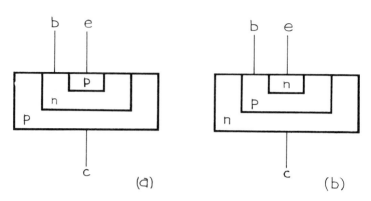

(a)   (b)

Fig. 10.1 Bipolar-junction-transistor construction

The three regions are called the emitter, base, and collector (e, b, and c), and each has a terminal connection as shown. There are thus two pn junctions: the emitter–base junction and the collector–base junction. Transistor operation is the control of the flow of current between emitter and collector by means of the voltage applied across the emitter–base junction.

Consider the operation of the pnp transistor shown in fig. 10.2.

In the doping process (discussed in chapter 9), the collector and emitter are heavily doped with p-type impurity (i.e. they have many free holes to act as current carriers). The n-type base region is relatively lightly doped (i.e has relatively few free electrons).

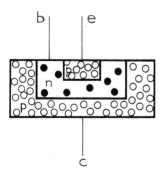

Fig. 10.2 Electrons and holes in a transistor

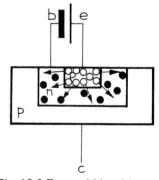

Fig. 10.3 Forward-biased base-emitter junction

When a forward bias is applied across the emitter–base junction, as shown in fig. 10.3, a current flows between emitter and base which is mainly due to holes flowing from emitter to base.

If now a reverse bias is applied across the base–collector junction, as shown in fig. 10.4, then most of the holes which have moved into the base region are immediately attracted into the collector region because of the negative voltage applied to it. We have thus arranged for current to flow from emitter to collector in the form of holes.

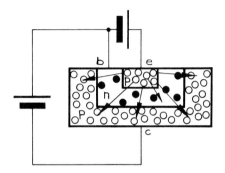

Fig. 10.4 Forward-biased base–emitter junction and reverse-biased collector-base junction

The transistor is now correctly *biased* for transistor action to take place. Notice that the holes injected from the emitter into the base may be considered as *minority carriers* once they are in the base region and are thus swept across the reverse-biased collector–base junction into the collector. Biasing a transistor for transistor action means that the base–emitter junction must have a *forward bias* while the base–collector junction must have a *reverse bias*.

Increasing the emitter–base bias voltage causes an increase in the current that flows from emitter to collector. The current flow is under the control of the emitter–base voltage, and the transistor may thus be considered as a control device. The action may be compared to controlling the flow of water through a rubber hose-pipe by tightening or releasing the grip around the pipe.

The main advantage of the transistor is that a very small amount of power applied to the control input will control a large amount of power at the output.

10.3 Transistor biasing
The symbol for the transistor is shown in fig. 10.5. Notice that the arrow is always on the emitter. The direction of the arrow shows the direction of flow of current through the transistor.

Since we are considering conventional current flow, then current flows from collector to emitter in the npn transistor, whereas current flows from emitter to collector in the pnp transistor.

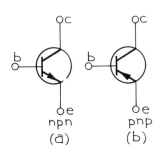

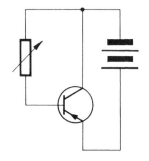

Fig. 10.5 Bipolar-junction-transistor symbols

Fig. 10.6 Transistor bias circuit

Figure 10.6 shows the usual method of *biasing* a pnp transistor, so as to forward bias the base–emitter (b–e) junction and reverse bias the collector-base (c–b) junction so that transistor action can take place. The forward biasing of the base–emitter (b–e) junction is provided via the resistor, which is referred to as the *base bias resistor*. Its value can be varied to provide the amount of bias current required. This circuit also provides the reverse bias for the collector–base (c–b) junction.

10.4 Current amplification
The transistor may be considered as a current-amplifying device (although it is also used to amplify voltage and power).

In the circuit of fig. 10.7 the currents in the collector, base, and emitter are represented by I_c, I_b, and I_e respectively. It may be seen that $I_e = I_c + I_b$,

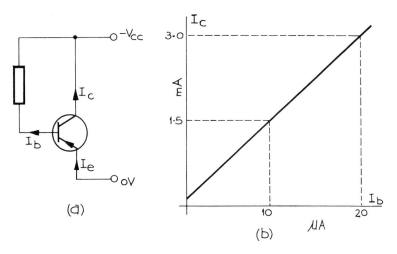

Fig. 10.7 Relationship between I_c and I_b

242

and this condition is true for both npn and pnp transistors. Also, the base current I_b is only a small fraction of the collector current I_c. The ratio $\Delta I_c / \Delta I_b$ is called the *current gain* and is given the symbol h_{fe}:

$$h_{fe} = \frac{\Delta I_c}{\Delta I_b}$$

where ΔI_c and ΔI_b represent small changes in current.

The graphical relationship between I_c and I_b is a straight line, as shown in fig. 10.7(b). The slope of this line is the current gain h_{fe}. The straight line does not pass exactly through the origin, since with $I_b = 0$ there is some small collector current called *leakage current*. It is symbolised as I_{ceo} (collector current with $I_b = 0$).

Consider the case shown in fig. 10.7(b), with $I_b = 10\,\mu A$ causing a collector current $I_c = 1.5\,mA$. Increasing the base current to $I_b = 20\,\mu A$ causes the collector current to increase to $I_c = 3.0\,mA$; therefore

$$\text{current gain } h_{fe} = \frac{(3.0 - 1.5)\,mA}{(20 - 10)\,\mu A}$$

$$= \frac{1.5\ mA}{10\,\mu A} = \frac{1500\,\mu A}{10\,\mu A} = 150$$

i.e. the current gain is 150.

Example A transistor has a current gain of 400. Calculate the collector and emitter current if the base current is $20\,\mu A$. (Assume negligible I_{ceo}.)

Since I_{ceo} is negligible, we may say that

$$I_c = h_{fe} I_b$$

where $h_{fe} = 400$ and $I_b = 20\,\mu A = 20 \times 10^{-6}$ A

$\therefore$ $I_c = 400 \times 20 \times 10^{-6}$ A

$= 8 \times 10^{-3}$ A $= 8\,mA$

$I_e = I_c + I_b$

$\therefore$ $I_e = 8000\,\mu A + 20\,\mu A$

$= 8.02\,mA$

i.e. the collector current is 8 mA and the emitter current is 8.02 mA. Notice that I_e is approximately equal to I_c.

10.5 Voltage amplification
We have seen that by varying the base current we can cause a much larger variation in collector current.

In order to obtain a *voltage* variation, it is necessary to include a load resistor R_L in the basic circuit as shown in fig. 10.8. (Although in fig. 10.7

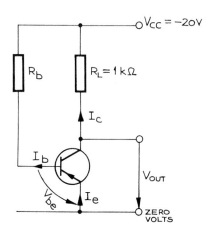

Fig. 10.8 Biased transistor with load resistor

the collector current may be varied, the collector voltage is fixed at $-V_{cc}$, where V_{cc} is the term used for the d.c. supply voltage.)

In fig. 10.8, as the current varies, the voltage across the resistor R_L also varies. The *output* of the circuit is taken between the collector and emitter of the transistor, where there will of course also be a voltage variation:

$$V_{ce} = V_{cc} - I_c R_L$$

Suppose R_b is chosen such that the base-emitter voltage (V_{be}) is 0.6 V and that $I_b = 50\ \mu A$. For a current gain of $h_{fe} = 200$, then (assuming negligible I_{ceo})

$$I_c = h_{fe} I_b = 200 \times 50\ \mu A = 10\ mA$$

With $R_L = 1\ k\Omega$, the voltage across the load resistor is $10\ mA \times 1\ k\Omega = 10\ V$.

With a total supply voltage of 20 V, the voltage remaining across the transistor output (V_{ce}) is then

$$V_{ce} = V_{cc} - I_c R_L$$
$$= 20\ V - 10\ V = 10\ V$$

If now the base resistance R_b is reduced such that the base current becomes $I_b = 60\ \mu A$ and V_{be} becomes 0.62 V, then

$$I_c = h_{fe} I_b$$
$$= 200 \times 60\ \mu A = 12\ mA$$

$\therefore$ voltage across $R_L = 12\ mA \times 1\ k\Omega = 12\ V$

The voltage remaining across the output (V_{ce}) is now $20\ V - 12\ V = 8\ V$.

The two conditions are shown below:

| V_{be} | 0.6 V | 0.62 V |
| V_{ce} | 10 V | 8 V |

$\therefore$ output voltage change $= 10\,V - 8\,V$

$$= 2\,V$$

input voltage change $= 0.62\,V - 0.6\,V$

$$= 0.02\,V$$

$\therefore$ voltage gain $(A_v) = \dfrac{2\,V}{0.02\,V} = 100$

i.e. the voltage gain is 100.

Notice that the output voltage change is in the opposite direction to the input voltage change. There is thus $180°$ phase inversion through a single-stage voltage amplifier, and this should be remembered.

10.6 A.c. voltage amplification

The circuit of fig. 10.9 shows the circuit modification required to provide a.c. voltage amplification. A d.c. blocking capacitor is included at the input and output of the amplifier. This allows the a.c. signal voltage to be superimposed on the base–emitter voltage.

Assuming a voltage gain of 200, then an input signal change of 20 mV peak to peak will provide an output voltage change of 2 V.

Figure 10.9 shows the a.c. input and output voltages, with the output voltage $180°$ out of phase with the input.

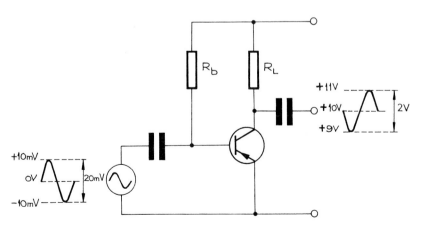

Fig. 10.9 A.c. voltage-amplifier circuit

245

Practical voltage amplifiers

In practice, the voltage amplifier is as shown in figs 10.10(a) and (b), where the arrangements for both the pnp and the npn transistor are given.

The potential-divider R_1 and R_2 provides the necessary base bias, while the resistor R_E connected in the emitter circuit provides the necessary *stabilisation*. This means that it minimises the effect of any change in the transistor parameters with temperature. It also minimises any variation in the output voltage due to variation in current gain (h_{fe}) from one transistor to another. The capacitor C_E acts as a bypass capacitor and is required to allow a.c. voltage variation at the output.

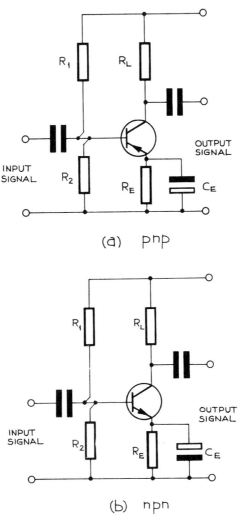

Fig. 10.10 Practical voltage amplifier with stabilisation circuit: (a) pnp, (b) npn

The amplifier will thus amplify a.c. signals but not d.c. signals. Other forms of amplifier are used for d.c. amplification if this is required.

10.7 Circuit configurations

So far we have considered only one type of amplifier circuit configuration, this being the common-emitter (CE) amplifier. This is so called because the emitter is common to both the input and the output signals, so far as the a.c. signal is concerned. This arrangement is the most usual and provides amplification of current, voltage, and power.

Two other configurations are possible, these being the common-base (CB) and common-collector (CC). All three cases are shown using an npn transistor in fig. 10.11. Notice that the d.c. bias arrangement is the same in all three cases, since the bias is necessary to produce transistor action.

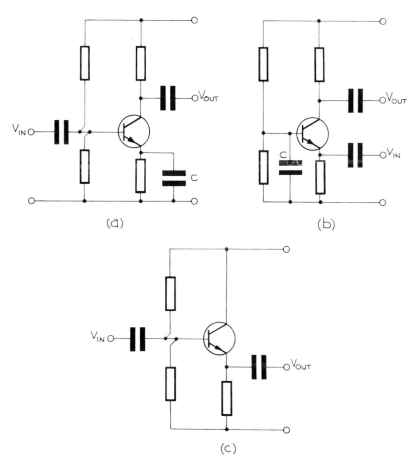

Fig. 10.11 Amplifier configurations: (a) common-emitter, (b) common-base, (c) common-collector

As far as a.c. signals are concerned, in fig. 10.11(a) the emitter is common via capacitor C. The input signal is applied to the base, and the output signal is taken from the collector.

In fig. 10.11(b) the base is common via C. The input signal is applied to the emitter, and the output signal is taken from the collector.

In fig. 10.11(c) the collector is common, being connected directly to V_{cc}. The input signal is applied to the base, and the output signal is taken from the emitter.

Each of the three possible configurations has its own particular advantages, and their parameters are given in Table 10.1.

Table 10.1 Circuit-configuration parameters (typical)

	Configuration		
	Common-base	Common-emitter	Common-collector
Current gain	0.98	90	90
Voltage gain	200	200	0.98
Input resistance	$20\,\Omega$	$400\,\Omega$	$10\,k\Omega$
Output resistance	$500\,k\Omega$	$50\,k\Omega$	$100\,\Omega$
Power gain	Medium	High	Low
Phase inversion	0	$180°$	0

The common-collector amplifier is also called the *emitter follower*, since the voltage gain between base and emitter is approximately unity and the emitter voltage virtually follows that of the base. The main advantage of the emitter follower is that it has a high input resistance and a low output resistance and can thus act as a *buffer* stage between one circuit stage and another. This means that the buffer stage takes only a small current from the signal source, but can feed a larger current into the following circuit.

10.8 Transistor characteristics

Any device has a *characteristic* which shows how one variable (say voltage) varies with another (say current).

With the transistor we are most interested in the relationship between voltage and current at the input (the *input characteristic*) and the relationship between the voltage and current at the output (the *output characteristic*). We shall consider both of these characteristics for the common-emitter and common-base configurations.

Common-emitter input characteristic

The circuit of fig. 10.12(a) may be used to obtain the input characteristic for the common-emitter configuration. The resistor in the base circuit is used to limit the base current so that the transistor cannot be damaged.

248

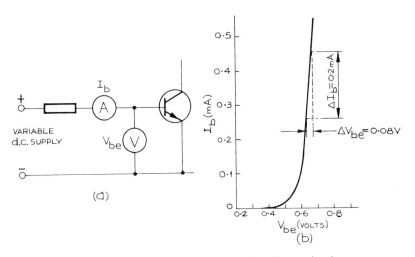

Fig. 10.12 Common-emitter input characteristic and test circuit

The input characteristic is shown in fig. 10.12(b) and is the same shape as the diode characteristic (it is in fact the characteristic of the base–emitter junction). When the voltage exceeds about 0.4 volts, I_b starts to increase. Typical values of V_{be} for a silicon transistor range between 0.5 V and 0.8 V, depending on the current.

The transistor input resistance in common-emitter configuration may be calculated from the slope of the input characteristic. From fig. 10.12(b),

$$R_{in} = \frac{\Delta V_{be}}{\Delta I_b} = \frac{0.08\,\text{V}}{0.2\,\text{mA}} = \frac{0.08\,\text{V}}{0.2 \times 10^{-3}\,\text{A}} = 400\,\Omega$$

i.e. a typical value of input resistance is $400\,\Omega$.

Common-emitter output characteristic

The circuit of fig. 10.13(a) may be used to obtain the output characteristic for the common-emitter configuration. The characteristic of fig. 10.13(b) shows that a *family* of characteristics may be obtained. With $I_b = 0$, the characteristic is in fact the leakage current between collector and emitter (I_{ceo}). Increasing I_b causes I_c to increase, and the family of output characteristics is shown for various step values of I_b.

The transistor is normally used in the region above the 'knee' of the characteristic, where the collector current changes only slightly with variation of collector–emitter voltage (V_{ce}). The output resistance of the transistor in common-emitter configuration may be calculated from the slope of the characteristic in this region. From fig. 10.13(b) the output resistance is given by

249

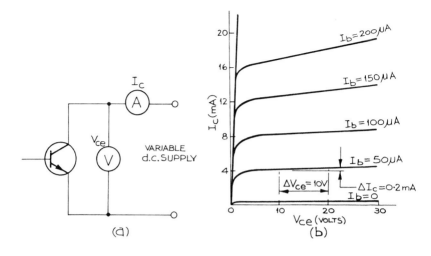

Fig. 10.13 Common-emitter output characteristic and test circuit

$$R_{\text{out}} = \frac{\Delta V_{ce}}{\Delta I_c} = \frac{10\,\text{V}}{0.2\,\text{mA}} = \frac{10\,\text{V}}{0.2 \times 10^{-3}\,\text{A}} = 50\,\text{k}\Omega$$

i.e. a typical value of output resistance is $50\,\text{k}\Omega$.

The current gain may also be calculated from the output characteristic. From fig. 10.12(b) it may be seen that, for $V_{ce} = 20\,\text{V}$,

when $\quad I_b = 50\,\mu\text{A} \quad$ then $\quad I_c = 4.3\,\text{mA}$

and when $\quad I_b = 150\,\mu\text{A} \quad$ then $\quad I_c = 13.3\,\text{mA}$

$$\therefore \quad h_{\text{fe}} = \frac{\Delta I_c}{\Delta I_b} = \frac{(13.3 - 4.3)\,\text{mA}}{(150 - 50)\,\mu\text{A}} = \frac{9\,\text{mA}}{100\,\mu\text{A}} = 90$$

i.e. at this voltage the current gain is 90.

Common-base input and output characteristics

A similar set of measurement circuits and corresponding characteristics for the common-base configuration are shown in figs 10.14 and 10.15.

From these characteristics, a typical input resistance is $20\,\Omega$ and a typical output resistance is $500\,\text{k}\Omega$. Notice that the input resistance is lower than that for the common-emitter configuration, but that the output resistance is higher. This result is also evident from the slope of the output characteristic above the knee.

The common-base current gain is given the symbol h_{fb} and is defined by

$$h_{\text{fb}} = \frac{\Delta I_c}{\Delta I_e}$$

250

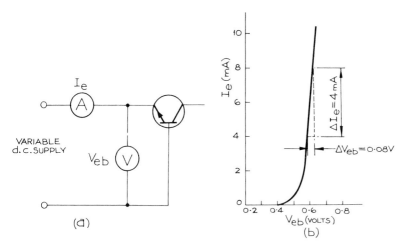

Fig. 10.14 Common-base input characteristic

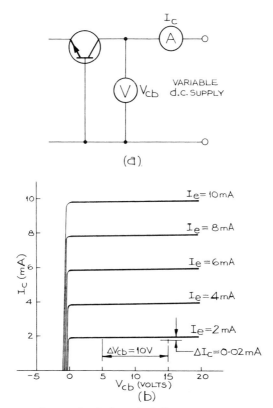

Fig. 10.15 Common-base output characteristic

251

It may be calculated from the common-base output characteristic as follows:

when $I_e = 2\,\text{mA}$ then $I_c = 1.94\,\text{mA}$

and when $I_e = 4\,\text{mA}$ then $I_c = 3.9\,\text{mA}$

$$\therefore \quad h_{fb} = \frac{\Delta I_c}{\Delta I_e} = \frac{(3.9 - 1.94)\,\text{mA}}{(4 - 2)\,\text{mA}} = \frac{1.96\,\text{mA}}{2\,\text{mA}} = 0.98$$

i.e. a typical value of common-base current gain is 0.98.

These parameters are listed in Table 10.1.

Example 1 For the circuit of fig. 10.16, calculate (a) the base-emitter bias voltage (V_{be}), (b) the collector–emitter voltage (V_{ce}). (Ignore the effect of any base current flowing in the 56 kΩ resistor.)

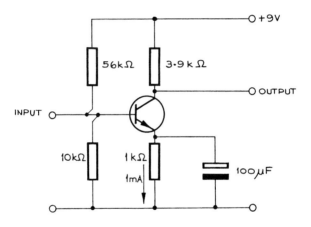

Fig. 10.16 Common-emitter alternating-voltage amplifier

a) Voltage across emitter resistor $= I_e R_e$

where $I_e = 1\,\text{mA}$ and $R_e = 1\,\text{k}\Omega$

$$\therefore \quad V_e = 1\,\text{mA} \times 1\,\text{k}\Omega = 1\,\text{V}$$

The base voltage is obtained from the potential-divider of 56 kΩ in series with 10 kΩ.

Ignoring the base current,

$$V_b = \frac{10\,\text{k}\Omega}{10\,\text{k}\Omega + 56\,\text{k}\Omega} \times V_{cc}$$

$$= \frac{10\,\text{k}\Omega}{66\,\text{k}\Omega} \times 9\,\text{V} = 1.36\,\text{V}$$

$$\therefore \quad V_{be} = V_b - V_e = 1.36\,V - 1\,V$$
$$= 0.36\,V$$

b) We may assume that I_c is approximately equal to I_e; therefore the voltage (V_L) across the 3.9 kΩ load resistor is given by

$$V_L = I_c R_L$$

where $I_c \approx 1\,mA$ and $R_L = 3.9\,k\Omega$

$$\therefore \quad V_L = 1\,mA \times 3.9\,k\Omega = 3.9\,V$$

The voltage across the transistor (V_{ce}) is therefore given by

$$V_{ce} = V_{cc} - V_L - V_e$$
$$= 9\,V - 3.9\,V - 1\,V$$
$$= 4.1\,V$$

i.e. $V_{be} = 0.36\,V$ and $V_{ce} = 4.1\,V$.

Example 2   A transistor has a common-base current gain (h_{fb}) of 0.98. Calculate the corresponding common-emitter current gain (h_{fe}).

$$I_e = I_c + I_b \qquad\qquad\qquad (i)$$

and $h_{fb} = I_c/I_e$

$$\therefore \quad I_e = I_c/h_{fb}$$

Substituting in equation (i),

$$I_c/h_{fb} = I_c + I_b$$
$$\therefore \quad I_c = h_{fb}I_c + h_{fb}I_b$$
$$\therefore \quad I_c(1 - h_{fb}) = h_{fb}I_b$$
$$\therefore \quad \frac{I_c}{I_b} = \frac{h_{fb}}{1 - h_{fb}}$$

But $I_c/I_b = h_{fe}$

$$\therefore \quad h_{fe} = \frac{h_{fb}}{1 - h_{fb}}$$

where $h_{fb} = 0.98$

$$\therefore \quad h_{fe} = \frac{0.98}{1 - 0.98} = \frac{0.98}{0.02} = 49$$

i.e. the common-emitter current gain is 49.

Example 3   A transistor with a common-emitter current gain of 120 is connected as a common-emitter voltage amplifier with a collector load of

2.2 kΩ. Estimate the voltage gain if the effective input resistance to the amplifier is 500 Ω.

$$\text{Input voltage} = I_{in} \times R_{in}$$

$$\text{output voltage} = I_{out} \times R_L$$

$$\therefore \quad \text{voltage gain} = \frac{\text{output voltage}}{\text{input voltage}}$$

$$= \frac{I_{out} \times R_L}{I_{in} \times R_{in}}$$

But $I_{out}/I_{in} \approx h_{fe}$ in common-emitter configuration

$\therefore$ voltage gain $= h_{fe} \times R_L/R_{in}$

where $h_{fe} = 120$ $R_L = 2.2 \, k\Omega$ and $R_{in} = 500 \, \Omega$

$$\therefore \quad \text{voltage gain} = 120 \times \frac{2200 \, \Omega}{500 \, \Omega}$$

$$= 528$$

i.e. the voltage gain is approximately 530.

Exercises on chapter 10

1　Explain the operation of an npn bipolar transistor and state the necessary bias across b–e and c–b for transistor action to take place.

2　What is the bias polarity of the base with respect to the emitter in a common-emitter connection of an npn transisitor? Show one method how this bias may be achieved, and explain how the base current is limited to a safe value.

3　Draw the circuit symbol for the npn and the pnp transistors and show, with the aid of sketches, how each may be connected in a simple d.c. bias circuit. Indicate the polarities on the sketch.

4　Sketch a typical set of output characteristics for the common-base connection of a npn transistor and show on them how values of output resistance and current gain may be obtained. Give typical values for the output resistance and current gain for this method of transistor connection.

5　The current-amplification factor of a transistor is 0.97. Calculate the current gain of the transistor when connected in (a) common-base, (b) common-emitter configuration.　[0.97; 32]

6　a) Draw a circuit diagram for obtaining the characteristics of a common-emitter-connected transistor.

　b) For a common-emitter-connected transistor, sketch (i) typical input characteristics, (ii) typical current-transfer characteristics, (iii) typical collector characteristics.

7　a) Explain why a common-base-connected transistor can be used as a voltage amplifier although its current gain is less than unity.

254

b) Draw a circuit diagram for obtaining the collector current/collector voltage characteristic of a transistor. Indicate all instruments needed. For two different values of base current, sketch the curves that would be expected for a common-emitter-connected transistor.

8 Draw the basic circuits of a transistor connected in (a) common-base, (b) common-emitter mode. Show clearly the bias polarities and briefly compare the input resistance, output resistance, and current gain for each method of connection.

9 A transistor has a current-amplification factor of 0.99 and it is used as a common-emitter amplifier with a resistive load of 2.2 kΩ. Estimate the current and voltage gain. Assume that the input resistance of the amplifier is 400 Ω. [99; 544.5]

10 Draw the circuit of a single-stage common-emitter transistor amplifier. Describe how the voltage gain of the amplifier can be measured and any precautions which must be taken to prevent errors. List the equipment required and show on the circuit diagram where it would be connected.

11 Explain why bias-stabilisation is normally used in a common-emitter voltage amplifier. Draw the circuit diagram of a single-stage common-emitter voltage amplifier. Identify the bias components and explain the stabilising action.

12 A transistor has a family of common-emitter output characteristics given below. Estimate the common-emitter current gain and output resistance at $V_{ce} = 30$ V and (a) $I_c = 15$ mA, (b) $I_c = 35$ mA. [250, 13 kΩ; 450, 2 kΩ]

I_b (µA)	40	60	80	100	120
$V_{ce} = 10$ V: I_c (mA)	9	13	18	24	29
$V_{ce} = 50$ V: I_c (mA)	12	17	28	44	56

13 For the circuit shown in fig. 10.17, calculate the quiescent values of collector current and voltage. Hence calculate the base current and the

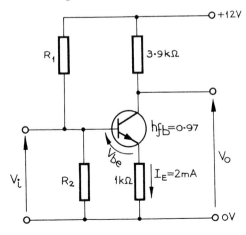

Fig. 10.17

255

collector–emitter voltage and choose suitable values for R_1 and R_2 if
V_{be} = 0.6 V.   [1.94 mA; 4.43 V; 60 μA; 2.34 V]

14   The circuit of fig. 10.18 is a common-emitter amplifier with the
base-bias current provided via R_B. Calculate the collector and base currents
and the voltage at the output and select a suitable value for R_B if V_{be} = 0.7 V.
[0.49 mA; 10 μA; 5 V; 330 kΩ]

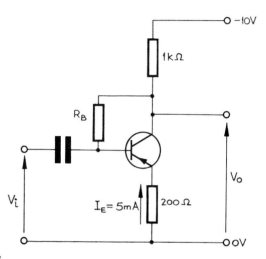

Fig. 10.18

15   For the circuit of fig. 10.19, calculate the current in the base of TR$_1$
and TR$_2$ and the current in R_L. Hence calculate the overall current gain
(h_{fe}) of the combination. Comment on your results.   [60 μA; 1.8 μA; 1110]

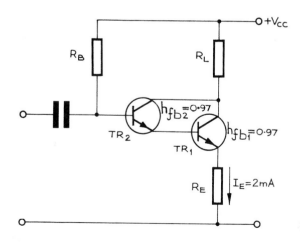

Fig. 10.19

Index